Nuclear Reactor Physics

Nuclear Reactor Physics

RAYMOND L. MURRAY

Professor of Physics
North Carolina State College
of Agriculture and Engineering

Englewood Cliffs, N.J.
PRENTICE-HALL, INC.
1957

To My Students

PREFACE

NUCLEAR REACTOR PHYSICS has come to connote the analysis of the behavior of an assembly of fissionable material. This book is intended to serve as an introduction to the physical concepts and calculation methods in this new branch of applied physics. It is designed for use by the first-year graduate student in science or engineering and the design engineer in the nuclear energy field. The principal emphasis is placed on the distributions in energy and space of neutron flux, the determination of the critical amount of fissionable material, and the transient behavior and control of the reactor as a heat source. It is assumed that the reader has familiarity with the fundamental facts of nuclear physics, but it is recognized that most of the description of the chain reactor is in terms of classical models. The goals that have been sought are to present the theory simply and logically, and to provide enough detail in the many numerical illustrations to achieve a degree of practical utility. Problems, with answers, are given at the end of each chapter.

The material presented is based on a series of undergraduate and graduate courses given by the author since 1950 in the Nuclear Engineering curriculum at North Carolina State College.

Valuable suggestions and assistance were provided by a number of people. Professor William M. Breazeale, Professor Richard A. Fayram, and Dr. Alfred M. Perry reviewed the first draft. Thanks are due also to Arthur Banister, Gene Baraff, Gerald Katzin, Harold Lamonds, Joseph Lundholm, Chreston Martin, and Charles Terrell of North Carolina State College for reading certain sections. The encouragement and assistance from the author's wife, Ilah Mae Rengler Murray, is gratefully recognized.

RAYMOND L. MURRAY

Raleigh, North Carolina

CONTENTS

Chapter 1

THE NUCLEAR REACTOR

||||||||||||||||||||||||||||||||||||||||||||||||||||||||||||||||||||||||||||||||||||||||||||||||||||||||||||||

A nuclear reactor may be defined as a device in which nuclear energy is liberated as a result of a chain reaction involving neutrons and fissionable elements. It is a source of thermal and radiant energy that utilizes nuclear reactions rather than chemical or electrical processes. As in other systems, the factors that must be considered in design and operation are the components or ingredients, the arrangement, and the method of control. The nuclear aspect introduces problems and methods of analysis that are unique in industrial practice. The behavior of the system often may be treated by the classic kinetic theory of gases and by methods conventional in the analysis of heat transfer and electric circuits. The interactions of component particles, however, are described by the concepts of nuclear physics. On the assumption that the reader has studied the equivalent of an introductory course in nuclear physics, we shall restrict attention to the reactions of special application to the theory of nuclear reactors.

1.1. *Nuclear reactions with neutrons*

The neutron plays a central role in the nuclear reactor since it serves as the agent by which nuclear fission occurs. Having no electric charge, it is not influenced by the presence of matter unless it comes within a distance of about 10^{-12} cm of the nucleus. Once within this range, it is subject to one of two events—scattering or absorption. The conventional classification of such neutron reactions follows.

1

(a) *Elastic collision.*   The collision of a neutron with a nucleus may be elastic, with momentum and kinetic energy conserved. This will result simply in a transfer of part of the neutron kinetic energy to the target nucleus, with a change in the direction of neutron motion.   Details of the relations between energy, speed, and angles in the elastic scattering process will be given in the next chapter.

(b) *Inelastic collision.*   In heavy elements such as iron or uranium, a neutron with energy in the vicinity of 1 mev may produce excitation of the nucleus.   The neutron thus may lose a large fraction of its initial energy.   The nucleus returns to the ground energy state by the emission of a gamma ray.

(c) *Radiative capture.*   Neutron absorption may convert the nucleus into a different isotope.   The formation of Co^{60} from Co^{59} is typical.   Excess energy resulting from the absorption of the neutron is released almost instantaneously by the nucleus as a capture gamma ray; if the product isotope is radioactive, it will emit beta particles and additional gamma rays according to its half-life.

(d) *Capture with charged particle emission.*   If the neutron energy is high enough, a transmutation with the ejection of a proton or alpha particle will occur.   The production of N^{16}, by the reaction with O^{16} of neutrons with energy above 10 mev, is an important example.

(e) *Fission.*   The neutron may induce fission.   In the isotopes U^{235}, Pu^{239}, and U^{233}, fission can be produced by either low or high energy neutrons, with the probability of fission particularly high for slow neutrons. U^{238} will fission only with neutrons of energy above 1 mev.   This event results in the emission of several fast neutrons, which may be used to sustain a chain reaction.

(f) *Fissionable isotope production.*   Radiative capture of neutrons in the isotopes $_{92}U^{238}$ and $_{90}Th^{232}$ leads to new fissionable elements, plutonium $_{94}Pu^{239}$ and $_{92}U^{233}$, according to the sequence of events below:

$$_{92}U^{238} + _{0}n^{1} \longrightarrow _{92}U^{239}$$

$$_{92}U^{239} \xrightarrow[23.5 \text{ min}]{} _{93}Np^{239} + _{-1}e^{0}$$

$$_{93}Np^{239} \xrightarrow[2.3 \text{ days}]{} _{94}Pu^{239} + _{-1}e^{0}$$

Table 1.1

Neutron Reactions and Radioactive Products

Unless otherwise noted, the neutron energy is 0.0253 ev.   Beta energies are maximum values.

Target Isotope	Cross Section (barns)	Maximum Capture Gamma Energy (mev)	Product Isotope(s)	Product Radiations and Energy (mev)	Half-life	
$_1H^1$	0.330	2.23	$_1H^2$		Stable	Secondary radiation in hydrogenous shields
$_4Be^9$	0.010	6.81	$_4Be^{10}$	β (0.56)	2.9×10^6 yr	Reactor construction material
$_5B^{10}$	4010	0.478	$_2He^4$ $_3Li^7$		Stable	Control elements, neutron detectors, shielding
$_6C^{12}$	0.0032	4.95	$_6C^{13}$		Stable	Capture gammas in graphite thermal columns
$_7N^{14}$	(>10.75 mev)		$_1H^1$ $_6C^{14}$	β (0.155)	5568 yr	Production of radioactive tracer
$_8O^{16}$	0.07 at 14 mev		$_1H^1$ $_7N^{16}$	80% γ (6.2-7)	7.35 sec	Water activation, shielding
$_8O^{18}$	2.1×10^{-4}		$_8O^{19}$	30% β (4.5) 70% β (2.9) γ (1.6)	29.4 sec	Water activation, shielding
$_{11}Na^{23}$	0.505	6.41	$_{11}Na^{24}$	β (1.39) γ (2.76, 1.38)	15.1 hr	Shielding
$_{13}Al^{27}$	0.230	7.72	$_{13}Al^{28}$	β (3.0) γ (1.8)	2.27 min	Structural activation, shielding
$_{18}A^{40}$	0.62		$_{18}A^{41}$	β (2.13) γ (1.37)	109 min	Radioactivity in air
$_{27}Co^{59}$	37.0	7.35	$_{27}Co^{60}$	β (0.31) γ (1.17, 1.33)	5.27 yr	Radioactive isotope for medical applications
$_{48}Cd^{113}$	20,800	9.05	$_{48}Cd^{114}$		Stable	Reactor control elements
$_{49}In^{115}$	145	5.86	$_{49}In^{116}$	β (1.0) γ (0.1-2.1)	53.9 min	Neutron detecting foils

$$_{90}\text{Th}^{232} + {_0}\text{n}^1 \longrightarrow {_{90}}\text{Th}^{233}$$

$$_{90}\text{Th}^{233} \xrightarrow[23.3 \text{ min}]{} {_{91}}\text{Pa}^{233} + {_{-1}}\text{e}^0$$

$$_{91}\text{Pa}^{233} \xrightarrow[27.4 \text{ days}]{} {_{92}}\text{U}^{233} + {_{-1}}\text{e}^0$$

These reactions relate to the *converter* and *breeder* reactors, in which useful fissionable materials not found abundantly in nature are formed.

Table 1.1 lists a number of other important neutron reactions, with the characteristics of the resulting radioactive isotopes. In this table, the cross section, to be discussed in detail in Chapter 2, is a measure of the probability of absorption. Two other non-fission nuclear reactions that provide neutrons are important in the reactor field. The photodisintegration of heavy hydrogen is given by

$$\gamma + {_1}\text{H}^2 \longrightarrow {_1}\text{H}^1 + {_0}\text{n}^1$$

The alpha particles from radium and its products react with beryllium according to

$$_2\text{He}^4 + {_4}\text{Be}^9 \longrightarrow {_6}\text{C}^{12} + {_0}\text{n}^1$$

1.2. *Fission*

The *fission* process consists of division of a nucleus such as U^{235} into two or more heavy fragments of much lower mass and atomic numbers than the original element. The first step is the absorption of a neutron:

$$_0\text{n}^1 + {_{92}}\text{U}^{235} \longrightarrow {_{92}}\text{U}^{236}$$

After emission of a capture gamma ray, the U^{236} nucleus may remain intact. In 16 per cent of all absorptions the result is essentially stable $(2.4 \times 10^7 \text{ yr})$ U^{236}; in the remaining 84 per cent the result is fission. The U^{236} may split in many ways. As a typical example,

$$_{92}\text{U}^{236} \longrightarrow {_{56}}\text{Ba}^{139} + {_{36}}\text{Kr}^{94} + 3{_0}\text{n}^1 + \text{energy}$$

The fission fragments have two important properties, kinetic energy and radioactivity. They are highly unstable, since they have a large neutron excess over the stable element of the same

atomic number.   They decay radioactively by a chain of beta and
gamma ray emissions.   The total *sensible* energy release from
fission is around 190 mev on the average, divided among the products approximately as follows:

> 167 kinetic energy of fission products
>   5 fast neutrons
>   7 instantaneously emitted gamma rays
>   5 fission product decay beta particles
> __6 fission product decay gamma rays__
> 190

An additional energy of about 11 mev, released in the form of
highly penetrating neutrinos, does not contribute to the practical
utilization of fission heat.   In spite of being large, the total energy
release is less than 0.1 per cent of the total mass-energy value of
the uranium nucleus.   The exact correlation of fission rate and
heat power in a nuclear reactor depends on the fraction of gamma
rays that escape from the system, as well as on the degree of
equilibrium of fission product production and decay.   Fortunately, precise numbers are not necessary.   Convenient relations
for estimates based on 190 mev/fission are

> 3.3×10^{10} fissions/watt-sec
> 1.3 gm U^{235} consumed per megawatt-day
> 10^7 kwh/lb of fuel fissioned

From 1 to 6 neutrons may be emitted in fission.   Table 1.2 shows

Table 1.2

Neutrons from Fissionable Elements

	ν	η (slow)	η (fast)
$_{92}U^{235}$	2.46	2.08	2.33
$_{94}Pu^{239}$	2.88	2.03	2.70
$_{92}U^{233}$	2.54	2.31	. .

the *average* number of neutrons per fission (ν) and the average
number of neutrons per absorption (η) in the principal fissionable
elements activated by low and high energy neutrons.   For natural uranium, with isotopic composition 0.7205 per cent U^{235}, 99.274
per cent U^{238}, the value of η is 1.34.

1.3. *The nuclear chain reactor*

If the number of neutrons in an assembly of fissionable materials can be maintained constant, a self-sustaining *chain reaction* exists. This is possible only because more than one neutron is produced for each neutron that sets off the fission process.

The basic interactions and components in a typical nuclear chain reactor are now presented. The reactor will be assumed to contain U²³⁵ as *fuel* and to operate with low-energy neutrons. The fission of a nucleus of U²³⁵ gives rise to around 2.5 neutrons on the average and 190 mev of useful energy. The kinetic energy of the fission fragments is the primary source of potentially useful heat, which can be removed by a circulating *coolant*. In a typical

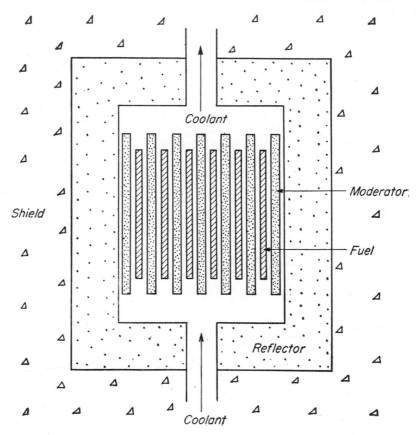

Figure 1.1. Schematic reactor

reactor, a *moderator* containing a light element such as hydrogen or carbon is intermixed with the fuel.   Successive collisions with moderator nuclei serve to reduce the energy of fission neutrons (2 mev average) to the thermal* level.   In the course of slowing down, many neutrons escape through the boundaries of the cen-

Table 1.3

Classification of Reactors

Energy of neutrons that produce fission
    fast
    intermediate (or epithermal)
    thermal

Nuclear fuel
    natural U (0.7% U^{235})
    slightly enriched U (1–2% U^{235})
    highly enriched U ($\simeq$90% U^{235})
    Pu^{239}
    U^{233}

Method of heat removal, by circulation of
    coolant only
    fuel mixed with coolant
    moderator-coolant
    fuel, moderator, and coolant

Purpose
    research
    prototype
    propulsion
    heat source
    electric power generation
    isotope production (fissionable or for industrial use)

Arrangement of fuel and moderator
    heterogeneous
    homogeneous

Materials used in the following reactor components
    moderator
    coolant
    structure
    reflector
    shield

---

* *Thermal* neutrons are those in equilibrium with a substance having thermal energy corresponding to temperature T.   Since room temperature corresponds to 0.025 ev neutron energy, the latter is a commonly quoted thermal value.

tral portion or *core*—a process called "leakage." A surrounding reflector has the function of reducing the number lost in this manner, while contributing additional moderation. Relatively few of the higher energy neutrons are removed from the cycle by absorption, unless an appreciable amount of U^{238} with its resonance absorption peaks is present. The choice of structural and moderating materials normally eliminates other capture losses at energies above thermal. Slow neutrons remain in the system for a relatively long time, since the chance of scattering is greater than that of absorption. Some are eventually absorbed by moderator, structure, U^{238}, or fission product isotopes, while a few escape from the assembly. The rest are absorbed by U^{235}. The reaction is self-sustaining or *critical* if the neutrons released from the fission of one U^{235} nucleus eventually produce one more fission (or if an initial fast neutron provides another to replace it at the end of the foregoing cycle). The sub-critical reactor is one sustained only by a separate supply of neutrons; in the super-critical reactor, neutrons will accumulate.

Figure 1.1 shows a schematic diagram of a reactor, with structural details omitted for simplicity. The radiation *shield* is not essential to the chain reaction, but must be provided for the protection of personnel from neutrons and gamma rays.

Reactors may be classified according to their function, materials of construction, and arrangement, as shown in Table 1.3.

1.4. *Reactor types and examples*

If one formed all the possible combinations of reactor features according to the classification in Table 1.3, about 1000 reactor types would be found. Many would not be feasible at all; others would be inordinately expensive. Some of the types that have been operated or show the most promise are now described briefly, to assist in orientation. First, consider six *power reactor* systems.

Heterogeneous, natural uranium, converter reactors. A chain reaction cannot be sustained in a mass of natural uranium metal, no matter how large, because of the unfavorable competition between neutron capture in U^{238} with fission. However, fuel may be arranged in lumps or rods separated by a material such as graphite or heavy water, in which neutrons are slowed to thermal energy with a minimum of capture. The first reactor built at Chicago in 1942 and the Hanford plutonium converter reactors are examples. The thermal X-pile at Oak Ridge, used for research and isotope production, consists of a 24-ft cube of graphite bars with 1248 diamond-shaped fuel channels on 8-in. centers. Cylindrical uranium rods 1.1 in. in diameter, 4 in. long, and coated with aluminum, are lined up end to end through the reactor. Cooling of the fuel rods is achieved by air flow through the passage formed by cylinder and diamond. In analogous power reactor designs, liquid sodium is used as a coolant because of its favorable heat transfer properties.

Heterogeneous, enriched uranium, thermal reactors. With water serving to reduce the energy of fission neutrons within a short distance, and with uranium enriched to the order of 90 per cent in U^{235}, giving an η value of over 2, it is possible to achieve criticality in a reactor volume of a few cubic feet. In the Materials Testing Reactor (MTR) at Arco, Idaho, thin (0.060-in.) plates of uranium-aluminum alloy, clad in aluminum, are used. A fuel assembly or element consists of 18 such plates in an array 3 in. square, 2 ft long, with water filling the 0.117-in. spaces between plates. The reactor core is critical with about 11 assemblies and 1760 gm of U^{235}, but is normally operated with about 30 fuel elements. This design has a large ratio of cooling surface area to volume of heat source, and has been adapted to high-temperature, high-power systems, by pressurization of the water.

Homogeneous, enriched uranium, circulating-fuel reactor. In this reactor a uranium salt such as UO_2SO_4 is dissolved in light or heavy water, and is contained in a corrosion-resistant metal vessel. The solution, heated by fission, is circulated to an external heat exchanger. This type admits the possibility of continuous chemical purification and refueling, which eliminates the costly fabrication of fuel elements. Since the fuel is in solution, a temperature limitation on fuel-metal structures is avoided. The Homogeneous Reactor Test (HRT) facility at Oak Ridge incorporates a 32-in. diameter zirconium alloy core tank, with approximately 90 per cent isotopic concentration U^{235} in D_2O.

Around the core, a "blanket" layer of thorium and D_2O, 14 in. thick, is used to produce U^{233}, which will eventually serve as core fuel. The system operates at about 300°C, 2000 psi pressure.

Fast breeder reactor. The fission in this reactor type occurs at a neutron energy of about 0.3 mev since there is no moderator to slow the neutrons. A fast reactor is characterized by compactness, but relatively large fuel mass (around 150 kg), and a high power density. Surrounding the U^{235} or Pu^{239} core is a blanket of natural uranium in which Pu^{239} is formed. Almost every fast neutron absorbed in fuel causes fission. As discussed in § 1.5, this makes possible an appreciable gain in fissionable material. The Experimental Breeder Reactor (EBR) at Arco, Idaho, consists of stainless-steel-clad U^{235} rods, cooled by circulating the liquid-metal alloy NaK, with a core volume of around 6 liters.

Boiling reactors. This type is based on the discovery that a water-moderated reactor will operate stably even if vigorous boiling of the fluid occurs. Fuel plates similar to those of the MTR may provide the heat to boil the water, or steam may be generated directly from a homogeneous solution. The advantages of direct boiling are the low pressure on the reactor vessel and the elimination of pumps and heat exchangers. The Experimental Boiling Water Reactor (EBWR) at Argonne National Laboratory has a cylindrical core 4 ft in each dimension, containing interchangeable natural and enriched uranium MTR-type fuel elements. Natural or forced circulation of the light-water coolant-moderator is possible.

Liquid-metal-fuel reactor. High thermal efficiencies can be attained with the use of a solution of fuel in a liquid metal such as bismuth, which can be circulated to an external heat exchanger for steam generation. Continuous chemical processing and breeding of U^{233} are also possible. Design studies at Brookhaven National Laboratory center about a solid-graphite moderated core, ultimately fueled with U^{233}, with a thorium-bismuth blanket in which additional U^{233} is formed.

Research reactors. All of the six reactor types discussed above are adaptable for use in research using radiations. For example, the CP-3 operated at Argonne National Laboratory for ten years was a heterogeneous, natural-uranium, heavy-water machine. Three partly or highly enriched thermal reactors have evolved as the most promising for research and training.

(1) *The Swimming Pool* or Bulk Shielding Facility, developed at Oak Ridge, was a prototype for the MTR. It consists of a 4-ft³ core of aluminum-clad U-Al alloy plates, with 3.6 kg of U^{235}. Natural convection cooling is provided by the water of the large tank in which the core is immersed. The water serves also as reflector and shield. A power level of more than 100 kw is possible if forced circulation is provided. The advantages of this type are simplicity of construction, ability of the metal cladding to retain hazardous fission products, and flexibility of core configuration.

(2) *The Water Boiler*, developed at Los Alamos, is a low-power version of the HRT. A water solution of a uranium salt is contained in a 0.5-ft³ spherical or cylindrical metal container surrounded by a graphite reflector. Cooling for this 50-kw core is provided by internal water tubing. Two of its advantages are small critical mass (less than 1 kg) and ability to utilize the radioactive fission gases as a separate gamma ray source. It also has the highest degree of inherent safety of the research reactors.

(3) *The Heavy-Water Reactor* or CP-5 type was developed at Argonne National Laboratory. Fuel elements similar to those of the MTR are immersed on 6-in. centers in a tank of circulating D_2O. Many spaces for irradiation are provided within and around the core. Its principal advantage is the large volume of moderator in which the thermal neutron flux is high.

1.5. *Criticality and neutron economy*

The elementary arithmetic that governs the fate of neutrons in a nuclear reactor is based on three processes: fission, capture that does not produce fission, and neutron escape from the assembly. In order to arrive at the essential features of the cycle we consider a reactor fueled with a pure fissionable element (U^{235}, U^{233}, or Pu^{239}). Let us select a typical neutron for observation, starting at the instant it is absorbed in the fissionable element. The number of neutrons produced by this absorption is η. Of these, only a fraction $\mathfrak{L}$ (labeled the non-leakage probability) will remain in the reactor, i.e., a number $\eta\mathfrak{L}$. The capture by other elements besides fuel will reduce this further, by a factor f (the ratio of absorption in fuel to the total absorption), to $\eta f\mathfrak{L}$. These neutrons are now available for absorption in fuel, and the cycle is complete. The original neutron has been *multiplied* by an amount equal to $k_e = \eta f\mathfrak{L}$, which is called the effective multiplication factor. When $k_e = 1$, the reactor is exactly self-sustaining, or critical. The quantity η is dependent on the choice of fuel as shown in Table 1.2; f approaches its maximum value of 1 if extraneous absorption in moderator, coolant, and structure is minimized by choice of materials; $\mathfrak{L}$ is dependent on the size of the reactor, approaching 1 for an infinite dimension.

We now turn to the possibility of creating fissionable material to replace or even exceed that consumed in the reactor. The most optimistic assumption is that no neutrons escape, $\mathfrak{L} = 1$, and that the neutrons not absorbed in the fissionable element go into the production of new fissionable isotopes from "fertile" elements. For example, consider a thermal reactor fueled with U^{233}, in which Th^{232} is converted to U^{233} by neutron absorption. The number of neutrons per absorption in U^{233} is $\eta = 2.31$. One of these neutrons is needed to maintain the cycle, and another must be absorbed in Th^{232} to replace the U^{233} burned. The number of neutrons left for purposes of *accumulating* fuel is $2.31 - 1 - 1 = 0.31$. The maximum or *theoretical breeding gain* is thus given by $\eta - 2$. The actual breeding gain will of course be somewhat lower, because of absorption and leakage losses. At high neutron energies, almost every neutron absorbed produces fission, i.e., η approaches ν. Inspection of Table 1.2 reveals that the *fast* breeding gain for Pu^{239} (0.70) would exceed that for U^{235} (0.33) and presumably also U^{233}. Qualitatively then, one would expect plutonium to be used in fast breeders and U^{233} to be used in thermal breeders.

The natural or slightly enriched uranium reactor is subject to a somewhat different set of formulas for criticality and isotope conversion, because of fast fission and the phenomenon of resonance capture in U^{238}. Instead of the $\eta f\mathfrak{L}$ neutrons previously found to be absorbed in uranium, there will be only ϵp times as many, where ϵ is the fast fission factor, around 1.03, and p is the resonance escape probability. The multiplication factor is

$$k_e = \epsilon p \eta f \mathcal{L}$$

In a graphite moderated reactor with the best arrangement of fuel and moderator, $\epsilon p f$ is only about 0.8, and with $\eta = 1.34$, the non-leakage probability $\mathcal{L}$ must be as high as 0.93 for the reactor to be critical. This can be achieved only by making the reactor very large, about 20 ft on a side. The analysis of isotope conversion must take into account the production of Pu^{239} by both resonance and thermal capture. Consider a limiting case in which there is negligible leakage, $\mathcal{L} = 1$, no absorption except in U^{235} or U^{238}, $f = 1$, and assume $\epsilon \simeq 1$ also. The disposition of η fast neutrons is as follows: $\eta(1 - p)$ are captured in U^{238} at energies above thermal to give Pu^{239}, ηp are absorbed by U^{235} (64.5 per cent) and U^{238} (35.5 per cent) at thermal energy. The ratio of plutonium production to *uranium* consumption is

$$\frac{Pu}{U} = \frac{\eta(1 - p) + 0.355\eta p}{\eta}$$

However, for criticality, $\eta p = 1$, which reduces the ratio to 0.519. This reveals that a thermal natural uranium reactor is limited to a conversion process, in contrast to breeding, as in a fast reactor. It will be noted that the number of Pu atoms *per* U^{235} *atom used* is $0.695/0.645 = 1.08$, which is the same as η for U^{235}, less one neutron to maintain the cycle.

1.6. *Design problems*

The principal problem faced by a reactor physicist is determination of the *compatibility* of a certain choice of reactor configuration and component materials with the intended function of the system. This compatibility includes many factors: economy of materials and of neutrons; shape, size, and weight; ability to produce the desired neutron flux and power levels; stability and life of operation; safety from accident and radiation hazard. A specific case may be most useful to illustrate. Assume that the following specifications for a power reactor have been set:

> highly enriched uranium fuel
> light-water moderator-coolant, pressurized

zirconium structure
100 megawatt total heat power
steam turbine, generator conversion of energy

Answers are needed to the questions below.   They are not necessarily listed in order of determination or of importance.

How does the critical size of the assembly and mass of fuel vary with the proportions of Zr and H_2O?

What choice of Zr/H_2O volume ratio best accomplishes the requirements of low fuel inventory, structural strength, and adequacy of heat transfer?

What is the distribution of neutron density and heat generation through core as function of time?

What effect does fuel consumption have on critical mass?

How much difference is there between the critical masses at low and high coolant temperature?   What degree of inherent safety from accidental power rise is provided by temperature changes?

What materials, shape, and arrangement of neutron-absorbing control elements are needed to guarantee shut-down and sensitive adjustment of power level?

How much effect does neutron absorption by fission products have on the neutron multiplication?

What effect will a sudden change in demand of electric power have on the stability of the reactor?

What is the radiation level at a neutron or gamma ray detector placed at a given location in the system?

What precautionary procedures should be adopted for a safe critical experiment and the initial start-up?   What measurements are essential?

How much radioactivity is induced in the cooling water and its impurities?

What should be the materials of construction and thickness of the radiation shield?

What hazard would result from a major accident, in which all safety devices failed and the core fission products were violently released?

A somewhat different set of questions might be asked in the design of a low-power research reactor, where more attention would be given to the prediction of radiation flux levels at many points.   In a breeder reactor planned for the production of U^{233} from thorium, more emphasis would be given to the loss of neutrons due to absorbers and leakage from the system.

1.7. *Nuclear Reactor Theory*

Before embarking on the presentation of methods of nuclear reactor analysis, it may be helpful to provide an outline of the role of theory, along with its possibilities and limitations.

The function of theory, as in all fields of engineering and applied science, is to provide a framework of logic for predicting system behavior, interpreting experimental results, and inventing new machines. Theory cannot substitute for actual measurements, but it can assist in the choice of materials and arrangement for most effective performance. The success of reactor theory for this purpose at this stage of its evolution depends on several factors—the type of system under consideration, the adequacy of fundamental constants, and the complexity and detail of the method of analysis used. It probably can be stated safely that reactor theory is capable of predicting results to an accuracy comparable or superior to theory in other engineering problems, but that its application still remains an *art*, subject to the need for considerable judgment and the use of empirical recipes.

The most common problem to which reactor theory is applied is calculation of the amounts of fissionable material and the arrangement of components that will sustain a chain reaction. In the steady state, the total number of neutrons in the system is constant, but with a spatial variation. The criterion for the steady state is that the rate of production of neutrons in fission be exactly equal to the rate at which they are lost to the system by capture or escape. The analysis thus brings in the mechanisms of neutron motion and interaction with nuclei, with reference to a large number of individual particles.

This problem will have been solved if it is possible to specify the number of neutrons n per unit volume, and in particular ranges of direction and energy for each point in the system, for any time of observation. This statement of the situation is deceptively simple in view of the multiplicity of possible approaches to the determination of n.

The number of neutrons present at any instant is in the billions. Thus n can be considered a continuous variable, subject to description by differential equations, as in the case of a fluid in the theory of hydrodynamics, or of temperature in the subject of heat transfer. Classic equations of continuity, conservation, or balance may then be applied. The most general reactor equation is an adaptation of that devised by Boltzmann in the kinetic theory of gases. It states in differential form that the time rate of accumulation of neutrons with a particular energy and direction at a point is equal to the sum of all the rates of gain and loss from the selected set, because of the processes of scattering, absorption, and free flow in space. Most of the descriptions of the steady state reactor are versions of the Boltzmann equation, simplified to a form amenable to mathematical operations. One such description divides the neutrons into classes according to energy, disregards directional aspects, and assumes that neutrons of each class obey the rules of gas diffusion. Although this so-called group-diffusion theory is adequate to represent gross behavior of neutrons, certain fine details related to directions of neutron motion are lost. Further, a good analytical method to describe the transfer of neutrons between energy groups has not yet been devised.

Fortunately, there are some reactor types that can be analyzed by the simpler approximate methods. For example, a unit cell of the heterogeneous natural uranium-graphite reactor can be imagined to contain a spatially uniform source of thermal neutrons, which obey a one-group diffusion theory. In an intermediate reactor with a beryllium moderator, a continuous neutron slowing process may be assumed, which provides a physically simple connection between energy groups. The reactor that is slightly off-critical is usually described by a one-group differential equation in the variables n and time t, that is merely an extension of the familiar growth equation of chemical reactions or population changes.

A simplified, approximate theory obviously cannot be expected to give uniformly accurate results when applied to many situations. It is necessary to compromise to the extent of choosing certain physical constants semi-empirically, in order to force agreement between theory and experiment. This will be unpalatable to the purist, but quite acceptable to the individual who needs to extend known information to predictions in new systems.

As analytical methods develop and experimental results accumulate, the crude calculation techniques now widely used will give way to elegant and rigorous approaches. The urgent demand for *answers* in the rapidly growing field of reactor design, construction, and operation justifies the present use of theories that admittedly give first-order approximations.

References

Semat, Henry, *Introduction to Atomic and Nuclear Physics.*   New York: Rinehart and Co. (1954).

Lapp, R. E., and H. L. Andrews, *Nuclear Radiation Physics*, 2nd Ed. Englewood Cliffs, N. J.: Prentice-Hall, Inc. (1954).

Halliday, David, *Introductory Nuclear Physics*, 2nd Ed.   New York: John Wiley and Sons (1955).

Murray, Raymond L., *Introduction to Nuclear Engineering.*   Englewood Cliffs, N. J.: Prentice-Hall, Inc. (1954).

Stephenson, R., *Introduction to Nuclear Engineering.*   New York: McGraw-Hill Book Co., Inc. (1954).

Glasstone, Samuel, *The Principles of Nuclear Engineering.*   New York: D. Van Nostrand Co. (1955).

Research Reactors: Selected reference material, United States Atomic Energy Commission.   Washington: Superintendent of Documents, U. S. Government Printing Office (1955).

Glasstone, Samuel, and Milton C. Edlund, *The Elements of Nuclear Reactor Theory.*   New York: D. Van Nostrand Co. (1952).

Peaceful Uses of Atomic Energy: Proceedings of the International Conference in Geneva, August 1955.   Volume 2, *Physics, Research Reactors* and Volume 3, *Power Reactors.*   New York: Columbia University Press.

Kinsman, Simon, ed., *Radiological Health Handbook.*   Cincinnati: U. S. Department of Health Education and Welfare (April 1954).   (Contains table of isotopes by J. M. Hollander, I. Perlman, and G. T. Seaborg that also appears in *Reviews of Modern Physics*, April 1953.)

Hughes, Donald J., and John A. Harvey, *Neutron Cross Sections*, BNL-325.   Washington: U. S. Government Printing Office (1955). See also *Heavy Element Cross Sections Presented at Geneva, August 1955 Addendum to BNL-325*, same authors.

Nuclear Engineering, Parts I, II, III.   New York: American Institute of Chemical Engineers (1954).

Charpie, R. A., J. Horowitz, D. J. Hughes, D. J. Littler, editors, *Progress in Nuclear Energy, Series I, Physics and Mathematics.* New York: McGraw-Hill Book Co., Inc. (1956).

Littler, D. J., and J. F. Raffle, *An Introduction to Reactor Physics.* New York: McGraw-Hill Book Co., Inc. (1956).

Chapter 2

NEUTRON MOTION

Each neutron in a reactor experiences a different history from the time it is released in a fission event until it disappears. Its motion may be described in terms of three microscopic phenomena: (a) collision with a nucleus, which results in a change in neutron energy and direction of motion; (b) capture by a nucleus; (c) free flight between collisions. Ultimately, it may leave the system for a region of space where its influence on the reactor is no longer felt. Radioactive decay of the neutron is of no consequence on the time scale of reactor cycles.

The large-scale behavior of a reactor depends on, and must be described in terms of, the total number of neutrons within it at any time. Since this number is so large, one may disregard the discreteness of the particle and consider neutron number as a continuous variable of position and energy. In this connection, the distribution function, which states the fraction of the total that possess a given attribute, is a useful concept. One may also employ the concept of the *typical* neutron, if the probability that it will experience a particular sequence of events can be calculated.

2.1. *Cross sections*

The probability of interaction between neutron and nucleus is measured numerically by the *microscopic cross section* σ, which may be considered as the *effective target area* of a nucleus. If, in each second, a beam of j neutrons crosses a 1-cm² area of a material which contains N nuclei per cm³, each of effective area σ, the number of particles removed from the beam per second by collision events in an infinitesimal layer of thickness dx is $jN\sigma\,dx$. It is noted that the product $N\sigma\,dx$ is the total area presented by all nuclei in this layer and, relative to the 1-cm² area, is a probability of collision within the layer. The symbol σ is usually reserved for total cross section, which includes all of the possible component processes. Thus

$$\sigma = \sigma_s + \sigma_a$$

where s refers to scattering and a to absorption. In turn,

$$\sigma_s = \sigma_{se} + \sigma_{si}$$
$$\sigma_a = \sigma_c + \sigma_f$$

where the subscripts are e elastic, i inelastic, c radiative capture, f fission. As illustration, the measured total cross section of a U^{235} nucleus for neutrons of 2200 meters/sec speed, 0.0253 ev energy, is $\sigma = 697 \times 10^{-24}$ cm², or using the conversion $1\ barn = 10^{-24}\ cm^2$, 697 barns. This may be broken down into

$$\sigma_s = 10 \text{ barns} \quad \text{scattering}$$
$$\sigma_c = 107 \text{ barns} \quad \text{capture}$$
$$\sigma_f = 580 \text{ barns} \quad \text{fission}$$

The absorption cross section is thus 687 barns. The product $N\sigma$, denoted by Σ, called the *macroscopic* cross section with units cm⁻¹, signifies the total nuclear target area per cubic centimeter. Appropriate subscripts are again attached to refer to specific processes.

Numerical Illustration: Find the macroscopic *absorption* cross section Σ_a for 2200-meters/sec neutrons in pure U^{235} metal, density 18.7 gm/cm³.

Solution: The number of nuclei per cubic centimeter is $18.7/235.1 \times$ Avogadro's number 6.023×10^{23}/mole, or $N = 0.0479 \times 10^{24}$ cm⁻³. Thus

$$\Sigma_a = N\sigma_a = (0.0479 \times 10^{24} \text{ cm}^{-3})(687 \times 10^{-24} \text{ cm}^2)$$
$$= 32.9 \text{ cm}^{-1}$$

We note that the factors 10^{24} and 10^{-24} cancel out; hence the number of atoms N may be expressed in *units of 10^{24}* and cross sections in *barns* for future such products.

Neutron attenuation. The rate of removal with distance of neutrons from a beam j is

$$\frac{dj}{dx} = -jN\sigma$$

from which the exponential attenuation formula is obtained.

$$j = j_0 e^{-\Sigma x}$$

where j_0 is the number incident on the plane $x = 0$. The mean free path λ, or average distance a neutron travels between events, can be shown to be the reciprocal of the macroscopic cross section Σ, as follows. In a layer dx, the number removed from the beam by collisions is $dj = -j\Sigma\, dx = -\Sigma e^{-\Sigma x}\, dx$. The average distance at which collision occurs is

$$\bar{x} = \frac{\int_0^\infty x\, dj}{j_0} = \frac{1}{\Sigma} = \lambda$$

where j_0 is both the initial beam and the eventual total number of collisions. For example, in water with a scattering cross section σ_s of 45 barns per molecule at 1 ev, and N of 0.0334, $\Sigma_s = 1.50$ cm^{-1} and $\lambda_s = 0.67$ cm.

Cross section values are dependent on the speed or energy of the neutron and on the particular nucleus bombarded. A few useful generalizations can be made.

(a) At most energies and with most elements, scattering cross sections change slowly with energy. For most materials at energies near 1 mev, σ_s is a few barns, and is slowly decreasing with increasing energy. For example, σ_s for hydrogen is 4.3 barns at 1 mev and 2.9 barns at 2 mev.

(b) The absorption cross section of most nuclei for thermal neutrons, those having energy comparable to that of atoms in a substance, decreases with increasing neutron speed, i.e., $\sigma_a \sim 1/v$. The absorption cross sections of reactor moderators and structural materials should be appreciably lower than 1 barn in order to avoid loss of neutrons needed to maintain the cycle. Values of σ_a at 2200 meters/sec neutron speed (0.0253 ev) for several common elements in pure form are listed in Table 2.1.

Table 2.1

**Absorption Cross Sections of
Moderators and Structural Materials**

Element	σ_a (barns)
H	0.330
D	4.6×10^{-4}
C	0.0032
Be	0.010
Al	0.23
Zr	0.18
Fe	2.53

(c) Many elements exhibit strong absorption in a narrow neutron energy range. A few important cases of this *resonance absorption* are given in Table 2.2.

Table 2.2

Cross Sections at Resonance Peaks

Isotope	Neutron Energy (ev)	σ_a at Peak (barns)
Cd^{113}	0.175	7800
In^{115}	1.46	3.0×10^4
Xe^{135}	0.065	3.4×10^6
Au^{197}	4.9	3.0×10^4
U^{238}	6.7	7000

(d) The cross sections for nuclear fuels at thermal energy is very high, as seen in Table 2.3. A complete compilation of cross

Table 2.3

Cross Sections for Fissionable Materials

Fuel	Cross Sections (in barns, at 2200 meters/sec)			
	σ_a	σ_c	σ_f	σ_s^*
U^{235}	687	107	580	10
Pu^{239}	1065	315	750	9.6
U^{233}	585	52	533	
U (natural)	7.68	3.50	4.18	8.3
U^{238}	2.75	2.75	. . .	8.3

sections is given in the report *Neutron Cross Sections*, BNL-325 (see References). Therein appear values for most elements and stable isotopes, with graphs of σ as a function of energy from the low ev region to 100 mev.

---

* Average for thermal neutrons.

Numerical Illustration: Find the total absorption cross section Σ_a for 0.0253 ev neutrons in a reactor core composed of U^{235}, water, and aluminum. The volume fractions of each component are $f_{U\text{-}235} = 0.002$, $f_{H_2O} = 0.600$ and $f_{Al} = 0.398$.

Solution.   A tabular calculation form will be useful. The numbers of nuclei per cm^3 are obtained from the densities and molecular weights; oxygen is ignored as having a negligible cross section.

Element	ρ (gm/cm³)	N	σ_a (barns)	Σ_a (cm⁻¹)	$f\Sigma_a$ (cm⁻¹)
U^{235}	18.7	0.0479	687	32.9	0.0658
H	0.1117	0.0668	0.33	0.0220	0.0132
Al	2.71	0.0605	0.23	0.0139	0.0055
				Total $\Sigma_a =$	0.0845

2.2. Neutron flux

The neutron flux, one of the most widely used concepts in reactor physics, has several representations and interpretations. An understandable confusion as to its meaning often arises, particularly in connection with the term *neutron current*.

Consider again the *beam* of neutrons of common direction and speed v, impinging on a square centimeter normal to the beam. If the neutron number per unit volume is n, then the number crossing the plane unit area each second is clearly nv. Now if a centimeter cube containing N nuclei, each of cross section σ cm² as seen by the neutrons, is placed behind the plane, the total target area seen is the macroscopic cross section $\Sigma = N\sigma$. The number of collisions or reaction events per cubic centimeter, assuming negligible "shadowing" of particles by each other, is $R = nv\Sigma$ per sec.

Definition of flux.   Now, examine the situation in a nuclear reactor, composed of a homogeneous material with macroscopic cross section Σ, where there are again n neutrons per cm³, of speed v, but with random direction. The reaction rate in this case is the same as it was in the case of a beam, $R = nv\Sigma$, direction being meaningless in connection with the neutron. However, we may now define the *flux* in a medium as

$$\phi = nv = \frac{R}{\Sigma} = \frac{\text{reaction rate per cubic centimeter}}{\text{macroscopic cross section}} \qquad (2.1)$$

No reference to a number crossing a specific area needs to be made. Indeed, there exists no plane unit area to which the flux can be referred.

> **Numerical Illustration:** Find the average thermal neutron flux in a reactor core for which the macroscopic fission cross section is 0.05 cm⁻¹ and the power density is 20 kw/liter. Recall that 1 watt = 3.3×10^{10} fissions/sec.
>
> *Solution:* The reaction rate R is (3.3×10^{10} fissions/watt-sec)(20 watts/cm³) = 6.6×10^{11} fissions/sec-cm³. The flux is $\phi = R/\Sigma_f = (6.6 \times 10^{11}$ fissions/sec-cm³$)/(0.05$ cm⁻¹$) = 1.32 \times 10^{13}$/cm²-sec.

It is to be noted that the units of flux are

$$n\left(\frac{\text{neutrons}}{\text{cm}^3}\right)v\left(\frac{\text{cm}}{\text{sec}}\right) = \phi\left(\frac{\text{neutrons}}{\text{cm}^2\text{-sec}}\right)$$

Should one insist on a connection with area, two facts can be proved: (a) ϕ is the number of neutrons that enter an imaginary sphere each second, of total surface area 4 cm², diametral plane area 1 cm²; (b) ϕ is equal to *twice* the total number of neutrons that cross a plane area each second from both sides. The most convenient definition of flux is simply the product nv, which is seen to be the sum of all of the speeds of the neutrons in a cubic centimeter. An extension to the case where the neutrons selected have a variety of speeds can be made by writing the flux as an integral:

$$\phi_0 = \int n(v)v \, dv \tag{2.2}$$

where $n(v)$, the neutron speed *distribution function*, is the number of neutrons in a unit speed range evaluated at v. If both sides of Equation (2.2) are divided by n_0, the total number of neutrons in the group, the resulting right side is the average speed

$$\bar{v} = \frac{\int n(v)v \, dv}{\int n(v) \, dv} \tag{2.3}$$

and the total flux is

$$\phi_0 = n_0\bar{v} \tag{2.4}$$

This flux may be considered for many purposes to be equivalent to one composed of neutrons of a *single speed*. For instance, if an appropriate average cross section $\bar{\Sigma}$ is chosen, the rate of inter-

action with nuclei per unit volume may be written as $R = \phi_0 \overline{\Sigma}$, as
in Equation (2.1). It is in this way that the detailed structure
of the thermal neutron distribution can often be ignored. Except
where the distribution feature is important, we shall drop the
subscript, and write simply ϕ for the total flux of a group of
neutrons.

2.3. *Neutron current*

Having noted previously that ϕ does *not* represent the number
of neutrons crossing a plane square centimeter area per second,
we ask, "What does?" The following derivation will yield the

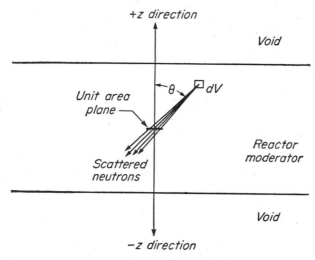

Figure 2.1. Geometry for analysis of current.

answer, and also some understanding of the limitations of the
method labeled *diffusion theory*. Picture, as in Figure 2.1, a plane
square centimeter lying somewhere in a large block of reactor
moderator. Within limits, it is immaterial whether or not the
block contains nuclear fuel. The method by which neutrons are
supplied is not specified, but it is supposed that the flux varies
from point to point. This is a reasonable expectation because
neutrons continually escape from the boundaries of the moderator,
resulting in a low value of n near these surfaces. In this sense
the flux is analogous to the temperature in an internally heated

metal maintained at fixed surface temperature. For simplicity, let the block be an infinitely broad slab of finite vertical thickness, so that there is a variation of flux in the z direction only. The number of neutrons that cross the plane each second *from above* is the sum of all those that start out in the right direction after making a collision, and are not lost by absorption or scattering aside. The rate of scattering in any element of volume dV is $\phi \Sigma_s \, dV$; assuming that the colliding neutrons were uniformly distributed in direction, they will be so distributed after scattering. A fraction $\cos \theta / 4\pi r^2$ are aimed correctly toward the square centimeter plane. A fraction $e^{-\Sigma r}$ of these get to it without further collision. The total number crossing a square centimeter toward the negative z direction is denoted by the term *directed current density* or simply *current*, and labeled j_-.

$$j_- = \int \phi \Sigma_s \, dV \, \frac{\cos \theta}{4\pi r^2} \, e^{-\Sigma r} \qquad (2.5)$$

At this point certain simplifications and assumptions are made:

(1) The absorption cross section of the medium is taken to be much less than the scattering cross section, so that $\Sigma = \Sigma_a + \Sigma_s$ may be replaced by Σ_s. In a reactor moderated with water or graphite and with low fuel concentration, this criterion is readily met; in a metal uranium fuel element, it is not.

(2) The reactor medium is homogeneous, so that Σ_s does not depend on position and may be removed from within the integral. This condition can be met far from the boundary between two dissimilar materials, e.g., water core and graphite reflector. The condition that the cross section be independent of neutron direction is easily achieved except in certain crystalline materials.

(3) The flux ϕ varies linearly with distance away from the plane at $z = 0$, i.e.,

$$\phi(z) = \phi + \frac{d\phi}{dz} \, z$$

where ϕ is the flux and $d\phi/dz$ is the slope of the flux *at* the plane. This cannot be correct everywhere because the neutron density n drops off more and more rapidly as the top surface of the block is approached. Use of what amounts to two terms of a Taylor's series expansion of ϕ about the origin does not provide a sufficiently accurate representation except far from boundaries.

(4) The integration is performed over all space above the plane, i.e., $r = 0$, to $r = \infty$. So long as the product $\Sigma_s r$, evaluated at the boundary, is much greater than unity, i.e., scattering sources are all much farther away than a mean free path $\lambda_s = 1/\Sigma_s$, there is no serious error in using $r = \infty$. This restriction again implies that the results will not apply for planes located near boundaries.

(5) Wherever λ_s appears, a replacement is made with the *transport mean free path* $\lambda_t = \lambda_s/(1 - \overline{\cos \theta})$ where $\overline{\cos \theta}$ is the average cosine of the angle of neutron scattering. This modification anticipates a consequence of transport theory (see Chapter 9), which takes account of the distribution in neutron direction.

Integration of Equation (2.5) with these changes gives

$$ j_- = \frac{\phi}{4} + \frac{\lambda_t}{6}\frac{d\phi}{dz} \qquad \begin{array}{l}\text{negative } z \\ \text{directed current}\end{array} \qquad (2.6) $$

where the flux and its derivative are evaluated at the plane. A repetition of the process for neutrons crossing from below gives

$$ j_+ = \frac{\phi}{4} - \frac{\lambda_t}{6}\frac{d\phi}{dz} \qquad \begin{array}{l}\text{positive } z \\ \text{directed current}\end{array} \qquad (2.7) $$

The total number of neutrons that cross the square centimeter each second, or *total current* is

$$ j_T = j_- + j_+ = \frac{\phi}{2} \qquad \text{total current} \qquad (2.8) $$

This factor of 2 should be noted carefully. Another special definition of flux in § 2.2 may now be verified. For instance, the average current density entering the surface of a sphere will be simply $\phi/4$ according to Equations (2.6) and (2.7), the effect of flux variation being negligible. For a sphere of surface area 4 cm², the entering current is ϕ.

Wherever there is any variation of neutron density and flux with position, there will be more neutrons flowing in one direction than the other. The *net current* is the resultant flow, given simply by

$$ j = j_+ - j_- = -\frac{\lambda_t}{3}\frac{d\phi}{dz} \qquad \text{net current} \qquad (2.9) $$

Note that the units of current are

$$(\text{cm})\left(\frac{\text{neutrons}}{\text{cm}^2\text{-sec}} \cdot \frac{1}{\text{cm}}\right) = \frac{\text{neutrons}}{\text{cm}^2\text{-sec}}$$

the same as for flux. The analysis above was based on a slab geometry for which there was a variation in flux only in one direction. In general, ϕ will depend on x, y, and z, or whatever set of coordinates is used. Equation (2.9) may be generalized to the fundamental formula of diffusion theory,

$$j = -D\,\nabla\phi \qquad \text{Fick's law of diffusion} \qquad (2.10)$$

where $D = \lambda_t/3$ is the diffusion coefficient and ∇ is the gradient operator, written in vector notation

$$\nabla = i\,\frac{\partial}{\partial x} + j\,\frac{\partial}{\partial y} + k\,\frac{\partial}{\partial z} \qquad (2.11)$$

Fick's law states that the net current of neutrons is in the direction away from the region of greater neutron density and proportional to the maximum rate of change. It was derived many years before the discovery of neutrons or the development of the nuclear reactor, in connection with the diffusion of gases. Its counterpart is recognized in other processes, such as heat transfer, where the rate of flow of heat is proportional to the gradient of the temperature.

Under the conditions of the derivation just completed, application of the formula must be restricted to regions of the medium far from boundaries. We should like, however, to know the value of the outward-directed leakage current at the surface.

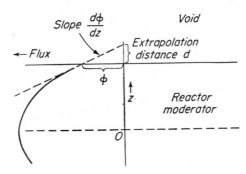

Figure 2.2. Extrapolation distance at boundary of core.

According to advanced theory (and experiment) the flux would drop off as shown in the solid curve in Figure 2.2. If the slope of this correct flux, evaluated slightly within the boundary, is extended outward as shown by the dashed line, it will go to zero at a distance outside

$$d = -\frac{\phi}{d\phi/dz} = 0.71\lambda_t \tag{2.12}$$

called the *extrapolation distance*. (This is a better result than would be obtained by formal application of the diffusion theory, Equation (2.6), with the assumption that $j_- = 0$ at the boundary, because no neutrons return from the void. For this *incorrect* version, d is $\frac{2}{3}\lambda_t$.)

We imagine for purposes of calculating reactor flux distributions that the system is extended in each direction by the extrapolation distance. For instance if a slab of moderator of height H contained enough fuel to be exactly critical, the vertical flux distribution would be found to be

$$\phi = \phi_c \cos \frac{\pi z}{H'} \tag{2.13}$$

where $H' = H + 2d$ is the "extrapolated height." The difference between flux and current may now be examined. According to Equation (2.9) the current is

$$j = -D\frac{d\phi}{dz} = \phi_c D \frac{\pi}{H'} \sin \frac{\pi z}{H'}$$

Now at $z = 0$, j is zero, because there are equal flows from above and below this plane; the flux is a maximum there however. At $z = H/2$, the flux becomes small, but the current is large, of amount $\phi_c(D\pi/H') \sin(\pi H/2H')$.

Numerical Illustration: Estimate the thermal neutron leakage current at the surface of a slab reactor, height 150 cm, composed of graphite with transport mean free path 2.7 cm, when the central flux is 2×10^{12}/cm²-sec.

Solution: The extrapolation distance is $d = 0.71\lambda_t = 1.9$ cm, and $H' = 150 + 3.8 = 153.8$ cm. The diffusion coefficient is $D = \lambda_t/3 = 0.9$ cm, and the surface current is approximately

$$j_s = \phi_c \frac{D\pi}{H'} \sin 0.975 \frac{\pi}{2} = \frac{(2 \times 10^{12})(0.9)(\pi)(0.999)}{153.8}$$

$$= 3.67 \times 10^{10}/\text{cm}^2\text{-sec}$$

2.4. *Maxwellian flux distribution*

After several collisions, neutrons reach an energy that is comparable to that of the atoms in the moderator, and are as likely to gain as to lose energy in subsequent collisions. Their energy is then determined by the thermal distribution of the moderator at absolute temperature T. Thermal neutrons are rather accurately distributed in speed v according to the gas equation of Maxwell,

$$n(v) = n_0 A v^2 e^{-mv^2/2kT} \qquad \text{maxwellian distribution} \qquad (2.14)$$

where n_0 is the total number of neutrons per cubic centimeter and

$$A = 4\pi \left(\frac{m}{2\pi kT} \right)^{3/2} \qquad (2.15)$$

This distribution is plotted in Figure 2.3. By application of Equations (2.3), (2.4), (2.14) and (2.15), with integration from

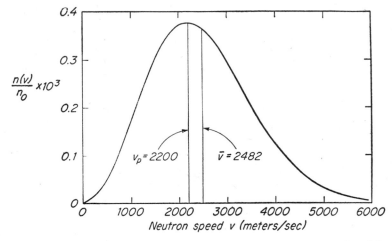

Figure 2.3. Maxwellian distribution of neutrons in medium at 20°C.

$v = 0$ to $v = \infty$, it is found that

$$\bar{v} = \sqrt{\frac{8kT}{\pi m}} \qquad \text{average speed} \qquad (2.16)$$

The peak of the speed distribution, found by equating the derivative of $n(v)$ in Equation (2.14) to zero, is

$$v_p = \sqrt{\frac{2kT}{m}} \qquad \text{most probable speed} \qquad (2.17)$$

The ratio $\bar{v}/v_p$ is seen to be $2/\sqrt{\pi} = 1.128$. For neutrons in equilibrium with a medium at room temperature, 293°K, the most probable speed is 2200 meters/sec. Measured thermal neutron cross sections are normally quoted for this particular speed, or its equivalent in energy, 0.0253 ev.

Numerical Illustration: Find the most probable neutron speed for a distribution in a medium at temperature 320°C.

Solution: From the table of atomic constants, Appendix B, the neutron mass is $m = 1.675 \times 10^{-24}$ gm, and $k = 1.380 \times 10^{-16}$ erg/deg. At the absolute temperature $T = 593°K$,

$$v_p = \sqrt{\frac{(2)(1.380 \times 10^{-16})(593)}{1.675 \times 10^{-24}}} = 3.13 \times 10^5 \text{ cm/sec}$$

The *effective* cross section for a neutron distribution in a substance for which the cross section depends on neutron speed is defined by an equality of reaction rates per unit target nucleus

$$\frac{R}{N} = \phi_0 \bar{\sigma} = \int \phi(v)\sigma(v)\, dv$$

or

$$\bar{\sigma} = \frac{\int n(v)v\sigma(v)\, dv}{\int n(v)v\, dv} \qquad \begin{array}{l}\text{effective} \\ \text{cross section}\end{array} \qquad (2.18)$$

A common and simple situation is the combination of maxwellian distribution and absorber with $1/v$ cross section, $\sigma = K/v$. The constant K may be any product of speed and known cross section at that speed; the most probable conditions are tabulated and thus are most convenient. Thus,

$$\sigma(v) = \frac{\sigma_p v_p}{v} \qquad \begin{array}{l}\text{cross section for} \\ 1/v \text{ absorber}\end{array} \qquad (2.19)$$

Combination of Equations (2.14), (2.18) and (2.19) gives

$$\bar{\sigma} = \frac{\sigma_p v_p}{\bar{v}} = \sigma(\bar{v}) \qquad (2.20)$$

Thus the effective cross section is equal to the cross section *evaluated at the average speed*. Since $v_p/\bar{v} = 1/1.128$, the effective cross section for a $1/v$ absorber with maxwellian neutrons is lower than the commonly quoted thermal value by a factor 1.128. For maxwellian neutrons and absorbers that do not follow the $1/v$ law because of resonances near thermal energy, it is necessary to find a correction factor experimentally or by integration of Equation (2.18) with appropriate $n(v)$.* The 2200-meter/sec values must be multiplied by a "not-$1/v$ factor," examples of which are listed in Table 2.4. This correction is a function of neutron tempera-

Table 2.4

Cross Sections of Not-$1/v$ Absorbers

Element	σ_p (barns)	Not-$1/v$ Factor (20°C)
$_{48}$Cd	2550	1.3
$_{62}$Sm	5500	1.5
$_{63}$Eu	4600	0.95
$_{64}$Gd	46000	0.85
$_{80}$Hg	380	0.95
$_{92}$U^{235}	687	0.981
$_{94}$Pu^{239}	1075	1.075
$_{92}$U (natural)	7.68	0.99

ture; the value quoted corresponds to room temperature.

Some authors, e.g., Hughes, choose to define flux in a different way, as the product $\phi_p = n_0 v_p$. The reaction rate with $1/v$ absorber and maxwellian flux is thus

$$R = \phi_0 \bar{\sigma} = \left(\phi_p \frac{\bar{v}}{v_p}\right)\left(\sigma_p \frac{v_p}{\bar{v}}\right) = \phi_p \sigma_p \qquad (2.21)$$

i.e., the product of flux and cross section at most probable speed. For many purposes this definition of flux is more convenient than Equation (2.4). Care should be exercised in the correlation of data from various sources because of these differences in definition.

Numerical Illustration: Find the effective cross section for a maxwellian distribution in the U^{235}-H$_2$O-Al reactor core (§ 2.1) in a medium at room temperature. In addition,

---

* If the thermal absorption cross section is of the order of magnitude of the scattering cross section, the distribution will not be maxwellian. See Cohen, E. Richard, "A Survey of Neutron Thermalization Theory," Geneva Paper P/611, Volume 5 (References).

calculate the *thermal utilization* defined as (absorption in uranium)/(total absorption).

Solution: The not-1/v factor of 0.981 must be applied to the uranium cross section and the factor 1/1.128 applied to each material to convert the cross sections to the maxwellian average values. In tabular form,

Element	$f\Sigma_a$ (0.0253 ev)	$f\Sigma_a$ (maxwellian)
U^{235}	0.0658	0.0572
H	0.0132	0.0117
Al	0.0055	0.0049
		$\bar{\Sigma}_a = 0.0738$

The fractional absorption in uranium is 0.0572/0.0738 = 0.7751.

2.5. *Neutron energy losses*

Elastic scattering of a neutron with a nucleus results in a discrete loss of neutron energy of an amount varying from zero to the maximum allowable by the laws of conservation of momentum and energy. The largest possible loss is now derived for the case of a target nucleus with mass A times as large as the neutron mass, which will be taken as m. The particular collision in which the neutron is reversed in direction gives rise to the greatest energy exchange, and is simplest mathematically. Table 2.5 lists

Table 2.5

Collision Analysis

	Before		After	
	neutron	target	neutron	target
Mass...............	m	Am	m	Am
Velocity............	v_0	0	$-v$	V
Momentum.........	mv_0	0	$-mv$	AmV
Energy.............	$E_0 = mv_0^2/2$	0	$E = mv^2/2$	$AmV^2/2$

conditions before and after the collision as would be observed by an experimenter in the laboratory (*not* according to an observer at the center of mass of the colliding particles). Conservation of momentum and kinetic energy requires that

$$v_0 = -v + AV$$
$$v_0^2 = v^2 + AV^2$$

Elimination of V gives

$$\frac{E}{E_0} = \frac{v^2}{v_0^2} = \left(\frac{A-1}{A+1}\right)^2 \qquad (2.22)$$

For future convenience, we define

$$\alpha = \left(\frac{A-1}{A+1}\right)^2$$

The maximum fractional loss is

$$\frac{\Delta E}{E_0} = \frac{E_0 - E}{E_0} = \frac{4A}{(1+A)^2} = 1 - \alpha \qquad (2.23)$$

From this formula it can be seen that in the collision of a neutron with a carbon nucleus, $A = 12$, the largest energy loss possible is 28 per cent. In contrast, a neutron may lose *all* of its initial energy in a collision with hydrogen, for which $A = 1$. This comparison, which shows hydrogenous materials to be the best moderators for reactors, is important in the theory of the complete slowing-down process, involving many collisions. As will be shown later, the *age theory* of slowing, which is applicable if there is only a small loss of energy in each collision, will be questionable for hydrogen.

In the more general collision, the neutron is deflected through an angle θ from its original direction of motion. A relation between the energy after collision E and the scattering angle θ may be derived by use of the *center-of-mass coordinate system*. As a neutron approaches the target nucleus, the center of mass of the system as viewed by the laboratory observer moves in the same line. Its speed V_c is determined by the fact that the total momentum of the system is equal to that of the neutron. Thus

$$(m + Am)V_c = mv_0$$

or
$$V_c = \frac{v_0}{1+A} \qquad (2.24)$$

To an observer remaining on the *center of mass*, the neutron appears to recede after collision at an angle ϕ (not to be confused with flux) from the point of impact, with a velocity v_n, speed equal to that of approach, which was

$$v_0 - V_c = \frac{Av_0}{1+A} \qquad (2.25)$$

The true velocity in the laboratory is the vector sum of the neutron velocity relative to the center of mass and the velocity of the center of mass itself:

$$v = v_n + V_c \tag{2.26}$$

as shown in Figure 2.4. Application of the cosine rule and Equations (2.24) and (2.25) yields the formula

$$\frac{E}{E_0} = \frac{v^2}{v_0^2} = \frac{1 + 2A \cos \phi + A^2}{(1 + A)^2} = \frac{1 + \alpha}{2} + \frac{1 - \alpha}{2} \cos \phi \tag{2.27}$$

Another useful property of the vector triangle is that

$$\cos \theta = \frac{1 + A \cos \phi}{\sqrt{1 + 2A \cos \phi + A^2}} \tag{2.28}$$

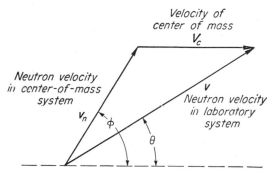

Figure 2.4.   Velocity vector diagram for neutron-nucleus collision.

In addition to its convenience for evaluating the energy after collision, the center-of-mass concept is useful for the derivation of two important parameters: $\overline{\cos \theta}$, the average cosine of the (laboratory) scattering angle used in connection with λ_t (see § 2.3), and ξ, the average change in the natural logarithm of the energy upon collision with a nucleus. We start with the fact that when low energy neutrons collide elastically with nuclei, each direction of motion after collision is equally probable as viewed from the center of mass. Scattering is said to be *spherically symmetric in the center of mass system*. Stated in another way, if n neutrons were scattered from a given type of nucleus, the number emerging in any unit area on a sphere of unit radius would be independent of angle, and equal to $n/4\pi$. Of greater interest is the number passing through the fraction of the total surface area associated with a range of angles $d\phi$ at ϕ. The absolute area of a ring of radius $\sin\phi$, width $d\phi$ on a sphere of unit radius, is $2\pi \sin\phi\, d\phi$. The fraction of the total sphere area of 4π is thus $\frac{1}{2}\sin\phi\, d\phi = -d(\cos\phi)/2$. The differential number scattered through this area is

$$dn = \frac{-d(\cos\phi)}{2}\, n \qquad (2.29)$$

Now the average cosine of the scattering angle is

$$\overline{\cos\theta} = \frac{\int \cos\theta\, dn}{n} \qquad (2.30)$$

It is necessary to invoke Equations (2.28) and (2.29) to put the integrand in terms of a common variable $\cos\phi$. Integration of Equation (2.30) over the variable $\cos\phi$ from -1 to 1 gives

$$\overline{\cos\theta} = \frac{2}{3A} \qquad \begin{array}{l}\text{average cosine of}\\ \text{scattering angle}\end{array} \qquad (2.31)$$

Numerical values for several materials are listed in Table 2.6.

Table 2.6

Values of $\overline{\cos\theta}$ and ξ

Element	A	$\overline{\cos\theta}$	$\bar\theta$	ξ
H	1	0.667	48°	1
D	2	0.333	70.5°	0.7261
Be	9	0.074	86°	0.2078
C	12	0.056	87°	0.1589
O	16	0.042	87.5°	0.1209
U	238	0.0028	89°50′	0.0084

$\bar\theta$ is not the average angle, but that corresponding to the average cosine. The scattering by hydrogen is highly in the forward direction, while at the other extreme with uranium, it is almost completely symmetric.

The average *logarithmic* energy change per collision is

$$\xi = \frac{\int \Delta(\ln E)\, dn}{n} \qquad (2.32)$$

In order to integrate, we differentiate Equation (2.27) and compare with Equation (2.29) to show that the fraction of neutrons of initial energy E_0 that are scattered into a range dE at energy

E is

$$\frac{dn}{n} = \frac{-dE}{E_0(1 - \alpha)} \qquad (2.33)$$

Also $\Delta(\ln E) = \ln E_0 - \ln E = \ln (E_0/E)$. Substituting and integrating from E_0 to αE_0, the *lowest* possible final energy, gives

$$\xi = 1 + \frac{\alpha \ln \alpha}{1 - \alpha} \simeq \frac{2}{A + 2/3} \qquad \begin{array}{l} \text{average logarithmic} \\ \text{energy change} \\ \text{per collision} \end{array} \qquad (2.34)$$

Values of ξ for common moderators are also given in Table 2.3. In order to obtain an accurate value of ξ by the rigorous form of Equation (2.34), it is necessary to use at least five significant figures. The approximate form of Equation (2.34) is good to within a fraction of a per cent for A greater than 10. The function ξ may be used to calculate the *average* number of collisions to slow down from an energy E_0 to an energy E_1. The total change in the natural logarithm of energy is $\ln E_0 - \ln E_1 = \ln (E_0/E_1)$. The number of collisions is this *total change* divided by ξ, the *average change*,

$$C = \frac{\ln (E_0/E_1)}{\xi} \qquad (2.35)$$

For example, if $E_0 = 2 \times 10^6$ ev and $E_1 = 0.025$ ev, and the scattering element is H, $\xi = 1$, $C = \left(\ln \frac{2 \times 10^6}{0.025} \right) \Big/ 1 = 18.2$. This may be compared with the remark that *one* collision with H can remove all of the neutron energy. For graphite, C is 114, and for U^{238}, C is greater than 2000. This fact makes it possible to assume that in a heterogeneous natural-U reactor, essentially no neutrons become thermal in the metal fuel elements.

2.6. *Epithermal and fast flux distributions*

Neutrons above the thermal energy constitute a flux that must be described by a distribution function, e.g., the flux per unit range of energy. The energy-dependent flux distribution is now defined. The number of neutrons in a range dE at energy E (speed v) is $n(E)\, dE$, and the corresponding flux is $\phi(E)\, dE = n(E)\, dE\, v(E)$. Thus $\phi(E)$ is the flux per unit energy at energy E. In the region from about 1 ev up to about 100 kev in most reactor moderators, the distribution function $\phi(E)$ is *inversely proportional to the energy*. In the energy region above 100 kev, however, the flux is strongly determined by the energy distribution of neutrons recently emitted by fission. A derivation of a formula that displays the flux variation with energy for both regions will now be presented.

It is first convenient to introduce a new useful dimensionless variable, the *lethargy*, as a substitute for energy. The lethargy u is defined by the differential

$$du = -d(\ln E) = \frac{-dE}{E} \qquad (2.36)$$

and if an arbitrary reference high energy E_R is chosen, by the integral form

$$u = \ln \frac{E_R}{E} \qquad (2.37)$$

The energy $E_R = 10$ mev is the commonly accepted reference energy since there are few fission neutrons above that level. As a neutron slows down, its lethargy increases, appropriately to the name of the variable. For example, for $E = 2$ mev, $u = \ln (10/2)$ $= \ln 5 = 1.609$; for $E = 0.025$ ev, $u = \ln (4 \times 10^8) = 19.8$. The inverse relation is

$$E = E_R e^{-u} \qquad (2.38)$$

We may now express the flux distribution in the lethargy variable u. $\phi(u)$, the flux per unit lethargy at u, is chosen such that the flux in an infinitesimal range du is $\phi(u)\,du$. The number of neutrons being the same regardless of variables used,

$$\phi(u)\,du = -\phi(E)\,dE$$

where the negative sign takes account of the fact that E decreases as u increases. Using Equation (2.36) relating u and E,

$$\phi(u) = E\phi(E) \qquad (2.39)$$

The energy distribution of fission neutrons, usually called the fission spectrum, has been measured accurately over a wide range of energies, from 0.1 mev to 17 mev. The number of neutrons produced per unit energy interval in U^{235} fission is given by a semi-empirical relation*

---

* Improvements in this formula have been and will continue to be made, because of its empirical nature. Its simplicity makes this form convenient for approximate calculations.

$$S(E) = Ae^{-E} \sinh \sqrt{2E} \qquad (2.40)$$

where E is in mev, $A = \sqrt{2/(\pi e)} = 0.484$, and $S(E)$ is normalized so that its integral from 0 to ∞ is unity. Figure 2.5 shows the fission spectrum $S(E)$. The most probable fission neutron energy is 0.72 mev. The average energy can be shown to be exactly 2 mev. The number of neutrons per unit *lethargy* interval, $S(u)$

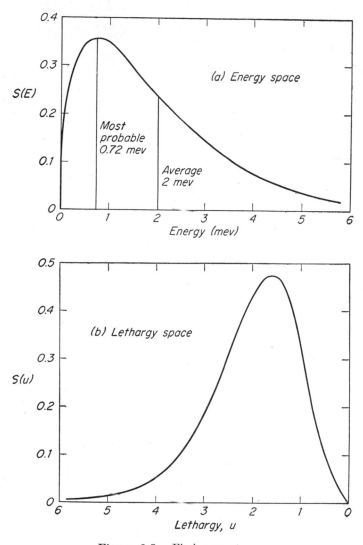

Figure 2.5. Fission spectrum.

is given by the equivalence

$$S(u) \, du = -S(E) \, dE$$

or
$$S(u) = ES(E) \qquad (2.41)$$

We now seek an indication of the shape of the flux distribution $\phi(u)$ in the high energy region. Since the rigorous calculation for an element of any mass is too involved for presentation at this point, we shall resort to two special cases.

Large hydrogen-moderated reactor. Visualize a very large uniform mixture of fissionable material and water that is just critical, with one fission neutron emitted per cubic centimeter each second. The system is large enough to allow spatial variations in flux to be ignored. We shall assume that hydrogen atoms are *wholly responsible* for neutron slowing. The gains and losses of neutrons in an infinitesimal lethargy range du in the vicinity of u will be calculated, neglecting absorption. See Figure 2.6. (a) Neutrons are lost by scattering collisions, at a rate $\phi(u)\Sigma_s(u) \, du$. (b) Neutrons arise in fission, at a rate $S(u) \, du$. (c) Neutrons of smaller lethargy u' are scattered and lose just enough energy to fall in the range du. The scattering rate per

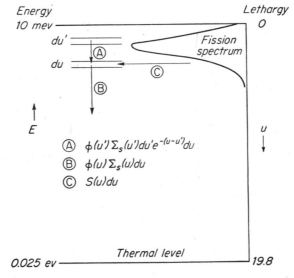

Figure 2.6. Neutron balance in slowing-down process: hydrogen moderator.

unit volume at lethargy u' is $\phi(u')\Sigma_s(u')\,du'$. The probability of experiencing a change in lethargy $u - u'$ to land in a unit lethargy range can be deduced to be $e^{-(u-u')}$, by converting Equation (2.33) into lethargy notation, and using the fact that $\xi = 1$ and $\alpha = 0$ for hydrogen. The total supply by scattering is the integral over all possible initial lethargies,

$$du \int_0^u \phi(u')\Sigma_s(u')e^{-(u-u')}\,du'$$

Equating gains and losses, and cancelling a common factor du,

$$\phi(u)\Sigma_s(u) = S(u) + \int_0^u \phi(u')\Sigma_s(u')e^{-(u-u')}\,du'$$

This may be solved by various methods. By substitution, it can readily be verified that a solution is

$$\phi(u) = \frac{S(u)}{\Sigma_s(u)} + \frac{\int_0^u S(u)\,du}{\Sigma_s(u)} \tag{2.42}$$

Each of these terms has a physical meaning. The first denotes the flux due to neutrons that have made no collisions, the so-called virgin flux; the second is the flux due to neutrons that have experienced one or more collisions. Inspection of Figure 2.5 reveals that for u greater than about 5, practically no neutrons are emitted and the uncollided flux of large lethargy neutrons is negligible. Therefore, to a good approximation for lethargies between $u \simeq 5$ and thermal,

$$\phi(u) \simeq \frac{q_T}{\Sigma_s(u)} \tag{2.43}$$

or in energy space, using Equation (2.39),

$$\phi(E) \simeq \frac{q_T}{\Sigma_s E}$$

Here, q_T is the total neutron emission rate, the complete integral of the spectrum $S(u)$. Figure 2.7 shows a plot of $\phi(u)$ for the range of energies 0–10 mev for the infinite hydrogen moderator. The thermal flux in Figure 2.7 was calculated from the maxwellian distribution. In order to effect a plot in lethargy coordinates, an alternate form of Equation (2.14) was used,

$$\phi(E) = \frac{\phi_0}{(kT)^2}\,Ee^{-E/kT} \tag{2.44}$$

along with Equation (2.40). The peak at small lethargy is due
to the continual supply of fission neutrons; the peak at large
lethargy is due to the fact that the thermal neutrons can neither
gain nor lose energy, but "pile up" until they are absorbed. Since
the simple models for the slowing-down process and the equilibrium thermal distribution are different, it is necessary to join the
thermal and epithermal fluxes arbitrarily. Each curve was taken
to be valid up to the point of intersection.

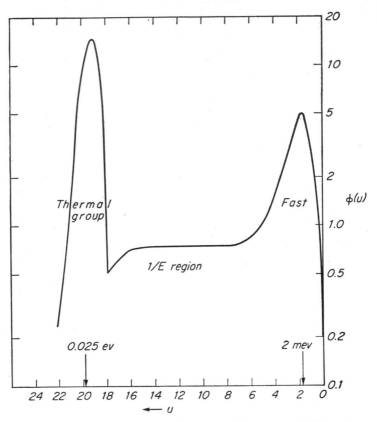

Figure 2.7.   Flux distribution: infinite water reactor.

Large reactor with heavy moderator. A simple neutron
balance argument is now used to derive the flux far from the fission
spectrum with no losses by escape or capture. If the moderator
nuclei are heavy, ξ is small, and many collisions are required to
effect a given lethargy change. Neutrons "flow" through a *unit*

lethargy range at u, by the slowing process. The number of collisions required to cross the interval, with an average change in $\ln E$ of amount ξ, is simply

$$\frac{\Delta \ln E}{\Delta \ln E} = \frac{1}{\xi}$$

The number of collisions per second in the interval, however, is $\phi(u)\Sigma_s(u)$. Thus the number that emerges each second is $\phi(u)\Sigma_s(u)\xi$. With no losses, this is also equal to the number entering the interval, the total fission rate q_T. Thus

$$\phi(u) = \frac{q_T}{\xi\Sigma_s(u)} \qquad (2.45)$$

Now using Equation (2.41),

$$\phi(E) = \frac{q_T}{\xi\Sigma_s E} \qquad \text{epithermal flux} \qquad (2.46)$$

which demonstrates that the flux per unit energy is proportional to $1/E$, in the low energy region. This result is noted to be the same as for the hydrogen moderator. The $1/E$ part of the spectrum is also labeled the "resonance flux," because neutrons in this energy range are strongly absorbed by materials that exhibit resonance cross section peaks.

Numerical Illustration: Estimate the epithermal flux per unit lethargy at the U^{238} resonance 6.7 ev, for a natural-U, graphite reactor. Assume a thermal flux of 2×10^{12} and a macroscopic *uranium* absorption cross section, averaged over the reactor, of 0.0050 cm^{-1}.

Solution: The maxwellian cross sections of natural uranium, using Tables 2.3 and 2.4 are

$$\sigma_{aU} = \frac{(7.68)(0.99)}{1.128} = 6.74 \text{ barns}$$

and

$$\sigma_{fU} = \frac{(4.18)(0.981)}{1.128} = 3.635 \text{ barns}$$

The ratio of fission to absorption is thus $3.635/6.74 = 0.539$, and Σ_{fU} for the whole reactor is $(0.539)(0.0050) = 0.00270$. The fission rate per unit volume is $\phi\Sigma_{fU}$ and the total neutron fission source density q_T is

$$\phi \Sigma_{fU} \nu = (2 \times 10^{12})(0.00270)(2.46) = 1.33 \times 10^{10}/\text{cm}^3\text{-sec}$$

At 6.7 ev, the microscopic carbon scattering cross section is 4.7 barns, and at a graphite density of 1.65 gm/cm³, N_C is 0.0827 and $\Sigma_s = 0.389$ cm⁻¹. Thus

$$\phi(u) = q_T/(\xi \Sigma_s) = \frac{1.33 \times 10^{10}}{(0.1589)(0.389)}$$

$$= 2.15 \times 10^{11}/\text{cm}^2\text{-sec, per unit lethargy}$$

Problems

2.1. Calculate the *macroscopic* absorption cross section at 0.025 ev of uranium enriched to 20 per cent in U^{235}, using the following data: $(\sigma_a)_{235} = 687$ barns, $(\sigma_a)_{238} = 2.75$ barns.
    Answer.   6.6 cm⁻¹.

2.2. Find the scattering and transport mean free paths in water for 2 mev neutrons, using the following cross sections: $(\sigma_s)_H = 2.2$ barns, $(\sigma_s)_O = 1.6$ barns.
    Answer. $\lambda_s = 5.0$ cm, $\lambda_t = 10.0$ cm.

2.3. Calculate the thermal utilization for maxwellian neutrons in a reactor containing the following materials.

Element	ρ (gm/cm³)	Volume Fraction
U^{235}	18.7	0.0010
Zr	6.4	0.2490
D_2O	1.1	0.7450
H_2O	1.0	0.0050

    Answer.   0.941.

2.4. Calculate the plane extrapolation distance d for thermal neutrons at room temperature in graphite, with density 1.65 gm/cm³, scattering cross section 4.8 barns.
    Answer.   1.89 cm.

2.5. Determine the speed at which the maximum of the maxwellian *flux* distribution occurs.
    Answer. $\sqrt{3kT/m}$.

2.6. By measuring the counting rate from a sample activated in a reactor, which of these two quantities can be found, flux $\phi_0 = n_0 \bar{v}$ or neutron density n_0?
    Answer. n_0.

2.7. What is the largest angle of scattering of a neutron with a free proton in the laboratory system?

Answer. 90°.

2.8. The scattering cross sections of H and O are approximately constant at 20 barns and 3.8 barns respectively in the energy range 1000 ev to 1 ev. Calculate the effective ξ and the number of collisions required for a typical neutron to slow through this range in water.

Answer. $\xi = 0.924$, $C = 7.5$.

2.9. Find the effective cross section for a $1/v$ absorber in a $1/E$ flux over an energy range E_1 to E_2.

Answer.

$$\bar{\sigma} = \frac{2[\sigma(E_1) - \sigma(E_2)]}{\ln (E_2/E_1)}$$

2.10. Prove that the average speed for a maxwellian distribution is 1.128 times the most probable speed *by integration* of the distribution function, Equation (2.14).

2.11. By series expansion methods, show that $\xi \simeq 2/(A + \frac{2}{3})$, and that the fractional error is approximately $1/(3A^2)$.

2.12. Evaluate u for $E = 0.72$ mev and E for $u = 5$.

Answer. $u = 2.63$, $E = 0.068$ mev.

2.13. Determine the magnitude of the *average* change in energy per collision of a neutron with a nucleus.

Answer. $\frac{1}{2}E_0(1 - \alpha)$.

2.14. A neutron detector whose sensitivity is proportional to $1/v$ is used to measure the cross section of a $1/v$ absorber of thickness Δx for a polyenergetic maxwellian beam of thermal neutrons from a reactor. Prove that the cross section measured by observing the reduction in counting rate Δc and computing $\Sigma = -\dfrac{\Delta c}{c\,\Delta x}$ is actually 1.128 *times* the value at the most probable speed.

2.15. Show that the ratio of epithermal fission to thermal fission in a reactor with $1/E$ flux joining a maxwellian flux at v_c and with $1/v$ fission cross section is $2v\Sigma_f(v_c)/\xi\Sigma_s$. How does this relate to the distinction between a thermal and an intermediate reactor?

References

Kennard, E. H., *Kinetic Theory of Gases.* New York: McGraw-Hill Book Co. (1938).

Hughes, Donald J., *Pile Neutron Research.* Cambridge, Mass.: Addison Wesley Press (1953), Chapters 1, 2.

Glasstone, Samuel, and Milton C. Edlund, *The Elements of Nuclear Reactor Theory.* New York: D. Van Nostrand Co. (1952).

Hughes, Donald J., and John A. Harvey, *Neutron Cross Sections*, BNL-325. Washington: U. S. Government Printing Office (1955).

Peaceful Uses of Atomic Energy: Proceedings of the International Conference in Geneva, August 1955. Volume 4, *Cross Sections Important to Reactor Design;* Volume 5, *Physics of Reactor Design.* New York: Columbia University Press.

The Reactor Handbook, Volume I, *Physics*, AECD-3645. Washington: U. S. Government Printing Office (March 1955).

The Reactor Handbook, Volume II, *Engineering*, AECD-3646. Washington: U. S. Government Printing Office (May 1955).

Chapter 3

FLUX DISTRIBUTIONS AND CRITICAL MASS

||||||||||||||||||||||||||||||||||||||||||||||||||||||||||||||||||||||||||||||||||||||||||||||||||||||||||||||||||||||||||||||

Methods for calculating the critical size and fuel content of simple reactors are displayed and compared in this chapter. According to most theories it is assumed that a steady state neutron flux exists in the reactor, governed by Fick's law of diffusion, Equation (2.10). As a necessary condition for a flux to satisfy this law and to have the proper form near boundaries, a relation between size, shape, and composition of the reactor core must be satisfied. Once all of the variables of the system have been fixed, the flux variation with position can be computed.

3.1. *The diffusion equation*

We shall now derive a differential equation that represents the balance of gains and losses of monoenergetic neutrons from a volume element of a reactor material. Three processes are operative: diffusion, absorption, and production. Consider the *diffusion* first, as it refers to an infinitesimal cube of volume $dx\,dy\,dz$, as in Figure 3.1. Across each surface of the cube there will be a net neutron current. If the flows at the opposite faces are different, there will be a continuous net rate of gain or loss in the volume element. Consider one pair of faces only, perpendicular to the z-direction. Letting subscripts refer to the point of evaluation of a quantity, the *net loss rate* with time is

$$j_{z+dz}\,dx\,dy - j_z\,dx\,dy \qquad (3.1)$$

The difference between the current densities is

$$j_{z+dz} - j_z = \left(\frac{\partial j}{\partial z}\right)_z dz \qquad (3.2)$$

while the z component of the current, Equation (2.10), is

$$j_z = -D\frac{\partial \phi}{\partial z} \qquad (3.3)$$

Combining Equations (3.2) and (3.3) with (3.1), the latter becomes

$$-\frac{\partial}{\partial z}\left(D\frac{\partial \phi}{\partial z}\right) dx \, dy \, dz$$

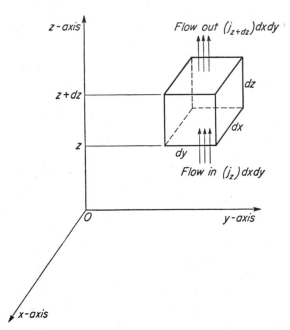

Figure 3.1. Neutron flows in volume element.

The loss rate due to flows in the other two directions may be found by analogy and added. The total leakage rate *per unit volume* is thus written as

$$L = -\left[\frac{\partial}{\partial x}\left(D\frac{\partial \phi}{\partial x}\right) + \frac{\partial}{\partial y}\left(D\frac{\partial \phi}{\partial y}\right) + \frac{\partial}{\partial z}\left(D\frac{\partial \phi}{\partial z}\right)\right] \qquad (3.4)$$

This form is applicable if the diffusion coefficients are different in the three directions, for example with cooling ducts running along one direction only. For materials in which D is independent of both direction and position,

$$L = -D\left(\frac{\partial^2\phi}{\partial x^2} + \frac{\partial^2\phi}{\partial y^2} + \frac{\partial^2\phi}{\partial z^2}\right) \equiv -D\,\nabla^2\phi \quad \begin{array}{l}\text{leakage}\\ \text{per unit}\\ \text{volume}\end{array} \quad (3.5)$$

The Laplacian operator ∇^2 takes on different forms in other co-ordinate systems. For a homogeneous sphere, radial coordinate (r) with no angular variation, it is

$$\nabla^2 = \frac{d^2}{dr^2} + \frac{2}{r}\frac{d}{dr} \tag{3.6}$$

In a cylinder, coordinates (r,z) with no angular variation, it is

$$\nabla^2 = \nabla_r^2 + \nabla_z^2 = \frac{\partial^2}{\partial r^2} + \frac{1}{r}\frac{\partial}{\partial r} + \frac{\partial^2}{\partial z^2} \tag{3.7}$$

The process of *absorption* is particularly simple. Neutrons are absorbed from a unit volume at a rate

$$A = \phi\Sigma_a$$

The third process is *production* by various methods—slowing down from other energies, fission and non-fission nuclear sources. Neutrons are supplied to a unit volume at a rate represented in general by the symbol S. In the *critical* reactor the number of neutrons in the volume is neither increasing or decreasing with time. Therefore there must exist a balance of the three rates given by

$$S = L + A$$

or, rearranging,

$$D\,\nabla^2\phi - \phi\Sigma_a + S = 0 \qquad \text{diffusion equation} \tag{3.8}$$

This second-order differential equation must be solved to find ϕ as a function of position, and to obtain the critical condition on materials and size. The equation is strictly applicable only to neutrons of a single energy, or to a group such as thermals. The source S has been deliberately left unspecified, since it depends on the nature of the reactor or at least on the theoretical assumptions made about the reactor.

3.2. *Solution of diffusion equation in a thermal reactor*

The neutron cycle in a thermal reactor starts with fission, which proceeds at a rate $\phi\Sigma_f$ per unit volume, giving a *fast* neutron production rate

$$S_f = \phi\Sigma_f\nu \qquad (3.9)$$

where ν is the number of neutrons per fission (2.46 for U^{235}). We shall assume the reactor to be homogeneous, in which case the fast fission factor ϵ (see § 1.5) is unity. Equation (3.9) can be put in a form involving the number of neutrons per absorption in fuel,

$$\eta = \frac{(\Sigma_f)_U}{(\Sigma_a)_U}\nu \qquad (3.10)$$

which is 2.08 for highly enriched uranium and 1.34 for natural uranium. The thermal utilization is also defined, as the fraction of all thermal neutrons absorbed that are absorbed in uranium

$$f = \frac{(\Sigma_a)_U}{\Sigma_a} \qquad (3.11)$$

Combining Equations (3.9), (3.10), and (3.11) the fast source is

$$S_f = \phi\Sigma_a f\eta \qquad (3.12)$$

Of these fast neutrons a fraction F, which may be called the fast neutron non-leakage probability, will slow down in the reactor, without escaping from the core. If the reactor contains U^{238} or another absorber whose absorption cross section remains large in the energy region above thermal, the neutrons are also subject to resonance capture. The probability that neutrons are *not* captured will be labeled p, and called the resonance escape probability. Of the S_f fast neutrons then only $S_f F p$ get to thermal, and the resulting thermal source will be $S_t = \phi\Sigma_a pf\eta F$. By defining the (infinite) multiplication factor k as

$$k = pf\eta \qquad (3.13)$$

the thermal source becomes

$$S_t = \phi\Sigma_a kF \qquad (3.14)$$

Substitute Equation (3.14) in Equation (3.8) and rearrange to the form

$$D\,\nabla^2\phi + \phi\Sigma_a(kF - 1) = 0 \qquad (3.15)$$

The constants depending on reactor materials are usually grouped into a single one, called the "buckling,"

$$B^2 = \frac{\Sigma_a}{D} (kF - 1) \tag{3.16}$$

so that Equation (3.15) simplifies to a form of the so-called wave equation,

$$\nabla^2 \phi + B^2 \phi = 0 \tag{3.17}$$

The flux distribution with position is given by its solution. At this point, it is necessary to select a core shape. Assume that it is an *unreflected* or bare *sphere* of radius R. In order to put Equation (3.17) into a form in which the solution is recognizable, let $\phi(r) = u(r)/r$ and make use of the Laplacian in spherical coordinates from Equation (3.6). The result is

$$\frac{d^2u}{dr^2} + B^2 u = 0 \tag{3.18}$$

This is the equation of simple harmonic motion, solutions of which are $\sin Br$ and $\cos Br$. The general solution of the original Equation (3.17) is a linear combination

$$\phi = A \frac{\sin Br}{r} + C \frac{\cos Br}{r} \tag{3.19}$$

where A and C are arbitrary coefficients, to be determined by information on the flux conditions at the boundary and the center of the core. First note that as r is allowed to approach zero, the second term increases indefinitely. Since an infinite flux is not allowed on physical grounds, C must be exactly zero, leaving

$$\phi = A \frac{\sin Br}{r} \tag{3.20}$$

According to § 2.3, the flux must go to zero at a distance d beyond the core boundary, i.e., at $R' = R + d$. Applying this boundary condition, Equation (3.20) becomes $\phi = A(\sin BR')/R'$. Since R' is finite, A cannot be zero without incurring a meaningless solution, so that $\sin BR' = 0$, $BR' = \pi$, or

$$B^2 = \left(\frac{\pi}{R'}\right)^2 \tag{3.21}$$

and finally

$$R = R' - d = \frac{\pi}{B} - d \tag{3.22}$$

In summary, the reactor size is determined by the constant B^2, which depends on the reactor materials according to Equation (3.16).

While proceeding as quickly as possible to the goal of critical size, we have failed to specify the function F representing the fraction of fast neutrons that slow down in the reactor. It clearly depends on the size, the shape, and the nature of the neutron slowing process. According to the *age theory* of Fermi for a bare reactor, as will be shown in § 3.3, the proper form is

$$F = e^{-B^2\tau} \qquad (3.23)$$

where B^2 is again the buckling, related to size according to Equation (3.21), and τ is the *age*, a measure of the distance neutrons travel in slowing from fission energy to thermal. Also we may group constants Σ_a and D in terms of the *diffusion length* L, defined by its square,

$$L^2 = \frac{D}{\Sigma_a} \qquad (3.24)$$

Combining Equations (3.16), (3.23), and (3.24),

$$1 = \frac{ke^{-B^2\tau}}{1 + B^2L^2} \qquad (3.25)$$

which is the *critical equation* of age-diffusion theory. It is a transcendental equation in B^2 that must be solved by successive trials.* We call the values of B^2 from Equation (3.25) the *materials* buckling, labeled B_m^2, since it depends only on the nuclear

Table 3.1

Geometric Bucklings for Different Reactor Shapes

Core Shape	Dimensions	$B_o{}^2$
sphere	radius R	$(\pi/R')^2$
slab	width H	$(\pi/H')^2$
parallelepiped	height H, width W, length L	$(\pi/H')^2 + (\pi/W')^2 + (\pi/L')^2$
cube	side S	$3(\pi/S')^2$
infinite cylinder	radius R	$(j_0/R')^{2*}$
finite cylinder	radius R, height H	$(j_0/R')^2 + (\pi/H')^2$

* Where j_0 is 2.4048, the first root of the Bessel function $J_0(r)$. See Appendix A for a review of Bessel equations and functions.

* A useful starting approximation is $B^2 \simeq \dfrac{\ln k}{L^2 + \tau}$, applicable for $B^2L^2 \ll 1$.

properties of the core. In contrast, the expression for B^2 in Equation (3.21) suggests that it be called the *geometric* buckling B_g^2, dependent only on the size and shape of the core. The critical condition may thus be written

$$B_m^2 = B_g^2 \qquad (3.26)$$

For other reactor shapes, different forms of B_g^2 are applicable, as shown in Table 3.1. Each B_g^2 is obtained by a solution of Equation (3.17) in the appropriate coordinate system and with the condition that the flux is zero at the extrapolated core boundary.

Numerical Illustration: Find the critical radius and mass of U^{235} in a water-moderated bare spherical core with the following materials constants (see example in § 2.4).

$$D = 0.223 \text{ cm} \qquad \tau = 50 \text{ cm}^2$$
$$(\Sigma_a)_U = 0.0572 \text{ cm}^{-1} \qquad f = 0.775$$
$$\Sigma_a = 0.0738 \text{ cm}^{-1} \qquad \eta = 2.08$$
$$f_U = 0.002 \qquad p = 1$$

Solution: From Equation (3.13), $k = (2.08)(0.775) = 1.612$; from Equation (3.24), $L^2 = 0.233/0.0738 = 3.02$ cm^2. As a first approximation, $B^2 \simeq (\ln 1.612)/53.02 = 0.00901$ cm^{-2}, and iteration of Equation (3.25) yields the same answer to the number of significant figures retained. Thus $R' = \pi/\sqrt{0.00901} = 33.1$ cm. The extrapolation distance by Equation (2.12) is $d = 0.71\lambda_t = 2.13\,D = 0.5$ cm and $R = 32.6$ cm. The volume of the core is $V = 145$ liters. The volume of uranium is $f_U V = (0.002)(145) = 0.290$ liters, which at a density of 18.7 kg/liter gives a critical U^{235} mass of 5.42 kg.

Flux distribution. Having found the critical size of the core, we may return to the flux distribution given last by Equation (3.20). No information on A has been revealed, which is to be expected since a critical reactor can be operated at any power and flux level (within the limits of resistance to temperature and radiation, of course). Let the flux at the center of the core be labeled ϕ_c, and note that for small r, $\sin Br$ approaches Br. Thus $A = \phi_c/B = \phi_c R'/\pi$, and

$$\phi = \phi_c \frac{\sin(\pi r/R')}{\pi r/R'} \qquad \begin{array}{l}\text{flux distribution} \\ \text{in bare sphere}\end{array} \qquad (3.27)$$

Figure 3.2 shows a plot of the thermal flux in the sphere.

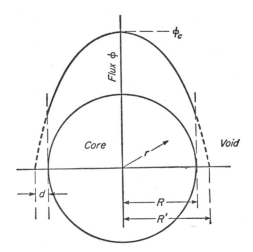

Figure 3.2.   Flux distribution in unreflected sphere.

Table 3.2 gives the flux distribution for all common geometrical shapes.

When the critical dimensions and flux distribution in a reactor are known, other useful information about the reactor can be found. Using the conversion factor from fissions to energy $c = 3.3 \times 10^{10}$ fissions/watt-sec, the local power density is simply $\phi \Sigma_f$ and the useful reactor power is

$$P = \frac{\overline{\phi} \Sigma_f V}{c} \tag{3.28}$$

where $\overline{\phi}$ is the average flux over the core. The average flux in a bare sphere can be shown to be approximately $3/\pi^2 = 0.304$ times the flux at the center of the core. (The approximation is that the extrapolation distance is negligible.) Once the power level is specified in a reactor of given composition and volume, the average flux can be computed from Equation (3.28). The ratio $\overline{\phi}/\phi_c$ appropriate to the core shape may then be applied, to obtain the central flux. The complete distribution is then available by use of Table 3.2.

Table 3.2

Flux Distributions for Different Reactor Shapes

Core Shape	$\dfrac{Average\ Flux}{Central\ Flux}, \dfrac{\bar{\phi}^*}{\phi_c}$	Flux
sphere......................	0.304	$\phi = \phi_c \dfrac{\sin\ (\pi r/R')}{\pi r/R'}$
slab.........................	0.637	$\phi = \phi_c \cos \dfrac{\pi z}{H'}$
parallelepiped................	0.258	$\phi = \phi_c \cos \dfrac{\pi x}{W'} \cos \dfrac{\pi y}{L'} \cos \dfrac{\pi z}{H'}$
cube.......................	0.258	$\phi = \phi_c \cos \dfrac{\pi x}{S'} \cos \dfrac{\pi y}{S'} \cos \dfrac{\pi z}{S'}$
infinite cylinder..............	0.432	$\phi = \phi_c J_0 \left(\dfrac{j_0 r}{R'}\right)$ †
finite cylinder................	0.275	$\phi = \phi_c J_0 \left(\dfrac{j_0 r}{R'}\right) \cos \dfrac{\pi z}{H'}$

* Approximate, disregarding extrapolation distance.
† $j_0 = 2.4048$.

Thermal leakage current. The total number of thermal neutrons escaping from the core per second is the integral of current density over the surface, $\int j\ dS$. For a sphere, this is simply $4\pi R^2 j(R) = -4\pi R^2 D\ (d\phi/dr)_R$. Now the total rate of absorption in the core is the integral $\int \phi \Sigma_a\ dV$, where r goes from 0 to R. Carrying out the indicated operations, we find that the ratio of neutrons lost to neutrons absorbed is (leakage)/(absorption) $= B^2 L^2$. The fraction of neutrons that become thermal and remain in the core to be absorbed will be called the thermal non-leakage probability.

$$\mathscr{L}_t = \frac{\text{absorption}}{\text{leakage} + \text{absorption}} = \frac{1}{1 + B^2 L^2} \qquad (3.29)$$

By comparison, the fast non-leakage probability from age theory is Equation (3.23)

$$\mathscr{L}_f = F = e^{-B^2 \tau} \qquad (3.30)$$

In this notation Equation (3.25) may be written

$$1 = k\mathscr{L}_f \mathscr{L}_t \qquad \text{general critical equation} \qquad (3.31)$$

This relation is more general than would be anticipated from the fact that the spherical bare core and age theory were employed in its formulation.   The form of the factors $\mathcal{L}_f$ and $\mathcal{L}_t$ will differ with theory, but the physical meaning is the same.   Assume that one thermal neutron is absorbed in uranium to give η fast neutrons. The number that escape the resonance and fast leakage processes is $\eta p \mathcal{L}_f$.   Of these, $\eta p \mathcal{L}_f \mathcal{L}_t$ are available for absorption, and $\eta p \mathcal{L}_f \mathcal{L}_t f$ are absorbed in uranium.   When this number is 1, as required by Equation (3.31), the cycle is complete, and the reactor is exactly critical.

Numerical Illustration: Calculate the total power and the thermal neutron leakage current for the baré spherical core of the previous illustration.   Assume that the central flux is $10^{12}/cm^2$-sec.

Solution: From Equation (3.10),

$$\Sigma_{fU} = \frac{\eta}{\nu} \Sigma_{aU} = \frac{2.08}{2.46} (0.0572) = 0.0484.$$

The average flux over the 145 liter volume is $(0.304)(10^{12})$ and

$$P = \frac{(0.304 \times 10^{12})(0.0484)(145)}{3.3 \times 10^{10}} = 6.5 \times 10^4 \text{ watts}$$

The total neutron absorption rate is $\bar{\phi}\Sigma_a V = (0.304 \times 10^{12})$ $(0.0738)(145) = 3.25 \times 10^{15}$/sec;   multiplying   by $B^2 L^2 =$ $(0.00901)(3.02) = 0.0272$, we obtain the thermal leakage rate $8.8 \times 10^{13}/cm^2$-sec.

One may properly question the value of the age-diffusion method since it is applicable only to the bare reactor, on the grounds that actual systems almost invariably employ a reflector to conserve neutrons.   Aside from its obvious advantage of simplicity that assists in understanding, the bare reactor concept can be applied to a reflected system, for example, a sphere.   For each critical reflected core of radius R and given composition, there will be a larger bare core of radius R_e that is also critical, the *bare equivalent* core.   If one can assign or estimate the difference in radii $R_e - R$, labeled the *reflector savings*, then the computation of R_e by age-diffusion theory immediately yields R.

3.3. *Fermi age theory*

The critical radius of the reactor was seen in the previous section to be dependent on the function $e^{-B^2\tau}$, which represented the non-leakage probability of fast neutrons. This quantity will now be derived by Fermi's theory of the slowing-down process, applicable to reactor moderators with nuclei that are relatively heavy, compared with the neutron. The slowing of neutrons in carbon, with $A = 12$, will be rather accurately described by the method. The slowing in water must be handled by other methods, as discussed in Chapter 10.

It will now be assumed that the flux is a function of two variables, lethargy u as defined in § 2.6 and position r, where r represents the vector coordinate needed to locate a point in space. We first select for consideration only those neutrons that lie in a unit volume in the vicinity of r. Out of these, pick those that are in a range of lethargy du at u. The number in this restricted group is $n(u,r)\,du$, and the flux due to them is $\phi(u,r)\,du$. Let us apply the diffusion equation (3.8) to this flux. The balance of neutrons $S = L + A$ in the range du and in a unit volume becomes

$$S(u)du = -D(u)\,\nabla^2\phi(u,r)du + \phi(u,r)du\Sigma_a(u)$$

The basic assumption of age theory is now made, that the slowing process is *continuous* rather than by discrete energy changes. Now we are able to interpret $S(u)$ as being a *net* source, due to slowing in the top of the lethargy range (from smaller u) and slowing out of the bottom (to larger u). The "flow" in and out may be expressed in terms of the *slowing-down density* $q(u,r)$, which is defined as the number of neutrons crossing a lethargy level u, per cubic centimeter per second. The number entering du is $q(u,r)$ and the number leaving du is $q(u+du,r)$. Thus

$$S(u)du = q(u,r) - q(u+du,r)$$

or

$$S(u)du = \frac{-\partial q(u,r)}{\partial u}\,du$$

Combining equations and cancelling a common du,

$$D(u)\,\nabla^2\phi(u,r) - \phi(u,r)\Sigma_a(u,r) = \frac{\partial q(u,r)}{\partial u} \qquad (3.32)$$

Omitting the designation of functional dependence,

$$D \nabla^2 \phi - \phi \Sigma_a = \frac{\partial q}{\partial u}$$

This is the *flux form* of the age equation. The special case of *no absorption* for epithermal neutrons, $\Sigma_a = 0$, will be considered first. In this form, Equation (3.32) becomes

$$D \nabla^2 \phi = \frac{\partial q}{\partial u} \tag{3.33}$$

Now the relation between flux and slowing-down density, for a region far below the fission spectrum, was found to be given by Equation (2.45),

$$\phi = \frac{q}{\xi \Sigma_s}$$

Substitution of this for ϕ puts Equation (3.33) in terms of the one variable q.

$$\frac{D}{\xi \Sigma_s} \nabla^2 q = \frac{\partial q}{\partial u} \tag{3.34}$$

A *new variable* τ called the *age* is introduced in differential form.

$$d\tau = \frac{D}{\xi \Sigma_s} du \tag{3.35}$$

Equation (3.34) becomes

$$\nabla^2 q = \frac{\partial q}{\partial \tau} \quad \begin{array}{l} \text{age equation,} \\ \text{no absorption} \end{array} \tag{3.36}$$

The term age is used because τ plays the same role in this equation as *time* in the corresponding differential equation of heat conduction,

$$\kappa \nabla^2 T = \frac{\partial T}{\partial t}$$

Integrating Equation (3.35) from initial lethargy u_0 to lethargy u,

$$\tau = \int_{u_0}^{u} \frac{D \, du}{\xi \Sigma_s} \quad \text{age} \tag{3.37}$$

It is difficult at this stage to recognize any physical meaning for τ except that it can be correlated with lethargy and therefore energy. The following analysis serves to establish a physical interpretation of τ.

Slowing-down distribution from point monoenergetic fast source. Consider a point source emitting q_0 neutrons of energy E_0 (lethargy u_0) at the origin in an infinite moderating medium. We wish to find the slowing down density $q(u,r)$ at a scalar distance r measured from the origin. By substitution, it can be verified that a solution of the age Equation (3.36) is

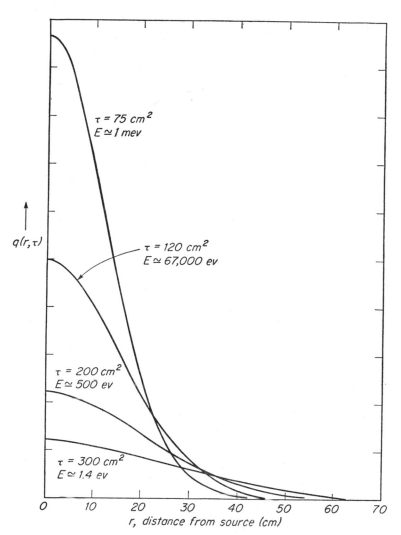

Figure 3.3. Slowing-down density distribution in graphite from 2-mev source (ordinate: arbitrary units).

$$q(u,r) = \frac{q_0 e^{-r^2/4\tau}}{(4\pi\tau)^{3/2}} \quad \text{slowing-down density distribution from a point fast source} \tag{3.38}$$

where τ is the function of u given by Equation (3.37). Figure 3.3 shows a graph of the slowing-down density for several ages. The curve drops and broadens as lethargy and age increase. The average of the squares of distances from the origin at which the neutrons reach the lethargy u is the integral over all space, $r = 0$ to $r = \infty$,

$$\overline{r^2(u)} = \frac{\int r^2 q(u,r)\, dV}{\int q(u,r)\, dV}$$

where $dV = 4\pi r^2\, dr$. The result is

$$\tau = \frac{\overline{r^2}}{6}$$

This means that τ is proportional to the average square of all the crow-flight distances between the source and the point where the neutrons reach lethargy u. The situation of greatest interest is the slowing from fission energy ($\simeq 2$ mev) to thermal (0.025 ev). For this case $\sqrt{\tau}$ is $1/\sqrt{6}$ times the root-mean-square distance a neutron takes to become thermal.

Neutron slowing and diffusion in a reactor. Fermi's age theory is now applied to a bare reactor, to find the probability F that a neutron arrives at thermal energy without being lost through the boundary. The slowing and thermal diffusion processes are connected by the fact that the source S in Equation (3.8) for thermal neutrons,

$$D\,\nabla^2\phi - \phi\Sigma_a + S = 0$$

is exactly the same quantity as the slowing-down density q at thermal energy. The latter is obtained from the differential equation (3.36),

$$\nabla^2 q = \frac{\partial q}{\partial \tau}$$

Let us propose that $q(u,r)$ can be separated into the product of a function of position and one of age, of the form

$$q(\tau,r) = \eta f \phi(r) \Sigma_a F(\tau) \tag{3.39}$$

At fission energy, $u = u_0$ (and thus $\tau = 0$ by Equation 3.37), $q(\tau,r)$ must equal the fission neutron production rate $\eta f \phi \Sigma_a$. Thus $F(0) = 1$. Substitute $q(\tau,r)$ into Equation (3.36) and differentiate as indicated. The result, rearranged, is

$$\frac{\nabla^2\phi}{\phi} = \frac{1}{F}\frac{\partial F}{\partial \tau}$$

From Equation (3.17) however, $\nabla^2\phi = -B^2\phi$ and thus

$$\frac{dF}{d\tau} = -B^2F$$

The solution, subject to the initial condition $F(0) = 1$ is

$$F(\tau) = e^{-B^2\tau} \qquad \text{fast non-leakage probability} \atop \text{by age theory} \qquad (3.40)$$

The fraction of neutrons that reach *thermal* is obtained by the use of the age-to-thermal value of τ calculated from Equation (3.37).

Resonance escape probability. No capture during slowing was assumed in the solution of the age equation for the slowing-down density from a point source, Equation (3.38). Similarly, in establishing the fast non-leakage probability for a reactor, capture during slowing was ignored, but the omission was corrected by incorporating a resonance escape probability p in the multiplication factor as in Equation (3.13). A more natural approach is to solve the *age equation with weak capture*, obtained by inserting Equations (2.45) and (3.35) into Equation (3.32),

$$\nabla^2 q_r - q_r\frac{\Sigma_a}{D} = \frac{\partial q_r}{\partial \tau} \qquad (3.41)$$

where the subscript r distinguishes this case with resonance capture from that without, q. We may try a solution of the form $q_r(u,r) = q(u,r)p(u)$ where p is the *resonance escape probability*. Substitution into Equation (3.41) and use of Equation (3.36) gives

$$\frac{1}{p}\frac{dp}{d\tau} = -\frac{\Sigma_a}{D}$$

or

$$p = e^{-\int_0^\tau \frac{\Sigma_a}{D}d\tau} = e^{-\int_E^{E_0} \frac{\Sigma_a}{\xi\Sigma_s}\frac{dE}{E}} \qquad \text{resonance escape probability, weak capture}$$

This result enables us to calculate the capture effect for the point source distribution, and to estimate the factor p for a reactor.

The restriction to weak capture may now be removed by an argument which, if not rigorous, helps to visualize the effect of resonance capture. The fractional number of neutrons that are removed by capture on transfer through a lethargy range du is the product of the number of collisions and the relative chance of absorption:

$$\frac{dn}{n} = -C \frac{\Sigma_a}{\Sigma_a + \Sigma_s}$$

Inserting $C = du/\xi$ and integrating from $u = u_0$, where the initial number of neutrons is n_0, to lethargy u,

$$n = n_0 e^{-\int_{u_0}^{u} \frac{\Sigma_a du}{\xi \Sigma}}$$

Thus the fraction escaping capture is

$$p = e^{-\int_{E}^{E_0} \frac{\Sigma_a}{\xi \Sigma} \frac{dE}{E}} \tag{3.42}$$

This differs from the previous expression for weak capture only in that Σ replaces Σ_s. Equation (3.42) may be shown to be generally applicable to homogeneous water-uranium mixtures and to other moderators if the resonances are widely spaced and narrow (in comparison with ξ, the average logarithmic energy change per collision). The exponent in Equation (3.42) may be written in various other forms:

$$-\int_{E}^{E_0} \frac{\Sigma_a}{\xi(\Sigma_s + \Sigma_a)} \frac{dE}{E}$$

$$-\int_{E}^{E_0} \frac{\Sigma_a}{\xi \Sigma_s} \frac{1}{1 + \Sigma_a/\Sigma_s} \frac{dE}{E}$$

$$-\frac{N_U}{\overline{\xi \Sigma_s}} \int_{E}^{E_0} \frac{\sigma_{aU}}{1 + \frac{N_U \sigma_{aU}}{\Sigma_s}} \frac{dE}{E}$$

where in the last form an average value of $\xi \Sigma_s$ has been taken outside the integral, and the fuel assumed to be the only absorber. It is noted that the integral depends on the cross section of uranium, and also on the total scattering cross section per uranium atom present Σ_s/N_U, which is a function of the moderator-fuel ratio. For a system containing *very little uranium*, Σ_s/N_U is large, and the integral reduces to

$$\sigma_r = \int_E^{E_0} \sigma_{aU}\, \frac{dE}{E} \qquad \text{resonance integral} \qquad (3.43)$$

This is simply the (logarithmic) integral of the uranium absorption cross section. The value of σ_r for natural U has been measured to be around 240 barns. For natural-U systems containing larger amounts of uranium, the approximation equation (3.43) is not valid because σ_a for U^{238} varies rapidly with energy. Resort must be made to empirical data. An *effective* resonance integral $(\sigma_r)_e$ with a corresponding macroscopic value $(\Sigma_r)_e$ deduced from experiment is used in the working formula for p:

$$p = e^{-(\Sigma_r)_e/\xi\Sigma_s} \qquad \begin{array}{l}\text{resonance escape probability} \\ \text{simplified form}\end{array} \qquad (3.44)$$

Table 3.3 gives values and formulas for the calculation of $(\sigma_r)_e$.

Table 3.3

Microscopic Resonance Integral

	$(\sigma_r)_e$ (barns)
Dilute homogeneous mixture of U and moderator..............	240
Concentrated homogeneous mixture of U and moderator.......	$3.9\left(\dfrac{\Sigma_s}{N_U}\right)^{0.415*}$
Pure U metal...	9.25
Cylindrical U metal slugs with surface-to-mass ratio S/M cm²/gm	
(a) Classic formula..................................	$9.25(1 + 2.67\, S/M)$
(b) Newer empirical formula (see Macklin and Pomerance, in References)......................................	$A\left(1 + \dfrac{\mu}{r_0 + M/S}\right)$

* Up to a ratio Σ_s/N_U of about 1000 *barns* per atom.

Numerical Illustration: Calculate the resonance escape probability for a homogeneous light-water-moderated reactor with atom ratio $N_H/N_{235} = 200$ at two isotopic concentrations of U^{235} (0.2 and 0.93).

Solution: First, find the scattering per U^{238} atom, in order to establish the proper empirical formula. In the region of prominent U^{238} resonances, the scattering cross sections of hydrogen and oxygen are approximately independent of energy $\sigma_{sH} \simeq 20$ barns, $\sigma_{sO} = 3.8$ barns. The scattering cross section associated with each H atom is thus 21.9 barns. At an isotopic concentration of 0.2,

$$N_{U\text{-}238}/N_H = (N_{U\text{-}238}/N_{U\text{-}235}) \cdot (N_{U\text{-}235}/N_H)$$
$$= (0.8/0.2)(1/200) = 0.020$$

Disregarding the small scattering due to U^{238}, we find $\Sigma_s/N_{U\text{-}238}$ = (50)(21.9) = 1095, and the effective resonance integral from Table 3.3 is

$$(\sigma_r)_e = 3.9(1095)^{0.415} = 71.2$$

The value of $\Sigma_s/N_{U\text{-}238}$ is only slightly above the limit of validity of the empirical formula. The average $\xi\Sigma_s$ is a composite for hydrogen and oxygen, using $\xi_H = 1$, $\xi_O = 0.1209$. $\xi\Sigma_s = N_H(\xi_H\sigma_{sH} + \frac{1}{2}\xi_O\sigma_{sO}) = 20.2N_H$. Thus the exponent of p is $(0.020/20.2)(71.2) = 0.0705$, and $p = 0.932$. For isotopic concentration 0.93, the scattering per U^{238} atom is far above 1000, and we make use of the limiting $(\sigma_r)_e$ of 240 barns. Now $N_{U\text{-}238}/N_H = (0.07/0.93)(1/200) = 0.000376$, and the exponent is $(0.000376)(240)/20.2 = 0.0045$. Thus $p = 0.995$. This shows that the resonance escape probability for a highly enriched reactor is very close to $p = 1$, and for some purposes can be ignored in the calculation of k.

3.4. *One-group theory*

The nature of source term S in the diffusion equation (3.8) distinguishes one theory from another. In another sense, a reasonable model of the slowing-down process is chosen to fit the conditions in the particular reactor under study. The specification of the source by age theory is but one of several methods. *One-group* theory, in which specific attention is given to neutrons of only one energy, may be used with three special source types.

(a) *Source independent of position, S = constant.* In the heterogeneous thermal reactor, rods or plates of fuel are regularly spaced through a moderator such as water or graphite. Because of the local variations in neutron absorption cross section, the flux will also vary from point to point. The slowing-down process is not greatly affected by the heterogeneity, and over a small region, the slowing down density q evaluated at thermal energy is essentially independent of position. The existence of a fast flux and the slowing process may be ignored, and attention given to the *one group* of thermals, S = constant. For the simple case of a plane section of moderator, the diffusion equation for thermal flux is

$$D\frac{d^2\phi}{dz^2} - \phi\Sigma_a = -S$$

an inhomogeneous equation that admits simple solutions. We shall reserve detailed discussion of the heterogeneous reactor until Chapter 4.

(b) *Source zero in the medium of diffusion, S = 0. Diffusion length.* This case is of special importance in that the physical meaning of the diffusion length, Equation (3.24) can be exhibited. Picture a *point* source that emits q thermal neutrons each second in non-multiplying infinite medium. If this idealization is objectionable on physical grounds, visualize instead thermal neutrons arising in a chosen limited region as a result of slowing down. If a sphere of radius a is drawn close about this point, there will be a net current density outward across its surface given by

$$j = \frac{q}{4\pi a^2}$$

This relation serves as a boundary condition for the solution of the diffusion equation for this system,

$$D \nabla^2\phi - \phi\Sigma_a = 0 \tag{3.45}$$

No term S appears, since there are no sources in the body of the medium. At this point it will be well to note a subtle but important difference between this equation and Equation (3.17). There the *positive* sign corresponds to a multiplying medium; here the *negative* sign applies to a non-multiplying region. In order to solve, invoke Equation (3.24) and let $\phi(r) = u(r)/r$. The result is

$$\frac{d^2u}{dr^2} - \frac{u}{L^2} = 0$$

Possible solutions are $e^{-r/L}$ and $e^{+r/L}$; hence

$$\phi = \frac{Ae^{-r/L}}{r} + \frac{Ce^{+r/L}}{r}$$

To avoid an infinite increase in flux as r increases indefinitely, C must be zero, and

$$\phi = \frac{Ae^{-r/L}}{r} \tag{3.46}$$

Now form the current at radius a,

$$j = -D\left(\frac{d\phi}{dr}\right)_a = ADe^{-a/L}\left(\frac{1}{a^2} + \frac{1}{La}\right) = \frac{q}{4\pi a^2}$$

and let a approach zero.   The result is $A = q/4\pi D$ and

$$\phi = \frac{qe^{-r/L}}{4\pi Dr} \qquad \begin{array}{l} \text{flux from thermal point source} \\ \text{in infinite medium} \end{array} \qquad (3.47)$$

The rate of absorption of neutrons per unit volume at a point r from the source is $\phi\Sigma_a$.   We may evaluate the average of the *squares* of distances at which neutrons are absorbed by

$$\overline{r^2} = \frac{\int r^2 \phi \Sigma_a \, dV}{\int \phi \Sigma_a \, dV} = \frac{\int r^2 \phi \, dV}{\int \phi \, dV}$$

Substituting Equation (3.47), $dV = 4\pi r^2 \, dr$, and integrating from $r = 0$ to $r = \infty$ gives

$$\overline{r^2} = 6L^2$$

This means that L is $1/\sqrt{6}$ times the root-mean-square displacement $\sqrt{\overline{r^2}}$ between the point of origin of a thermal neutron, and the point of absorption.   By rearrangement of Equation (3.24), the diffusion length can also be written

$$L = \sqrt{\frac{\lambda_t \lambda_a}{3}}$$

a modified geometric average of the transport and absorption mean free paths.

(c) *Source strength equal to production rate.* $S = \phi\Sigma_f\nu$.   For a thermal reactor, taking $S = \phi\Sigma_f\nu$ or $k\phi\Sigma_a$ would imply either that fission neutrons were born thermal or that the distance it took a neutron to slow down was exactly zero, both completely unrealistic concepts.   Only in a *fast reactor*, which operates as a result of fission by fast neutrons, is there a semblance of validity. Even in a fast reactor it is necessary to consider the flux distribution in energy, and application of one-group theory is a gross oversimplification.   Its use serves as a vehicle for introduction to the characteristic features of such reactors, however.   Two important differences from thermal systems should be noted.   Much of the neutron energy loss is due to inelastic scattering with heavy uranium nuclei.   Also, the cross sections for many materials that would be considered strong poisons in a thermal reactor are negligible, so far as fast neutrons are concerned.   Figure 3.4 shows the cross section variations with neutron energy of reactor fuels.

A solution of the one-group theory differential equation will

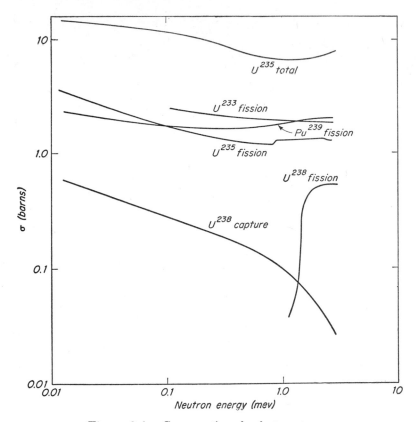

Figure 3.4.   Cross sections for fast neutrons.

be displayed for a *reflected* sphere of radius R, in which the use of
boundary conditions at an interface between two media is demonstrated.   The reflector will be assumed to be effectively infinite
in thickness.

The differential equations for the core (c) and reflector (r) are

$$D_c \, \nabla^2 \phi_c - \phi \Sigma_c + k\phi \Sigma_c = 0 \qquad (3.48)$$
$$D_r \, \nabla^2 \phi_r - \phi_r \Sigma_r \qquad = 0 \qquad (3.49)$$

It is noted that no source term appears in Equation (3.49) since
the reflector is presumed not to be appreciably fissionable.   The
solution of the core equation (3.48) by direct analogy with equation (3.17) is

$$\phi_c = \frac{A \sin B_c r}{r} \qquad (3.50)$$

where now
$$B_c^2 = \frac{k-1}{L_c^2}$$
(3.51)

and
$$L_c^2 = \frac{D_c}{\Sigma_c}$$

The solution of the reflector equation (3.49), by direct analogy with Equation (3.45), is

$$\phi_r = \frac{A'e^{-r/L_r}}{r}$$
(3.52)

where
$$L_r^2 = \frac{D_r}{\Sigma_r}$$

Whenever a neutron flux extends across a boundary between two dissimilar media, the following conditions must be met:

   (a) The flux ϕ must be a continuous function across the interface of core and reflector.

$$\phi_c(R) = \phi_r(R)$$
(3.53)

   (b) The current j must be a continuous function across the interface of core and reflector.

$$j_c(R) = j_r(R)$$
(3.54)

By recalling the physical meaning of flux and current, it is readily seen that the same values must be obtained, whether the boundary is approached from one side or the other. Applying Equation (3.53),

$$\frac{A \sin B_c R}{R} = \frac{A'e^{-R/L_r}}{R}$$

From Equation (3.54),

$$-D_c A \left(\frac{B_c \cos B_c R}{R} - \frac{\sin B_c R}{R^2} \right) = D_r A' e^{-R/L_r} \left(\frac{1}{L_r R} + \frac{1}{R^2} \right)$$

Dividing these equations and simplifying,

$$B_c R \cot B_c R = 1 - \frac{D_r}{D_c} \left(1 + \frac{R}{L_r} \right) \qquad \begin{array}{l} \text{critical condition} \\ \text{reflected sphere} \end{array}$$
(3.55)

For the special case in which $D_r = D_c$, this becomes

$$\tan B_c R = -B_c L_r$$
(3.56)

   Numerical Illustration: Find the critical radius and U^{235} mass of a spherical core with isotopically pure U^{235} as metal, surrounded by a blanket of pure U^{238}, of infinite extent.

Solution: The effective neutron energy will be taken as 0.3 mev based on flux spectra computed for existing reactors. The applicable cross sections are

$$U^{238} \qquad \sigma_a = 0.18 \text{ barns}, \quad \sigma_f = 0$$
$$U^{235} \qquad \sigma_f = 1.50 \text{ barns}, \quad \sigma_a = 1.78 \text{ barns}$$

We also take the microscopic transport cross sections σ_t of each isotope as 7.4 barns, and use $\nu = 2.51$, $k = \eta = 2.12$ as good average values. The densities of U^{235} and U^{238} are taken as 18.7 and 19.0 gm/cm³ respectively. With the atom number $N = 0.0479$ cm⁻¹, we find $\Sigma_c = 0.0853$ cm⁻¹, $\Sigma_r = 0.00862$ cm⁻¹, and $\Sigma_t = 0.354$ cm⁻¹. The common diffusion coefficient is $D = 1/(3\Sigma_t) = 0.940$ cm. Thus $L_r^2 = D/\Sigma_r = 109$ cm² and $L_c^2 = D/\Sigma_c = 11.0$ cm². The core buckling is $B_c^2 = (\eta - 1)/L_c^2 = 0.102$ cm⁻², and $B_c = 0.319$ cm⁻¹. Insertion of these numbers in Equation (3.56) leads to a core radius of 5.86 cm. The core volume is 843 cm³ and the critical U^{235} mass is 15.8 kg. This result, although based on a crude theory, agrees well with the experimental U^{235} mass of 16 kg in a natural-uranium-reflected sphere fueled with approximately 90 per cent U^{235}. It will be noted that the fuel mass is large compared with that computed for the water-moderated reactor. This is a characteristic feature of the fast reactor.

3.5. *Modified one-group theory*

The age-diffusion theory used in § 3.2 is not readily applicable to a reflected core. An approximate analysis that embodies the neutron slowing feature but retains the simplicity of the one-group approach is the *modified one-group* theory. It is principally useful for estimating the effect of a reflector on a *large reactor*. It will be recalled from § 3.2 that the critical buckling of a core by age theory could be approximated by $B^2 \simeq \dfrac{\ln k}{L^2 + \tau}$. If k is close to unity, as is the case for a low U^{235} enrichment or highly poisoned reactor, $\ln k$ is approximately $k - 1$. As a fundamental postulate, the buckling in modified one-group theory is assumed to be

$$B_c^2 = \frac{k - 1}{L^2 + \tau} \tag{3.57}$$

This is identical with the one-group equation (3.51) except for the insertion of τ in the denominator, hence the term "modified" one-group theory. Cognizance of the finite slowing-down dis-

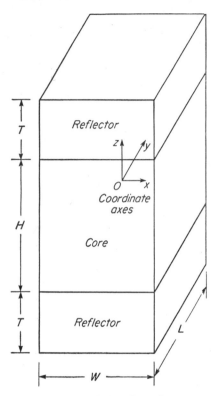

tance is thus incorporated. The solution procedure for the differential equations parallels closely the one-group method described in § 3.4. Opportunity will be taken here to display the method of *separation of variables* for calculating the critical size of core in which three coordinates are needed. Consider a large rectangular parallelepiped reactor of height H, width W, and length L, with a reflector of thickness T on the top and bottom, as sketched in Figure 3.5. The core differential equation is

$$\nabla^2\phi_c + B_c^2\phi_c = 0 \qquad (3.58)$$

where $\nabla^2\phi$ is given in (x,y,z) coordinates by Equation (3.5). It is proposed that the flux solution is a product of three separate functions, one for each coordinate:

Figure 3.5. End-reflected rectangular parallelepiped reactor.

$$\phi_c(x,y,z) = X(x)Y(y)Z(z) \qquad (3.59)$$

Substitution of Equation (3.59) in Equation (3.58) and rearrangement gives

$$\frac{1}{X}\frac{\partial^2 X}{\partial x^2} + \frac{1}{Y}\frac{\partial^2 Y}{\partial y^2} + \frac{1}{Z}\frac{\partial^2 Z}{\partial z^2} + B_c^2 = 0 \qquad (3.60)$$

The first three terms are functions of their respective coordinates only. If Equation (3.60) is to be true for all possible combinations of x, y, and z, each term must be a constant. Let the first two terms be labeled $-B_x^2$ and $-B_y^2$. Two equations result:

$$\frac{d^2 X}{dx^2} + B_x^2 X = 0 \qquad (3.61)$$

$$\frac{d^2Y}{dy^2} + B_y^2 Y = 0 \tag{3.62}$$

and if we let

$$B_z^2 = B_c^2 - B_x^2 - B_y^2 \tag{3.63}$$

a third equation is obtained,

$$\frac{d^2Z}{dz^2} + B_z^2 Z = 0 \tag{3.64}$$

B_z^2 is the *axial* buckling, equal to the *total buckling* less those associated with coordinates x and y. The solutions of (3.61) and (3.62) can be written by inspection as proportional to $\cos B_x x$ and $\cos B_y y$, the sines being forbidden because of the physical requirement that the flux be symmetric about the origin. In order for the flux ϕ_c to vanish at the extrapolated distance outside the bare-sided core, $B_x = \pi/W'$ and $B_y = \pi/L'$. We may now set this information aside for future reference, and proceed with the solution of Equation (3.64) as a strictly one-dimensional problem. The general solution that is symmetric about the origin is

$$Z(z) = A \cos B_z z \tag{3.65}$$

The reflector differential equation is

$$\nabla^2 \phi_r - B_r^2 \phi_r = 0 \tag{3.66}$$

where

$$B_r^2 = \frac{1}{L_r^2} = \kappa_r^2 \tag{3.67}$$

The same separation scheme is adopted, with the result that

$$\frac{d^2Z}{dz^2} - \bar{\kappa}_r^2 Z = 0 \tag{3.68}$$

with

$$\bar{\kappa}_r^2 = \kappa_r^2 + B_x^2 + B_y^2 \tag{3.69}$$

The differences between signs in the core and reflector cases should be noted carefully. The axial flux in the reflector may be written

$$Z(z) = F \sinh \bar{\kappa}_r (H/2 + T' - z) \tag{3.70}$$

which can be shown to satisfy (3.68) and the condition that it go to zero at $z = H/2 + T'$, the extrapolated boundary of the reflector. Assuming continuity of flux and current at $z = H/2$, Equations (3.53) and (3.54) become

$$A \cos B_z \frac{H}{2} = F \sinh \bar{\kappa}_r T' \qquad (3.71)$$

$$AD_c B_z \sin B_z \frac{H}{2} = D_r \bar{\kappa}_r F \cosh \bar{\kappa}_r T' \qquad (3.72)$$

The critical equation is their quotient,

$$\cot B_z \frac{H}{2} = \frac{D_c}{D_r} \frac{B_z}{\bar{\kappa}_r} \tanh \bar{\kappa}_r T' \qquad (3.73)$$

Several useful theorems may be deduced from this result.

(a) A finite reflector is comparable in value to an infinite reflector if it is a few diffusion lengths thick. The hyperbolic tangent is within 1 per cent of its limiting value of 1 at argument 2.65, i.e., for $\bar{\kappa}_r T' = 2.65$. For the large reactors to which this method applies, B_z^2 and B_y^2 are small, and $\bar{\kappa}_r \simeq \kappa_r = 1/L_r$. Thus $T' = 2.65 L_r$.

(b) If the thermal flux at the interface of core and reflector with similar properties were linearly extrapolated into the reflector, it would go to zero at about one diffusion length, as proved below. The "extrapolation distance" implied by this statement is

$$d = -\left(\frac{\phi_c}{\phi_c'}\right)_{H/2} = \frac{\cos B_z H/2}{B_z \sin B_z H/2} = \frac{\cot B_z H/2}{B_z}$$

According to Equation (3.73), with $D_r \simeq D_c$ and large T', this becomes

$$d = \frac{1}{\bar{\kappa}_r} \simeq \frac{1}{\kappa_r} = L_r$$

(c) By the use of a thick reflector on the sides of a large reactor, fuel layers on each side of width approximately one diffusion length can be saved. The critical height of the core *if unreflected* on the ends would be approximately $H_0 = \pi/B_z$, or $B_z H_0/2 = \pi/2$. Assume $D_c \simeq D_r$ and T' large in Equation (3.73), to yield

$$\cot B_z \frac{H}{2} \simeq \frac{B_z}{\bar{\kappa}_r}$$

For angles near $\pi/2$, the cotangent is approximately $\pi/2$ minus the angle, so that

$$\frac{\pi}{2} - \frac{B_z H}{2} \simeq \frac{B_z}{\bar{\kappa}_r}$$

Simplifying, the *reflector savings* is

$$S = \frac{H_0}{2} - \frac{H}{2} \simeq L_r$$

Numerical Illustration: Estimate the critical size of a cubical graphite moderated reactor, with thick graphite reflector, having the following materials constants:

$$k = 1.060 \qquad \tau = 350 \text{ cm}^2$$
$$L_c^2 = 250 \text{ cm}^2 \qquad L_r = 50 \text{ cm}$$

Also find the ratio of average to maximum flux in the core.

Solution: The first step is to find the dimensions of the *bare* reactor. The materials buckling is

$$B_c^2 = (1.060 - 1)/(250 + 350) = 0.00010$$

and $B_c = 0.01$. The geometric buckling for a bare cube, according to Table 3.1, is $3(\pi/S')^2$, where S' is a side, including two extrapolation lengths d. Equating bucklings, $S' = \pi\sqrt{3}/B_c = 544$ cm. Letting $\lambda_t = 2.7$ cm for graphite, and making use of Equation (2.12), we find $d = (0.71)(2.7) \simeq 2$ cm. Thus the actual bare side is $544 - 2d = 540$ cm. The thick reflector allows a total reduction of core side by approximately $2L_r = 100$ cm, leaving the reflected dimension $S = 440$ cm $= 14.4$ ft. The flux distribution in the core will be approximately

$$\phi(x,y,z) = \phi_c \cos\frac{\pi x}{S'} \cos\frac{\pi y}{S'} \cos\frac{\pi z}{S'}$$

where x, y, and z are of interest only up to $S/2$. Thus

$$\frac{\bar{\phi}}{\phi_c} = \frac{1}{S^3} \int_{-S/2}^{S/2} \left(\cos\frac{\pi x}{S'} \, dx \right)^3 = \phi_c(0.258) \left(\frac{S'}{S} \sin\frac{\pi S}{2S'} \right)^3 = 0.425 \, \phi_c$$

The considerable improvement over the value 0.258 for an unreflected reactor is noted.

3.6. *Integral formulation of neutron motion*

The slowing down and diffusion of neutrons in an infinite medium can be formulated in terms of *integral* equations instead of differential equations. Usually the two are equivalent, but for some problems the integral method is much more powerful. Consider a spatially distributed fast neutron source $q(r,0)$, where

r' is a vector coordinate and the initial age is zero. Recalling from Equation (3.38) that the slowing-down density at a distance from a unit fast point source at *scalar* distance r is

$$q(u,r) = \frac{e^{-r^2/4\tau}}{(4\pi\tau)^{3/2}}$$

we may write for a point of observation r,

$$q(r,\tau) = \int q(r,0) \frac{e^{-|r-r'|^2/4\tau}}{(4\pi\tau)^{3/2}} \, dr' \qquad (3.74)$$

where dr' means the volume element at r', and the integral is over all space. The function of r and r' which represents the slowing-down density of a unit point source, may be called the *point age kernel*, and given the symbol

$$G_{\text{point age}}(r,r') = \frac{e^{-|r-r'|^2/4\tau}}{(4\pi\tau)^{3/2}} \qquad (3.75)$$

Thus

$$q(r,\tau) = \int q(r',0) G_{\text{point age}}(r,r') \, dr' \qquad (3.76)$$

In general, a kernel represents the effect at an observation point produced by a unit source. The *point diffusion kernel* giving *flux* due to a unit point thermal source (compare Equation 3.47) would thus be

$$G_{\text{point diffusion}}(r,r') = \frac{e^{-|r-r'|/L}}{4\pi D|r-r'|} \qquad (3.77)$$

Relation of point and plane kernels. One may construct plane kernels, giving the results of plane sources of unit strength per unit area by integration of point kernels, as follows. Let $G_{\text{point}}(r,0)$ be a kernel with source at the origin, point of observation at a scalar distance r. The effect of a uniform plane at $z = 0$, which is a collection of point sources, is the integral

$$\int_{\rho=0}^{\infty} G_{\text{point}}(r,0) 2\pi\rho \, d\rho$$

where ρ is the radius of a ring of width $d\rho$ on the plane, as shown in Figure 3.6. Now since $r^2 = \rho^2 + z^2$ and $\rho \, d\rho = r \, dr$, this may be written

$$G_{\text{plane}}(z,0) = 2\pi \int_{z}^{\infty} G_{\text{point}}(r,0) \, r \, dr \qquad (3.78)$$

For the case of age slowing, with

$$G_{\text{point}}(r,0) = \frac{e^{-r^2/4\tau}}{(4\pi\tau)^{3/2}}$$

we find by integration that

$$G_{\text{plane}}(z,0) = \frac{e^{-z^2/4\tau}}{(4\pi\tau)^{1/2}}$$

For the case of neutron diffusion, with

$$G_{\text{point}}(r,0) = \frac{e^{-r/L}}{4\pi\,Dr}$$

it can easily be shown that

$$G_{\text{plane}}(z,0) = \frac{Le^{-z/L}}{2D}$$

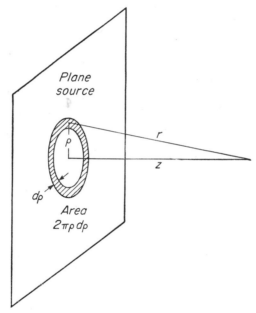

Figure 3.6.   Geometry for deriving plane
kernel from point kernel.

By replacing distances z from the plane $z = 0$ by the distance
$z - z'$ from the plane $z = z'$, these kernels may be generalized to

$$G_{\text{plane age}}(z,z') = \frac{e^{-|z-z'|^2/4\tau}}{(4\pi\tau)^{1/2}} \tag{3.79}$$

and

$$G_{\text{plane diffusion}}(z,z') = \frac{Le^{-|z-z'|/L}}{2D} \tag{3.80}$$

Combined slowing and diffusion. The thermal flux at z due to slowing of neutrons from plane source at $z = 0$ to the plane z', with subsequent thermal diffusion from z' to z, may be obtained by compounding kernels. Let G_f stand for the age kernel and G_t for the diffusion kernel. The flux is

$$\phi(z) = \int G_f(z',0) \, G_t(z,z') \, dz' \equiv G_{ft}(z,0) \qquad (3.81)$$

Invoking Equations (3.79) and (3.80),

$$G_{ft}(z,0) = \int_{-\infty}^{\infty} \frac{e^{-(z')^2/4\tau}}{(4\pi\tau)^{1/2}} \frac{Le^{-|z-z'|/L}}{2D} \, dz'$$

Integration results in the age-diffusion kernel,

$$G_{ft}(z,0) = \frac{L}{4D} \, e^{\tau/L^2}(g_1 + g_2) \qquad (3.82)$$

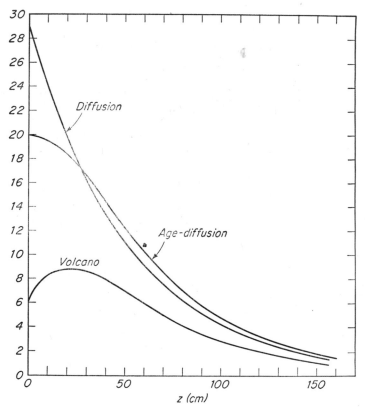

Figure 3.7. Plane kernels (graphite): $\tau = 364$ cm², $L = 52$ cm.

where

$$g_1 = e^{-z/L}\left[1 + \text{erf}\left(\frac{z}{2\sqrt{\tau}} - \frac{\sqrt{\tau}}{L}\right)\right]$$

$$g_2 = e^{z/L}\left[1 - \text{erf}\left(\frac{z}{2\sqrt{\tau}} + \frac{\sqrt{\tau}}{L}\right)\right]$$

and the tabulated *error function* is

$$\text{erf } x = \frac{2}{\sqrt{\pi}} \int_0^x e^{-\alpha^2}\, d\alpha \qquad (3.83)$$

Note that erf $(-x) = -\text{erf } x$. Figure 3.7 shows the diffusion and age-diffusion kernels for graphite with $\tau = 364$ cm^2 and $L = 52$ cm.

Application to reflected reactor. All of the kernels discussed above referred to an infinite, homogeneous medium. They may be adapted to the case of a reactor with infinite reflector if properly interpreted. The following method is described by Goertzel and Loeb.

Consider an infinite moderator such as graphite or water, in which a finite "core" region also contains fuel that contributes *additional absorption*. Fast neutrons from fission in the core region will slow down in the whole medium and diffuse to the points where they are absorbed. Were the medium completely uniform, the kernel G_{ft} could be used to determine the thermal flux. The fuel nuclei absorb thermal neutrons, however, and act as *negative* sources. If a *positive* source of thermals were located at a point, a flux distribution proportional to $e^{-r/L}/(4\pi Dr)$ would be set up. The sink due to fuel gives a negative effect, i.e., a depression in flux. The scale of this depression is determined by the fact that it takes $1/\eta$ absorptions in fuel to give one fast neutron. The proper kernel is thus

$$G_v = G_{ft} - \frac{1}{\eta}\, G_t \qquad (3.84)$$

which is called the "volcano" kernel, an appropriate name, as can be seen from Figure 3.7. With a fast neutron source density $\phi\Sigma_f\nu$ we may construct the thermal flux anywhere in the reactor as

$$\phi(z) = \int \phi(z')\Sigma_f\nu\left[G_{ft}(z,z') - \frac{1}{\eta}\, G_t(z,z')\right] dz' \qquad (3.85)$$

where integration is taken over the region containing fuel. It is important to note that the unknown flux function appears both inside and outside the integral, which is characteristic of integral equations.

Greuling has developed a method involving the calculus of variations for determining the critical loading as a function of core size. A rudimentary version of the approach may be demonstrated for one-group theory. For this case, $G_{ft}(z,z')$ is identical with $G_t(z,z')$ in Equation (3.85). Multiplication of both sides by $\phi(z)\ dz$ and integration yield

$$\frac{1}{\Sigma_{aU}} = \frac{\int \phi(z)\ dz \int \phi(z')(\eta - 1)G_t(z,z')\ dz'}{\int \phi^2(z)\ dz} \qquad (3.86)$$

As a first approximation for a reflected slab reactor of width H, a trial *constant flux* is inserted, and the indicated integration performed. The critical condition is

$$\frac{1 - f}{f(\eta - 1)} = 1 - \frac{L}{H}(1 - e^{-H/L})$$

The corresponding differential equations result can be rearranged to

$$\frac{1 - f}{f(\eta - 1)} = 1 - \cos^2 \frac{BH}{2}$$

which agrees in the limit of a large reactor with the integral solution. The next logical trial flux, the parabola, gives better agreement.

Problems

3.1. Find the ratio of height to diameter of a bare circular cylinder reactor, with fixed volume, that (a) has the smallest ratio of surface to volume, (b) has the minimum geometric buckling.

Answer. (a) $H/D = 1$; (b) $H/D = 0.924$.

3.2. For a fuel-moderator solution with materials buckling 0.010 cm^{-2} and volume 200 liters, what dimensions of a flat container of square cross section would be appropriate to guarantee that the solution would remain sub-critical?

Answer. Height less than 40.6 cm or sides greater than 70.2 cm.

3.3. Calculate the diffusion length for thermal neutrons in graphite of density 1.6 gm/cm³, $\bar{\sigma}_a = 3.5$ millibarns and $\sigma_s = 4.8$ barns.
Answer. 57.1 cm.

3.4. Prove that $\bar{r}^2 = 6\tau$ for the slowing-down density from a point source of monoenergetic neutrons.

3.5. Compute (a) by modified one-group theory and (b) by age theory, the critical radius and fuel mass of a spherical bare graphite-moderated, pure U²³⁵ reactor, with atom ratio $N_C/N_{235} = 15,000$, using $D = 0.9$ cm, $\tau = 350$, $\rho = 1.65$ gm/cm³, and maxwellian cross sections $(\bar{\sigma}_a)_C = 3.5$ millibarns and $(\bar{\sigma}_a)_{U\text{-}235} = 597$ barns.
Answer. (a) 78.7 cm; (b) 91.3 cm.

3.6. (a) Compute the age to thermal of 2 mev neutrons in graphite, of density 1.60 gm/cm³, using the following scattering cross section data:

E (ev)	σ_s (barns)
2×10^6	1.72
10^6	2.67
2×10^5	4.22
10^5	4.48
10^4 to 1	4.70
0.1 to 0.01	4.80

(b) What part of this is associated with the slowing between 1.45 ev (the usual measuring point) and thermal? Suggestion: Plot the age integrand with logarithmic energy scale and integrate numerically.
Answer. (a) $\simeq$345 cm²; (b) $\simeq$60 cm².

3.7. Estimate the resonance escape probability for a solution of natural uranium and water with atom ratios $N_H/N_U = 40$ and $N_H/N_U = 1000$.
Answer. 0.923, 0.988.

3.8. Why would the solution with $N_H/N_U = 40$ (Problem 3.7) not be suitable for use in a reactor?

3.9. Derive a formula for the flux distribution as a function of energy E and coordinate r, in the $1/E$ region above thermal, for a bare spherical core of radius R to which age theory is applicable.

Answer. $\phi(E,r) = \dfrac{k\Sigma_a \phi_c}{\xi \Sigma_s E} \dfrac{\sin (\pi r/R')}{\pi r/R'} e^{-(\pi/R')^2 \tau(E)}$.

3.10. Calculate, using the answer to Problem 3.9, the flux per unit lethargy interval at 1.45 ev at the center of a graphite, enriched-uranium

sphere of Problem 3.5, operated at a total power of 100 kw. Assume
$R' = 93.2$ cm, $\Sigma_a = 0.00358$ cm^{-1}, $k = 1.912$, $\Sigma_s = 0.397$ cm^{-1}, τ (1.45 ev)
$= 285$ cm^2.

Answer. 9.0×10^{10}/cm^2-sec per unit lethargy.

3.11. A rectangular parallelepiped reactor has ducts along one axis
that cause the diffusion coefficient to be larger in that direction by a
factor c.   If the length of the homogeneous version is H_0, what is the
length of this reactor?

Answer. $H_0\sqrt{c}$.

3.12. Show that the thermal flux distribution by modified one-group
theory in an infinitely long circular cylinder with infinite reflector is
given by

$$\phi_c = \phi_0 J_0(B_c r), \qquad \phi_r = C\phi_0 K_0(\kappa_r r)$$

3.13. For a graphite system with $k = 1.10$, $L_c^2 = 250$ cm^2, $\tau_c = 364$ cm^2, $L_r = 50$ cm, $R = 153$ cm, find the coefficient C in the reflector
flux (see Problem 3.12).   Plot the flux distribution from $r = 0$ to
$r = 350$ cm.

Answer.   7.76.

3.14. Find the flux distribution and thermal leakage per unit area
from a sphere of radius R with a unit point thermal source in the center.

$$Answer. \quad \phi(r) = \frac{1}{4\pi Dr} \frac{\sinh\left[(R - r)/L\right]}{\sinh R/L}$$

$$j(R) = \frac{1}{4\pi RL \sinh R/L}.$$

3.15. Derive formulas for the ratios of average to central flux in (a)
a reflected slab reactor, height H, bare equivalent height H', (b) a side-
reflected cylinder, radius R, bare equivalent radius R'.

$$Answer. \quad (a) \;\; \frac{\sin x}{x}, \text{ where } x = \frac{\pi H}{2H'},$$

$$(b) \;\; \frac{2J_1(x)}{x}, \text{ where } x = \frac{j_0 R}{R'}.$$

References

Soodak, Harry, and Edward C. Campbell, *Elementary Pile Theory.*
     New York: John Wiley & Sons, Inc. (1950).
Goodman, Clark, Ed., *The Science and Engineering of Nuclear Power.*
     Cambridge, Mass.: Addison Wesley Press (1949), Vols. I, II.
Glasstone, Samuel, and Milton C. Edlund, *The Elements of Nuclear
     Reactor Theory.*   New York: D. Van Nostrand Co. (1952).

Jahnke, Eugene, and Fritz Emde, *Tables of Functions*. New York: Dover Publications (1945). See also Appendix for other references on Bessel functions.

Peaceful Uses of Atomic Energy: Proceedings of the International Conference in Geneva, August 1955. Volume 5, *Physics of Reactor Design*. New York: Columbia University Press (1956).

    Macklin, R. L., and H. S. Pomerance, "Resonance Capture Integrals," Paper P/833.

    Cohen, E. Richard, "A Survey of Neutron Thermalization Theory," Paper P/611.

    Beyer, F. C. et al, "The Fast Exponential Experiment," Paper P/598.

    Okrent, D., R. Avery, and H. H. Hummel, "A Survey of the Theoretical and Experimental Aspects of Fast Reactor Physics," Paper P/609.

Salvetti, C., *Lectures on the Theory of Nuclear Reactors*, NP-3826. Oak Ridge, Tenn.: Technical Information Service, Atomic Energy Commission (1952).

Greuling, E., *Theory of Water-Tamped Water Boiler*, LA-399 (1945). Declassified 1956.

Tables of the Error Function and Its Derivative. National Bureau of Standards, Applied Mathematics Series 41. Washington: U. S. Government Printing Office (1954).

Goertzel, G., and William A. Loeb, "Non-Uniform Fuel Distributions in Nuclear Reactors," *Nucleonics*, September 1954, p. 42.

Dresner, Lawrence, "The Effective Resonance Integrals of U-238 and Th-232." *Nuclear Science and Engineering* 1, 68 (1956).

Chapter 4

THE HETEROGENEOUS REACTOR

|||||||||||||||||||||||||||||||||||||||||||||||||||||||||||||||||||||||||||||||||||||||||||||||||||||||||||||||||||||||||||||||||||||||||||||||||||||

When the first Chicago reactor CP-1 was built, the only fission-able fuel available was natural uranium. Since a homogeneous mixture of fuel and moderator would not yield a self-sustaining chain reaction under conditions of strong resonance capture in U^{238}, it was necessary to isolate the metal fuel from the moderator. This required a theory of the *heterogeneous reactor* to account for local flux variations superposed on a general distribution over the whole reactor. Many of the present power reactors fueled with enriched uranium are also heterogeneous, but for a different reason: to give a maximum heat transfer surface from the fuel to a circulating coolant. The fuel plates are sometimes so thin and closely spaced relative to characteristic distances neutrons move between collisions, that the system may be considered homogeneous from a mathematical standpoint. The term "quasi-homogeneous" may be used for such reactors. In § 4.1, the diffusion theory for mono-energetic neutrons in a two-region fuel-moderator system is developed. It will yield a first approximation for the thermal flux in a natural or slightly enriched uranium reactor or for the flux depressions in fuel for a highly enriched core. It should be noted that higher-order approximations based on transport theory are needed to obtain more accurate flux predictions, as discussed in Chapter 9.

The ideal combination of fuel and moderator from an economic standpoint would be natural uranium and ordinary water. It appears not to be possible to achieve a practical reactor with these materials because of the resonance capture of epithermal neutrons in U^{238} and the capture of thermals in hydrogen. This leads to the use of graphite and D_2O as moderators. Even with these materials in heterogeneous arrangement to minimize resonance capture, the reactor dimensions with natural uranium fuel must be about 20 ft with graphite and 10 ft with D_2O. Figure 4.1 shows the general arrangement of a natural uranium reactor. The enriched fuel reactor can be much smaller, of course.

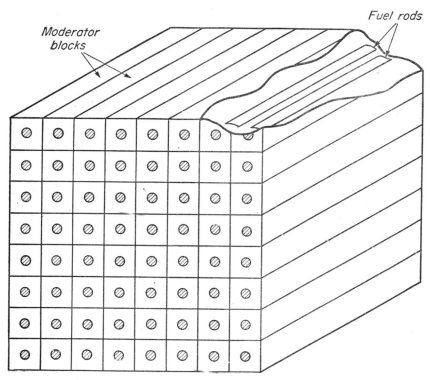

Figure 4.1. Natural or low-enrichment uranium reactor.

The analysis of criticality consists of four phases:

(a) To ascertain the average or effective values over the system at room temperature, of the four factors ϵ, p, f, and η, that go in the general infinite multiplication factor of a reactor.

$$k = \epsilon p f \eta \qquad (4.1)$$

(b) To deduce the characteristic distances that neutrons require to slow down and be absorbed, measured by τ and L^2, which differ from their counterparts in pure moderator because of the presence and orientation of fuel and coolant passages.

(c) To apply a "homogeneous" theory, typically two-group (Chapter 5), age-diffusion (§ 3.2) or modified one-group (§ 3.5), using k, L^2, and τ obtained previously, to obtain the critical size.

(d) To include effects of fission product poisons, operating temperature, fuel burnup, and excess multiplication for flexibility of control and safety, as corrections to the basic result from (c).

4.1. *Flux distribution and thermal utilization, f*

The thermal neutron flux in a heterogeneous reactor will be depressed in the absorbing fuel and adjacent moderator. This effect complicates the calculation of thermal utilization. The

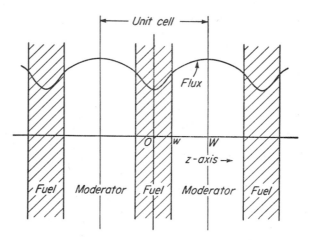

Figure 4.2.   Lattice and unit cell of plate-type heterogeneous reactor.

fractional absorption by fuel must include both average flux and volume weighting factors,

$$f = \frac{\overline{\phi}_U \Sigma_{aU} V_U}{\overline{\phi}_U \Sigma_{aU} V_U + \overline{\phi}_m \Sigma_{am} V_m} \tag{4.2}$$

where the $\overline{\phi}$'s are *average* fluxes over the uranium and moderator. In order to find the average values, the spatial variation of flux must be determined. The fact that the reactor is large relative to one unit of the repeated geometric pattern is fortunate from a mathematical standpoint, in that it can be assumed that little change in flux is observed on traversing one "cell." An individual cell may be studied independently, by reasoning that processes occurring within it are representative. Two typical cells are (a) a cylindrical fuel rod or line of slugs surrounded by a volume of moderator with square cross section, and (b) a thin metal plate with a layer of moderator on each side, with the cell width small compared with the other dimensions.

In order to demonstrate the principles most simply, we shall consider the effectively one-dimensional parallel plate system of Figure 4.2. Diffusion theory (Equation 3.8) for the thermal neutrons is assumed to be applicable in each medium. Letting the subscripts 0 and 1 designate the fuel and moderator,

$$D_0 \nabla^2 \phi_0 - \phi_0 \Sigma_0 + S_0 = 0 \qquad \text{fuel} \qquad (4.3)$$

$$D_1 \nabla^2 \phi_1 - \phi_1 \Sigma_1 + S_1 = 0 \qquad \text{moderator} \qquad (4.4)$$

Three assumptions that simplify these equations are made:

(a) The variation of flux in any plane parallel to the fuel plates may be ignored on the basis that relative absorptions in fuel and moderator will be the same everywhere. Only one coordinate is now necessary to solve the problem.

(b) The thermal source in the fuel S_0 may be set equal to zero, on the grounds that there is a small chance of a neutron becoming

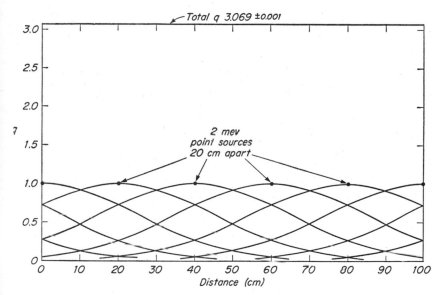

Figure 4.3. Superposition of slowing-down densities in graphite.

thermal in the heavy metal, with its very small ξ (for uranium, 0.0084).

(c) The thermal source in the moderator is independent of position, $S_1 =$ constant. This can be justified by recalling from § 3.3 that the slowing-down density just above thermal energy from a fast neutron source is a broad, flat distribution. Further, the actual q at a point in the reactor is a superposition of many such curves, because of sources located throughout the core. Figure 4.3 indicates schematically the composition of the thermal source for an arrangement of 2 mev *point* neutron sources. The diffusion equations become

$$\frac{d^2\phi_0}{dz^2} - \kappa_0^2\phi_0 = 0 \qquad (4.5)$$

$$\frac{d^2\phi_1}{dz^2} - \kappa_1^2\phi_1 + \frac{S_1}{D_1} = 0 \qquad (4.6)$$

where $\kappa_0^2 = \Sigma_0/D_0$ and $\kappa_1^2 = \Sigma_1/D_1$ are squares of inverse diffusion lengths.

Of the two possible solutions for the fuel, $\cosh \kappa_0 z$ and $\sinh \kappa_0 z$, only the former is admissible, since the slope of the flux must be zero at $z = 0$. Thus

$$\phi_0 = A \cosh \kappa_0 z \qquad (4.7)$$

where A is arbitrary.

The complete solution of Equation (4.6) is the sum of the complementary function ϕ_c and a particular integral ϕ_p. The solution ϕ_c of the homogeneous equation

$$\frac{d^2\phi_1}{dz^2} - \kappa_1^2\phi_1 = 0$$

is a linear combination of $\sinh \kappa_1 z$ and $\cosh \kappa_1 z$. It will be convenient to choose this combination in such a way that the slope of the flux is guaranteed to be zero at the boundary of the cell, $z = W$. This condition implies symmetry of flux about the median plane of the moderator (or zero net current between adjacent cells). It is proposed, therefore, that ϕ_c be written

$$\phi_c = C \cosh \kappa_1(W - z)$$

The particular integral is found to be a constant,

$$\phi_p = \frac{S_1}{\Sigma_1}$$

which can be tested by direct substitution in Equation (4.6).
Thus the moderator flux is

$$\phi_1 = C \cosh \kappa_1(W - z) + \frac{S_1}{\Sigma_1} \qquad (4.8)$$

The arbitrary coefficients are obtained by equating fluxes and
currents at the fuel-moderator interface, $z = w$, i.e., $\phi_0(w) = \phi_1(w)$
and $D_0\phi_0'(w) = D_1\phi_1'(w)$, where primes denote differentiation.

$$A \cosh \kappa_0 w = C \cosh \kappa_1(W - w) + \frac{S_1}{\Sigma_1}$$

$$D_0\kappa_0 A \sinh \kappa_0 w = -D_1\kappa_1 C \sinh \kappa_1(W - w)$$

from which we find

$$\frac{A}{S_1} = \frac{D_1\kappa_1 \sinh \kappa_1(W - w)}{\Delta} \qquad (4.9)$$

$$\frac{C}{S_1} = \frac{-D_0\kappa_0 \sinh \kappa_0 w}{\Delta} \qquad (4.10)$$

where $\Delta =$

$$\Sigma_1[D_1\kappa_1 \cosh \kappa_0 w \sinh \kappa_1(W - w) + D_0\kappa_0 \sinh \kappa_0 w \cosh \kappa_1(W - w)]$$

The flux distribution may be plotted with knowledge of the various constants in Equations 4.9 and 4.10. The thermal utilization, defined as (*absorption in fuel*)/(*total absorption*), is also equal
to (*absorption in fuel*)/(*total thermal source*), by virtue of the assumption that there is no net neutron leakage from the cell, and
thus all neutrons arising in the cell are absorbed in it. Specifically,

$$f = \frac{\int_0^w \phi_0\Sigma_0 \, dz}{V_1 S_1} \qquad (4.11)$$

where V_1 is the volume of a column of moderator of *unit area*,
width $W - w$. Inserting Equation (4.7) and integrating,

$$f = \left(\frac{A}{S_1}\right) \frac{\Sigma_0 \sinh \kappa_0 w}{V_1 \kappa_0} \qquad (4.12)$$

The only unknown factor in f is A/S_1, which has already been
found. Combining Equations (4.9) and (4.12) and simplifying,
the *reciprocal* of the thermal utilization is found to be

$$\frac{1}{f} = 1 + \frac{V_1\Sigma_1}{V_0\Sigma_0} F + (E - 1) \qquad (4.13)$$

where

$$F = \kappa_0 w \coth \kappa_0 w \qquad (4.14)$$

$$E = \kappa_1(W - w) \coth \kappa_1(W - w) \qquad (4.15)$$

A physical interpretation of the functions F and E may be deduced by rewriting the conventional definition of thermal utilization, Equation (4.2), as

$$\frac{1}{f} = 1 + \frac{V_1 \Sigma_1 \overline{\phi}_1}{V_0 \Sigma_0 \overline{\phi}_0}$$

Now let $\overline{\phi}_1 = \overline{\phi}_1 + \phi_1(w) - \phi_1(w)$, and substitute to obtain

$$\frac{1}{f} = 1 + \frac{V_1 \Sigma_1}{V_0 \Sigma_0} \frac{\overline{\phi}_1(w)}{\overline{\phi}_0} + \frac{V_1 \Sigma_1}{V_0 \Sigma_0} \frac{[\overline{\phi}_1 - \phi_1(w)]}{\overline{\phi}_0} \qquad (4.16)$$

Comparison with Equation (4.13) reveals that F is actually the ratio of flux at the fuel surface to the average over the fuel. Also $E - 1$ accounts for the fact that the moderator flux is not flat, but rises to a maximum at the cell boundary.

Before proceeding to the application of this formula, we take note of an improvement over simple diffusion theory that can be effected by use in Equation (4.13) of the transport theory prediction of κ (see § 9.3) in the case of the *fuel*.

$$\frac{\kappa}{\Sigma} = \tanh \frac{\kappa}{\Sigma_s} \qquad (4.17)$$

where $\Sigma = \Sigma_a + \Sigma_s$ denotes the total cross section. It is not necessary to invoke this correction for the calculation of κ for the moderator.

Numerical Illustration: Find the thermal utilization for a natural-uranium–graphite system with fuel plates 0.5 in. thick, separated by 12 in. on centers.

Solution. The first step is to assign constants. The dimensions are $w = 0.635$ cm $= V_0$, $W = 15.24$ cm, $W - w = 14.605$ cm $= V_1$. The absorption cross section for 2200 meters/sec neutrons in uranium is 7.68 barns. With a scale factor $1/1.128$ to a maxwellian distribution and a not-$1/v$ factor of 0.99, we obtain $\sigma_a = 6.74$ barns. Using a metal density of 19.0 gm/cm^3 and an atom density 0.0480, $\overline{\Sigma}_a = \Sigma_0 = 0.324$ cm^{-1}. Also $\sigma_s = 8.3$ barns, $\Sigma_s = 0.398$ cm^{-1}, and $\Sigma = 0.722$ cm^{-1}. Trial and error treatment of Equation (4.17) gives

$\kappa_0 = 0.675$ cm^{-1}. For the reflector, we assume graphite of density 1.65 gm/cm^3 with sufficient impurities to increase its microscopic cross section to 4.5 mb at 2200 meters/sec or 4.0 mb for a maxwellian flux. With $N = 0.0827$, $\Sigma_1 = 3.31 \times 10^{-4}$ cm^{-1}. The transport mean free path λ_t using $\sigma_s = 4.8$ barns, $\overline{\cos \theta} = 0.056$, is computed to be 2.67 cm, and $D_1 = 0.890$ cm. Thus $\kappa_1 = 0.0193$ cm^{-1}. Now $\kappa_0 w = 0.429$ and $\kappa_1(W - w) = 0.282$. From Equation (4.14), $F = 0.429$ coth $0.429 = 1.061$, and from Equation (4.15), $E = 0.282$ coth $0.282 = 1.026$. Finally,

$$\frac{1}{f} = 1 + \frac{(14.605)(3.31 \times 10^{-4})}{(0.635)(0.324)} (1.061) + 0.026 = 1.051$$

The thermal utilization is therefore 0.951. In passing, we note that the ratio of flux at the fuel surface to the average in the fuel is $F = 1.061$.

4.2. *Flux in cylindrical system*

The only simple mathematical method for treating a lattice of uranium *rods* makes use of a *cylindrical* unit cell. The square (or hexagonal) area associated with each fuel rod in the square (or triangular) lattice is replaced by a circle of equal area; this greatly simplifies the calculations, but with error of much less than 1 per cent. The flux is assumed not to vary along the rod axis, reducing the problem to one-dimensional, with coordinate r, rod radius r_0, and cell radius r_1. The analysis will be seen to resemble closely the plane case. The diffusion equation for the fuel in cylindrical coordinates is

$$\frac{d^2\phi_0}{dr^2} + \frac{1}{r}\frac{d\phi_0}{dr} - \kappa_0^2 \phi_0 = 0 \qquad (4.18)$$

If the substitution $x = \kappa_0 r$ is made, Equation (4.18) becomes

$$\frac{d^2\phi_0}{dx^2} + \frac{1}{x}\frac{d\phi_0}{dx} - \phi_0 = 0 \qquad (4.19)$$

which is the modified Bessel equation of zero order (see Appendix A). It has two possible solutions, $I_0(x)$ and $K_0(x)$, the modified Bessel functions of the first and second kind, respectively. These are tabulated, along with other types. The second solution can be ruled out immediately in this problem, because it goes to infinity at $x = 0$. The general solution of Equation (4.18) is thus

$$\phi_0(r) = AI_0(\kappa_0 r) \tag{4.20}$$

where A is an arbitrary constant. The diffusion equation for the moderator is of the inhomogeneous type,

$$\frac{d^2\phi_1}{dr^2} + \frac{1}{r}\frac{d\phi_1}{dr} - \kappa_1^2\phi_1 = \frac{-S_1}{D_1} \tag{4.21}$$

having a solution that is a sum of the characteristic solutions of the homogeneous equation, $K_0(\kappa_1 r)$ and $I_0(\kappa_1 r)$ and the particular integral, which is again S_1/Σ_1. Thus

$$\phi_1(r) = CK_0(\kappa_1 r) + GI_0(\kappa_1 r) + \frac{S_1}{\Sigma_1} \tag{4.22}$$

where C and G are arbitrary constants. To find A, C, and G in terms of S_1, the usual continuity of flux and current is assumed at r_0, along with the condition that $d\phi_1/dr = 0$ at r_1, which implies a slow variation of flux through the reactor and that as many neutrons enter as leave the cell. As preparation, we note the differentiation formulas $dI_0(x)/dx = I_1(x)$ and $dK_0(x)/dx = -K_1(x)$, where I_1 and K_1 are the first-order modified Bessel functions. A certain amount of algebraic complication can be avoided by first applying the condition of zero current at r_1. Then from Equation (4.22),

$$0 = -C\kappa_1 K_1(\kappa_1 r_1) + G\kappa_1 I_1(\kappa_1 r_1)$$

or

$$G = C\frac{K_1(\kappa_1 r_1)}{I_1(\kappa_1 r_1)}$$

Thus the moderator flux is

$$\phi_1(r) = CM_0(\kappa_1 r) + \frac{S_1}{\Sigma_1} \tag{4.23}$$

where we have defined the compound function

$$M_0(\kappa_1 r) = K_0(\kappa_1 r) + \frac{K_1(\kappa_1 r_1)}{I_1(\kappa_1 r_1)}I_0(\kappa_1 r) \tag{4.24}$$

Continuity of flux and current at r_0 gives the pair of equations

$$AI_0(\kappa_0 r_0) = CM_0(\kappa_1 r_0) + \frac{S_1}{\Sigma_1} \tag{4.25}$$

$$D_0\kappa_0 AI_1(\kappa_0 r_0) = -D_1\kappa_1 CM_1(\kappa_1 r_0) \tag{4.26}$$

where

$$M_1(\kappa_1 r) = K_1(\kappa_1 r) - \frac{K_1(\kappa_1 r_1)}{I_1(\kappa_1 r_1)} I_1(\kappa_1 r) \qquad (4.27)$$

Note that $\dfrac{dM_0(x)}{dx} = -M_1(x)$

Solving Equations (4.25) and (4.26) simultaneously,

$$\frac{A}{S_1} = \frac{D_1\kappa_1 M_1(\kappa_1 r_0)}{\Delta} \qquad (4.28)$$

$$\frac{C}{S_1} = \frac{-D_0\kappa_0 I_1(\kappa_0 r_0)}{\Delta} \qquad (4.29)$$

$$\Delta = \Sigma_1[D_1\kappa_1 I_0(\kappa_0 r_0)M_1(\kappa_1 r_0) + D_0\kappa_0 I_1(\kappa_0 r_0)M_0(\kappa_1 r_0)] \qquad (4.30)$$

Relative flux plots may be made by use of Equations (4.20), (4.23), (4.28), (4.29), and (4.30). By direct analogy with Equation (4.11) we write

$$f = \frac{\int_0^{r_0} \phi_0\Sigma_0 2\pi r\,dr}{V_1 S_1} = \left(\frac{A}{S_1}\right)\frac{2\pi\Sigma_0}{V_1}\int_0^{r_0} I_0(\kappa_0 r)r\,dr \qquad (4.31)$$

The integral is $r_0 I_1(\kappa_0 r_0)/\kappa_0$, using formulas in Appendix A. The combination of Equations (4.28), (4.30), and (4.31) yields the reciprocal of the thermal utilization,

$$\frac{1}{f} = 1 + \frac{V_1\Sigma_1}{V_0\Sigma_0} F + (E - 1) \qquad (4.32)$$

where now

$$F = \frac{\kappa_0 r_0}{2}\frac{I_0(\kappa_0 r_0)}{I_1(\kappa_0 r_0)} \simeq 1 + \frac{(\kappa_0 r_0)^2}{8} - \frac{(\kappa_0 r_0)^4}{192} \qquad (4.33)$$

and

$$E - 1 = \left[\frac{V_1}{V_0}\frac{\kappa_1 r_0}{2}\frac{M_0(\kappa_1 r_0)}{M_1(\kappa_1 r_0)}\right] - 1 \simeq \frac{(\kappa_1 r_1)^2}{2}\left[\ln\left(\frac{r_1}{r_0}\right) - \frac{3}{4}\right] \qquad (4.34)$$

The approximations, obtained from series expansions of Bessel functions, are accurate for $r_1 \gg r_0$, i.e., moderator volume considerably larger than fuel volume, and for small $\kappa_0 r_0$, i.e., relatively weak absorption in the fuel.

Numerical Illustration: Find the thermal utilization for a heterogeneous natural-uranium reactor similar to the Oak Ridge pile, with fuel rods 1.1-in. diameter, 8-in. rectangular cell.

Solution. The cell area is 64 sq in., which in circular shape has a radius $r_1 = 11.46$ cm. The radius of fuel rod is $r_0 = 1.397$ cm, considerably smaller than r_1. Using the constants calculated in an earlier example, $\kappa_0 = 0.675$ cm^{-1}, $\kappa_1 = 0.0193$ cm^{-1}, we find $\kappa_0 r_0 = 0.943$ and $\kappa_1 r_1 = 0.221$. Substitution in Equation (4.33) gives $F = 1 + 0.111 - 0.004 = 1.107$, and in Equation (4.34) gives $E - 1 = 0.0244$ (ln $8.20 - 0.75$) $= 0.0330$. Now $V_1/V_0 = (r_1/r_0)^2 - 1 = 66.3$, $\Sigma_0 = 0.324$ cm^{-1}, $\Sigma_1 = 3.31 \times 10^{-4}$ cm^{-1}, and $1/f = 1 + (66.3)(1.022 \times 10^{-3})$ $(1.107) + 0.0330 = 1.108$. The thermal utilization is **0.903**. The result obtained by the more exact forms of Equations (4.33) and (4.34) will agree within the accuracy of the theory itself.

4.3. *Resonance escape probability p*

The fraction of neutrons that reach thermal energy without experiencing capture in the resonances of U^{238} is given by the theory in § 3.3 as

$$p = e^{-\Sigma_{r_0}/\xi\Sigma_s} \qquad (4.35)$$

in a homogeneous medium. The heterogeneous equivalent is logically

$$p = e^{-(V_U\bar\phi_U\Sigma_{r_0})/(V_m\bar\phi_m\xi\Sigma_s)} \qquad (4.36)$$

since the "flux of resonance neutrons" will not be uniform and proper volume and average flux weighting factors must be applied. The exponent bears a resemblance to similar ratios appearing in the calculation of thermal utilization, a fact that will now be exploited. A resonance utilization is defined:

$$f_r = \frac{\text{resonance absorption in fuel}}{\text{resonance absorption in fuel + scattering "absorption" by moderator}} \qquad (4.37)$$

The physical meaning of the terms in Equation (4.37) will be explained below. By analogy with thermal flux absorption, the resonance absorption in uranium would be $\bar\phi_0 V_0 \Sigma_0$, where Σ_0 is an appropriately chosen average cross section of uranium over the resonance flux region. If we were dealing only with uranium, the average cross section would be written in the lethargy notation of § 2.6.

$$\bar\sigma_U = \frac{\int \sigma_{aU}(u)\phi(u)\,du}{\int \phi(u)\,du} \qquad (4.38)$$

Presuming that the flux over the resonance region is $1/E$ dependent, $\phi(u)$ is independent of lethargy, and cancels out. Thus the average cross section is related to the resonance integral by

$$\bar{\sigma}_U = \frac{\int \sigma_{aU} \dfrac{dE}{E}}{\int \dfrac{dE}{E}} = \frac{\sigma_r}{\Delta(\ln E)} \qquad (4.39)$$

where $\Delta (\ln E)$ is the width of the logarithmic energy interval in which absorption occurs. The presence of moderator and the nature of the geometry require that an effective resonance integral σ_{re} be used instead of σ_r. Also the effective $\Delta(\ln E)$ may be considered as a semi-empirical constant, to be derived from experiment. The classic recipe, Table 3.3, for the microscopic effective resonance integral for natural uranium reactors is

$$\sigma_{re} = 9.25\left(1 + 2.67 \frac{S}{M}\right) \qquad (4.40)$$

where S/M is the fuel surface-to-mass ratio (cm²/gm). The first term has to do with volume absorption, modified to account for scattering within the volume of the metal (see § 3.3). The second term takes cognizance of the fact that the resonance flux is depressed in the interior of the metal by the absorption in outer layers. One finds reference in the literature to many variations and elaborations on this semi-empirical formula. The effective $\Delta(\ln E)$ for U metal has been measured as 5.6. We may now construct the cross section

$$\Sigma_0 = \frac{N_U \sigma_{re}}{5.6} = \frac{N_U \, 9.25\left(1 + 2.67 \dfrac{S}{M}\right)}{5.6} = \frac{\Sigma_{re}}{5.6} \qquad (4.41)$$

The scattering "absorption" by moderator is represented by $\bar{\phi}_1 V_1 \Sigma_1$, where we define

$$\Sigma_1 = \frac{\int \xi \Sigma_s \dfrac{dE}{E}}{\int \dfrac{dE}{E}} = \frac{\overline{\xi \Sigma_s}}{5.6} \qquad (4.42)$$

Combining Equations (4.37), (4.41), and (4.42), we see that the magnitude of the exponent of p in Equation (4.36) is

$$\frac{V_U\overline{\phi}_U\Sigma_{re}}{V_m\overline{\phi}_m\xi\overline{\Sigma}_s} = \left(\frac{1}{f_r} - 1\right)^{-1} \tag{4.43}$$

The method of calculating thermal utilization in § 4.1 is now borrowed to find f_r, using Σ_0, Σ_1 and the inverse diffusion lengths κ_0 and κ_1. The latter constants are obtained from the empirical expression

$$\kappa_0 = 0.0222\rho \tag{4.44}$$

where ρ is the density of uranium in grams per cubic centimeter and

$$\kappa_1 = \sqrt{3\Sigma_1\Sigma_{t1}} \tag{4.45}$$

with Σ_{t1} as the actual transport cross section of the moderator averaged over the resonance flux region.

Numerical Illustration: Compute p for the natural-uranium–graphite plate system (see § 4.1).

Solution. The surface-to-mass ratio can be computed for a column of unit area extending from the central plane to the outside of the fuel plate as

$$\frac{S}{M} = \frac{1 \text{ cm}^2}{(19.0 \text{ gm/cm}^3)(0.635 \text{ cm})} = 0.0829$$

Thus $\sigma_r = 9.25[1 + (2.67)(0.0829)] = 11.3$ barns, and $\Sigma_0 = (0.0480)(11.3)/5.6 = 0.0969$ cm^{-1}. For graphite, with $\xi = 0.159$, $\overline{\cos\theta} = 0.056$, $N = 0.0827$ and $\bar{\sigma}_s = 4.8$ barns, we find $\Sigma_1 = (0.159)(0.397)/5.6 = 0.0113$ cm^{-1}, and $\Sigma_{t1} = (0.397)(0.944) = 0.375$ cm^{-1}. Thus $\kappa_1 = \sqrt{3(0.0113)(0.375)} = 0.1128$ cm^{-1}. Also, $\kappa_0 = (0.0222)(19.0) = 0.422$ cm^{-1}. Using $w = 0.635$ cm and $W - w = 14.605$ cm, we find $F = 0.268$ coth $0.268 = 1.024$ and $E = 1.647$ coth $1.647 = 1.774$. Finally, applying Equations (4.13), (4.14), and (4.15),

$$\frac{1}{f_r} = 1 + \frac{(14.605)(0.0113)}{(0.635)(0.0969)} (1.024) + (1.774 - 1)$$

$$= 1 + 2.746 + 0.774 = 4.520$$

The resonance utilization $f_r = 0.221$ is seen to be quite a bit smaller than the thermal utilization. Using

$$\left(\frac{1}{f_r} - 1\right)^{-1} = 0.284$$

the resonance escape probability is $p = e^{-0.284} = 0.753$.

4.4. *Fast fission factor* ϵ

The amount of fast fission in uranium is related to the chance that a fast neutron released in the fuel is capable of colliding with a uranium nucleus before escaping into the moderator. Relatively few of the neutrons that get into the moderator are able to return to the fuel (or proceed to the next element) with sufficient energy to cause fission in U^{238}, with its 1.0-mev threshold.

Out of the many fission neutrons that arise in the metal, a few will cause further fast fission, thus increasing the number of neutrons available. The *fast fission factor*, ϵ, is best defined by the relation

$$\epsilon - 1 = \frac{\text{gain in fast neutrons per starting}}{\text{fission neutron}} \qquad (4.46)$$

A typical value of $\epsilon - 1$ is 0.03, e.g., in widely spaced 1-in. diameter natural-uranium metal rods.

The average chance p that a neutron will escape from the fuel *without collision* is mutually dependent on collision cross section and dimensions of the body. In general,

$$p = \frac{\text{neutrons escaping}}{\text{neutrons produced}} = \frac{\int dS \int \phi(r)\Sigma_f \nu G(\rho)\, dV}{\int \phi(r)\Sigma_f \nu\, dV} \qquad (4.47)$$

where symbols are defined as follows: the fast neutron source due to fission in a volume element dV at r (see Figure 4.4) is $\phi(r)\Sigma_f\nu\, dV$; the fraction of these that escape through a unit area at the surface due to a volume element dV is $G(\rho) = e^{-\Sigma\rho}\cos\theta/4\pi\rho^2$. Integration over the total surface yields the numerator of p, the leakage rate. The denominator is the total neutron source. Values of the *chance of collision* $P = 1 - p$ are plotted in Figure 4.5 for the special case of a uniform thermal flux distribution in the metal.

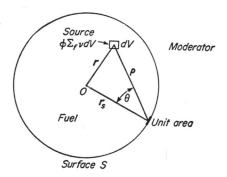

Figure 4.4. Geometry for calculating escape probability.

Upon collision, with total cross section $\sigma = 4.3$ barns, several fates are possible, represented by individual cross sections, averages over the fission spectrum:

(a) Capture, with neutron lost completely, $\sigma_c = 0.04$ barns.
(b) Elastic scattering, with small energy loss, but with a further chance of collision before escaping the metal, $\sigma_e = 1.5$ barns.
(c) Inelastic scattering, with the neutron energy reduced below the fission threshold, $\sigma_i = 2.47$ barns.
(d) Fission, $\sigma_f = 0.29$ barns, yielding $\nu_f = 2.55$ new neutrons.

The relation between ϵ and P is easily derived if we assume the primary source is approximately uniform over the fuel.

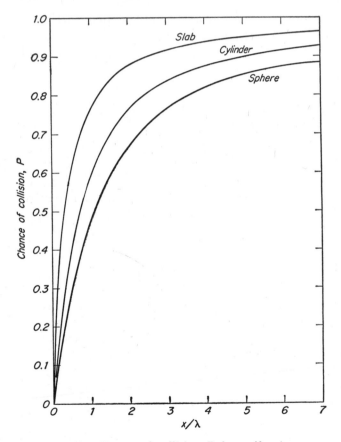

Figure 4.5. Chance of collision P for uniform source: x = half-thickness of slab, radius of cylinder or sphere; λ = mean free path.

For each starting fission neutron, a fraction P collide in the fuel and $P(\sigma_f/\sigma)\nu_f$ new neutrons plus $P(\sigma_e/\sigma)$ scattered neutrons are now available to continue the chain. Let the sum $P(\sigma_f\nu_f + \sigma_e)/\sigma$ be labeled x, which in turn generate x^2, x^3, $\cdots$ neutrons. At each generation, a fraction $1 - P$ escape and $P(\sigma_i/\sigma)$ are scattered inelastically. The total of these that become available for the lower energy processes in the reactor is thus $(1 + x + x^2 + \cdots)(1 - P + P\sigma_i/\sigma)$. Since x is less than 1, the series is equal to $1/(1 - x)$, and the total slowing below the threshold is

$$\epsilon = \frac{1 - P + P\dfrac{\sigma_i}{\sigma}}{1 - P\dfrac{\sigma_f\nu_f + \sigma_e}{\sigma}}$$

Rearranging,

$$\epsilon - 1 = \frac{(\sigma_f\nu_f - \sigma_f - \sigma_c)P}{\sigma - (\sigma_f\nu_f + \sigma_e)P} = \frac{0.0952P}{1 - 0.521P} \qquad (4.48)$$

Numerical Illustration: Calculate the fast fission factor for the plate reactor.

Solution. The total macroscopic collision cross section of uranium is $N\sigma = (0.0480)(4.3) = 0.206$ cm^{-1}, from which the mean free path λ is 4.85 cm. The fuel plate has a half-width 0.635 cm or $x/\lambda = 0.635/4.85 = 0.13$. From Figure 4.5, $P = 0.3$, and from Equation (4.48), $\epsilon = 1.034$.

In addition to the calculation of ϵ, it is of interest to compare the relative fission rates (and corresponding powers) attributed to fast and thermal fission. Suppose that a starting fast neutron has c chance of causing fast fission, $c\sigma_a/\sigma_f$ of absorption. The number of fission neutrons due to fast fission is $c\nu_f$, and the new total is $1 + c\nu_f - c\sigma_a/\sigma_f$, a gain of $c(\nu_f - \sigma_a/\sigma_f)$. This also is $\epsilon - 1$. Thus the number of fast fissions per starting fast neutron is $c = (\epsilon - 1)/(\nu_f - \sigma_a/\sigma_f)$. Now consider the source of the one starting neutron. If one thermal fission gives ν neutrons, then $1/\nu$ thermal fissions were responsible for the one neutron. The ratio of fission rates is thus

$$\frac{\text{fast fission rate}}{\text{thermal fission rate}} = \frac{(\epsilon - 1)/(\nu_f - \sigma_a/\sigma_f)}{1/\nu} = 1.74(\epsilon - 1) \quad (4.49)$$

where the constants for natural uranium, $\nu_f \simeq 2.55$ and $\nu = 2.46$, have been inserted. This shows that fast fission is somewhat more important practically than is implied by the size of $\epsilon - 1$ alone.

We can also answer the frequent question, "Can a fast natural uranium reactor, containing no moderator, be made critical?" Since resonance capture will take up almost all the neutrons that fall below the fast fission threshold, criticality will depend strictly on fast multiplication. Consider one starting neutron, which was due to $1/\nu_f$ fissions. As shown above, the number of fissions due to an initial neutron is c. The multiplication constant k is then

$$\frac{(\epsilon - 1)/(\nu_f - \sigma_a/\sigma_f)}{1/\nu_f}$$

In an infinite mass of uranium, $P = 1$ and $\epsilon - 1$ has a maximum value $0.0952/0.479 = 0.20$. Inserting this and $\nu_f = 2.55$, we find $k = 0.36$, which is definitely subcritical.

The analysis of ϵ in this section must be regarded as a first approximation, because the thermal flux distribution is *not* uniform, the effect of the moderator in returning neutrons is not negligible, and there will be interaction between closely adjacent fuel elements.

4.5. *Multiplication factor and critical dimensions*

According to Equation (3.10), the number of neutrons per absorption in uranium is $\eta = (\sigma_{fU}/\sigma_{aU})\nu$, where the microscopic cross sections refer to the particular isotopic composition. For natural uranium, $\sigma_{fU} = 4.18$ barns at 2200 meters/sec, and with a not-$1/v$ factor of 0.981 (since fission is due to U^{235}), the maxwellian cross section is $\bar{\sigma}_{fU} = (4.18)(0.981)/1.128 = 3.635$ barns. Applying the factors 0.99 and $1/1.128$ to the 2200-meters/sec absorption cross section of 7.68 barns, we find $\bar{\sigma}_{aU} = 6.74$ barns. Thus with $\nu = 2.46$,

$$\eta = \frac{(3.635)(2.46)}{6.74} = 1.327$$

In some design calculations older values that give better overall consistency of results, $\eta = 1.315$ or 1.32, are used. The number of neutrons per absorption at any other isotopic concentration may be calculated from the basic cross sections, isotopic abundances, and not-$1/v$ factors. The conversion factor $1/1.128$ to a maxwellian distribution actually need not be applied since a ratio is computed.

Numerical Illustration: Find η for maxwellian neutrons in 1-per cent U^{235}, i.e., $N_{235}/N_U = 0.01$.

Solution.   Using the 2200-meters/sec cross sections, $\sigma_{a238} = 2.75$, $\sigma_{f235} = 580$, $\sigma_{a235} = 687$, and a not-$1/v$ factor of 0.981 for U^{235},

$$\eta = \frac{(0.01)(580)(0.981)(2.46)}{(0.01)(687)(0.981) + (0.99)(2.75)} = 1.480$$

Were all other factors in k constant, an increase in multiplication (over that in natural uranium) of 12 per cent would be implied. The conclusion is that slight enrichment is very effective, particularly if the moderator is such that k is close to 1.

We may now collect the four factors in the infinite multiplication factor k for the continued plate problem. In summary, $\epsilon = 1.034$, $p = 0.753$, $f = 0.951$, and $\eta = 1.327$. Thus from Equation (4.1), $k = \epsilon p f \eta = 0.983$. We conclude that the arrangement chosen cannot be self-sustaining, regardless of volume of reactor. Several approaches to the solution of this dilemma are open.

(a) Increase the moderator-fuel volume ratio by the use of thinner plates. The resonance escape probability will experience a net increase, even though the surface-to-mass ratio is less favorable. The gain will be partially offset by the increased thermal neutron absorption in moderator and attendant drop in f.

(b) Replace the graphite moderator with a more highly purified type, or heavy water, with lower thermal absorption cross section.

(c) Use slightly enriched fuel, e.g. the 1 per cent for which η was found to be 1.480. The effect of uniform enrichment may also be simulated by distributing a few *highly enriched* plates through the assembly.

Effects of coolant structure and fission products.   Thermal neutron absorption by other elements besides fuel and moderator results in a reduction of the thermal utilization. Figure 4.6 shows a lattice cell complete with cladding, coolant, tubing, and possible insulation. Estimates of the effect of extra absorption can be made without resorting to a multi-region calculation, by assuming that any poisons that are tolerable do not appreciably disturb the basic flux distribution with fuel and moderator only. The reciprocal utilization *with poison* may be written

$$\frac{1}{f_p} = \frac{1}{f} + \frac{V_p \Sigma_p \bar{\phi}_p}{V_0 \Sigma_0 \bar{\phi}_0} \qquad (4.50)$$

where f is computed *without poison*, and the average flux in added absorber is $\bar{\phi}_p$. In the case of a thin metal cladding for a fuel element, an annulus of coolant, or a coolant duct, the ratio $\bar{\phi}_p/\bar{\phi}_0$ is approximately equal to $\phi_0(r_0)/\bar{\phi}_0$, which is recognized as the factor F (Equation 4.13). A slight refinement can be made by

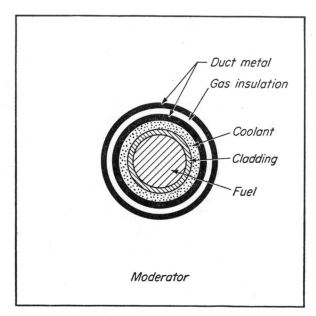

Duct metal

Gas insulation

Coolant

Cladding

Fuel

Moderator

Figure 4.6. General cylindrical lattice cell.

letting Σ_p be the difference between the actual cross section of the poison and the moderator that it replaces physically. If the product $V_p \Sigma_p \bar{\phi}_p$ is interpreted as a sum of several such terms, the composite effect of several absorbers may be determined.

The reduction in thermal utilization by fission product poisons may also be incorporated by the same addition process, but where $\bar{\phi}_p/\bar{\phi}_0$ is 1, since the fission product nuclei are exposed to the same flux as are the fissionable nuclei. The amount of the disturbance to $1/f$ will vary from point to point in the reactor, however, because Σ_p is in general dependent on the flux that both produces and removes the absorbing nuclei. Further discussion of this problem will appear in Chapter 8.

Age and diffusion length of reactor. The critical size of the heterogeneous reactor may be calculated by treating the multiplying medium as if it were homogeneous. The necessary factors are infinite multiplication constant k, derived for the cell, the age τ, and the square of the diffusion length, L^2. Several effects cause the diffusion length and age of the heterogeneous reactor to be different from those of a moderator. Absorption by fuel and poisons reduce L^2 sharply by a factor of about $1 - f$. Both thermal and fast neutrons find it easier to move parallel to the fuel than perpendicular to it. The inelastic scattering in fuel results in neutrons of lower than typical energy after scattering by moderator nuclei, which tends to reduce the average age. Kaplan and Chernick (see References) give a complete description of the method of correction for a graphite reactor. For rough estimates, one may assume the following expressions:

$$L^2 \simeq L_1^2 f_m \qquad (4.51)$$

$$\tau \simeq \tau_1[(V_1 + V_0)/V_1]^2 \qquad (4.52)$$

where the subscript 1 refers to experimental moderator constants and f_m is the fractional absorption in moderator. The age-diffusion theory critical condition,

$$1 = ke^{-B^2\tau}/(1 + B^2L^2)$$

Eq. (3.20), is most appropriately used, although for k close to 1, the approximations $B^2 \simeq \ln k/(L^2 + \tau)$ and $B^2 \simeq (k - 1)/(L^2 + \tau)$ may be sufficiently accurate.

Numerical Illustration: From the calculations performed during the design of the Brookhaven reactor, the following data are quoted for a 1.4-cm radius rod in an 8-in. lattice, with air channel area 36 cm^2 and Al/U volume ratio 0.2.

$\eta = 1.315$	$p = 0.8783$
$\epsilon = 1.0299$	$L^2 = 310.61$ cm^2
$f = 0.8984$	$\tau = 424.58$ cm^2

Find k, B^2 and the side of a bare cube for this reactor, using modified one-group theory. Compare the answer with that from age theory.

Solution. The multiplication factor from Equation (4.1) is $k = 1.0686$. From the modified one-group equation (3.57),

$$B^2 = \frac{k - 1}{L^2 + \tau} = \frac{0.0686}{735.19} = 93.3 \times 10^{-6} \text{ cm}^{-2}$$

Now from Table 3.1, $S' = \pi\sqrt{3}/B = 563.4$ cm. Subtracting two extrapolation distances of 1.9 cm, $S = 559.6$ cm or **18.4 ft**. According to age theory, by trial and error in Equation (3.20), B^2 is found to be 90.2×10^{-6} cm^{-2}, which yields a side $S' = 572.9$ cm, and S is 18.7 ft. The difference between age and modified one-group results is insignificant in this case.

4.6. *The exponential pile*

Experimental determination of the materials buckling for mixtures of fuel and moderator may be made by measurements of thermal flux in the *exponential pile*. It consists of a long rectangular or cylindrical block of material with a neutron source at one end that gives rise to a steady state thermal flux as shown in Figure 4.7. The cost of a sub-critical exponential pile is considerably lower than that for a critical assembly since special safety

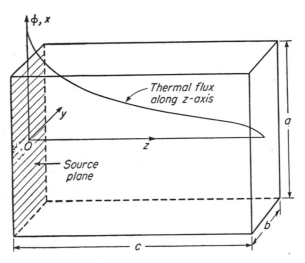

Figure 4.7. Exponential pile.

equipment is not needed, and because less fuel and moderator are used.   The principle of the exponential pile may be illustrated by the special case of a uniform plane thermal source at one end. This situation is actually approximated in the "thermal column," an extension of a reflector that filters out fast neutrons.   The diffusion equation for a rectangular column containing fuel and moderator is

$$\frac{\partial^2 \phi}{\partial x^2} + \frac{\partial^2 \phi}{\partial y^2} + \frac{\partial^2 \phi}{\partial z^2} + B^2\phi = 0 \qquad (4.53)$$

where B^2 is the materials buckling, to be determined.   The boundary conditions are: $\phi = \phi_0$, an arbitrary flux level over the whole surface plane $z = 0$; $\phi = 0$ at the planes $x = \pm a/2$, $y = \pm b/2$, $z = c$, where extrapolation distances are included in the dimensions.   As in the rectangular reactor, we assume the variables x, y, and z are separable, i.e.,

$$\phi(x,y,z) = X(x)Y(y)Z(z)$$

Thus

$$\frac{d^2X}{X\,dx^2} = -B_x^2, \qquad \frac{d^2Y}{Y\,dy^2} = -B_y^2, \qquad \frac{d^2Z}{Z\,dz^2} = \gamma^2$$

where $\gamma^2 = B_x^2 + B_y^2 - B^2$ is definitely a positive number, since the system is sub-critical.   The differential equation in x has solutions that go to zero at $\pm a/2$ and are symmetric about $x = 0$,

$$X = \cos B_x x = \cos \frac{m\pi x}{a}$$

where $m = 1, 3, 5, \cdots$.   Similarly,

$$Y = \cos B_y y = \cos \frac{n\pi y}{b}$$

where $n = 1, 3, 5, \cdots$.   The flux variation in the z-direction that satisfies the differential equation and the condition that the flux be zero at c is

$$Z = \sinh \gamma_{mn}(c - z)$$

where

$$\gamma_{mn}^2 = \left(\frac{m\pi}{a}\right)^2 + \left(\frac{n\pi}{b}\right)^2 - B^2$$

The general solution is the linear combination of all possible solutions

$$\phi(x,y,z) = \sum_{m=1}^{\infty} \sum_{n=1}^{\infty} A_{mn} \cos \frac{m\pi x}{a} \cos \frac{n\pi y}{b} \sinh \gamma_{mn}(c - z) \quad (4.54)$$

where the arbitrary constants A_{mn} are composites of those normally affixed to X, Y, and Z. The set of constants may be evaluated by applying the condition $\phi = \phi_0$ at $z = 0$, and making use of the orthogonality of the cosines.

$$\phi(x,y,0) = \phi_0 = \sum_{m=1}^{\infty} \sum_{n=1}^{\infty} A_{mn} \cos \frac{m\pi x}{a} \cos \frac{n\pi y}{b} \sinh \gamma_{mn}c$$

Multiply both sides by $\cos \dfrac{k\pi x}{a} \cos \dfrac{l\pi y}{b}$ and integrate x from $-a/2$ to $a/2$ and y from $-b/2$ to $b/2$. The result is

$$A_{mn} = \left(\frac{4}{\pi}\right)^2 \frac{\phi_0}{mn \sinh \gamma_{mn}c}$$

At large distances from the source plane, the higher harmonics are negligible. Since γ_{mn} increases with m and n, the z-variation, which approximates $e^{-\gamma_{mn}z}$, is a rapidly decreasing function, for $m > 1$ and $n > 1$. Thus the flux reduces to

$$\phi(x,y,z) \simeq \left(\frac{4}{\pi}\right)^2 \phi_0 \cos \frac{\pi x}{a} \cos \frac{\pi y}{b} \frac{\sinh \gamma_{11}(c - z)}{\sinh \gamma_{11}c} \quad (4.55)$$

where

$$\gamma_{11}^2 = \left(\frac{\pi}{a}\right)^2 + \left(\frac{\pi}{b}\right)^2 - B^2 \quad (4.56)$$

A circular cylinder of extrapolated radius R serves as an alternate exponential pile geometry. For this case, the flux at large z is

$$\phi(r,z) \simeq \frac{2\phi_0}{j_0 J_1(j_0)} J_0(j_0 r/R) \frac{\sinh \gamma_{11}(c - z)}{\sinh \gamma_{11}c} \quad (4.57)$$

where

$$\gamma_{11}^2 = \left(\frac{j_0}{R}\right)^2 - B^2 \quad (4.58)$$

Flux measurements along the z-axis ($x = y = 0$ or $r = 0$), by the use of small foils or counters, are correlated with Equation (4.55) or (4.57), from which γ_{11} can be computed. Using Equation (4.56) or (4.58), and the column dimensions, the buckling B^2 can be found.

The thermal diffusion length of a pure moderator, where $k = 0$, may also be measured by substituting $-1/L^2$ for B^2 in these formulas.

Numerical Illustration: Find the flux on the z-axis of a square graphite column 5 ft on a side and 6 ft long at a distance 4 ft from the source plane. Assume a thermal neutron flux at the reactor end, $z = 0$, to be $10^{10}/\text{cm}^2$-sec. Let $L = 50$ cm and $D = 0.9$ cm for graphite. Also, find the neutron current at $z = c$.

Solution. The column dimensions are $a = b = 152.4$ cm, and $c = 182.88$ cm. The point of interest is $z = 121.9$ cm. Substituting $1/L^2$ for $-B^2$ in Equation (4.56) gives the fundamental attenuation constant

$$\gamma_{11} = \sqrt{2\left(\frac{\pi}{152.4}\right)^2 + \left(\frac{1}{50}\right)^2} = 0.03535 \text{ cm}^{-1}$$

From Equation (4.55)

$$\phi(0,0,121.9) \simeq \left(\frac{4}{\pi}\right)^2 (10^{10}) \frac{\sinh 2.156}{\sinh 6.465} = 2.151 \times 10^8$$

The correction due to the first harmonic, $m = 1$, $n = 3$ and $m = 3$, $n = 1$, may be computed: $\gamma_{13} = \gamma_{31} = 0.0682 \text{ cm}^{-1}$; $A_{13} = A_{31} = 4.15 \times 10^4$, $\sinh \gamma_{13}(c - z) = \sinh \gamma_{31}(c - z) = 31.96$. Applying Equation (4.54), the two additional terms contribute a flux of 0.026×10^8. Thus the final value of ϕ is $2.177 \times 10^8/\text{cm}^2$-sec, assuming the higher harmonics to be essentially zero. The current at the end of the column from Equation (4.55) is

$$j(c) = \left(\frac{4}{\pi}\right)^2 \frac{D\phi_0 \, \gamma_{11}}{\sinh \gamma_{11}c}$$

Inserting numbers, $j(c) = 8.0 \times 10^7/\text{cm}^2$-sec.

Measurements of age, diffusion length, and effective absorption cross section. The exponential pile can be used to find the *age* in a lattice of fuel and moderator, by comparing bucklings with and without a uniformly disposed poison such as boron. In the age-diffusion critical equation,

$$1 = \frac{\epsilon p f \eta e^{-B^2\tau}}{1 + B^2 L^2}$$

only the factors f, B^2, and L^2 will be changed by the poison.

Taking logarithms of this equation under two conditions, (0) without poison, and (1) with poison,

$$(B_0^2 - B_1^2)\tau = \ln\left[\frac{(1 + B_1^2 L_1^2)f_0}{(1 + B_0^2 L_0^2)f_1}\right] \tag{4.59}$$

In an experiment reported by Cohen (see References), in a 4.9-lattice of 1-in. natural-uranium rods in D_2O using 150 mg of B_2O_3 per liter, the age was found to be 107 cm², vs. 125 cm² for pure D_2O.

The *diffusion length* for a fuel-moderator lattice is difficult to obtain because of the presence of the distributed fast sources. This problem can be avoided by the use of non-multiplying fuel elements with the same scattering and absorption properties as fuel, e.g., a PbCd alloy.

The *effective cross section* of the whole system can be computed by the cadmium ratio method. Since the element indium exhibits both resonance capture and thermal capture, if used alone as a detector it can only measure the total of the thermal and resonance fluxes. However, if an indium foil is covered with a cadmium layer that removes all neutrons up to the cadmium cut-off energy $E_c = 0.4$ ev, the activation gives a measure of resonance flux only. The *cadmium ratio* is the ratio of the two measurements,

$$R_{\text{Cd}} = \frac{A_t + A_r}{A_r} \tag{4.60}$$

According to theory, the ratio $A_t/A_r = R_{\text{Cd}} - 1$ is

$$\frac{A_t}{A_r} = \frac{\int_0^{E_c} N\sigma_a(E)\phi(E)\,dE}{\int_{E_c}^{\infty} N\sigma_a(E)\phi(E)\,dE} \simeq \frac{\phi_0 \bar{\sigma}_a}{\dfrac{q}{\xi\Sigma_s}\int_{E_c}^{\infty}\sigma_a\dfrac{dE}{E}} \tag{4.61}$$

where the resonance integral σ_r of indium is noted. This equation gives either the thermal to resonance flux ratio, or the slowing down density q as a function of thermal flux. In turn, q appears in the thermal neutron balance $D\,\nabla^2\phi_0 - \phi_0\Sigma_a + q = 0$, and since $\nabla^2\phi_0 = -B^2\phi_0$,

$$q = \phi_0(\Sigma_a + B^2 D) \tag{4.62}$$

A measurement of cadmium ratio and buckling, with the knowledge of σ_r for indium, yields the average cross section Σ_a for the lattice.

Problems

4.1. Show that the function F is equal to the ratio of fuel surface flux to average fuel flux for two geometries: (a) plane, (b) cylindrical, by use of flux functions and integration.

4.2. Find the corrected thermal utilization f_p of the ORNL-type reactor, § 4.2, including the effect of a 0.035-in. aluminum cladding ($\sigma_a = 0.23$ barns at 2200 meters/sec) and the removal of graphite to give a coolant channel of area 1 sq in.
Answer. 0.899.

4.3. Compute the effective microscopic resonance integral and the resonance cross section Σ_0 for the uranium cylinders for the ORNL-type reactor (Problem 4.2).
Answer. 11.1 barns, 0.0951 cm^{-1}.

4.4. Find p for the ORNL-type reactor (Problems 4.2 and 4.3), using $\Sigma_0 = 0.0951$, $\Sigma_1 = 0.0113$, $\kappa_0 = 0.422$ and $\kappa_1 = 0.1128$. What is the ratio of resonance flux at the fuel surface to the average over the fuel? (See Problem 4.1.)
Answer. 0.899, 1.043.

4.5. (a) Estimate the fast fission factor for natural-uranium rods of 1.1-in. diameter. (b) Using answers from Problems 4.2, 4.4, and $\eta = 1.327$, find k.
Answer. (a) 1.030, (b) 1.105.

4.6. Calculate η for a natural-uranium converter reactor after operation for a time such that the isotopic concentrations are U^{235} 0.005, Pu^{239} 0.002, U^{238} 0.99.
Answer. 1.39.

4.7. The diffusion length squared for a heterogeneous system including various poisons is often written $L_1^2 f_m$ or $L_1^2 f_m (V_R/V_1)$, where f_m is the "moderator utilization," i.e., (absorption in moderator)/(total absorption) and V_R is the total cell volume. Justify these relations.

4.8. Derive a working formula for the ratio

$$\frac{\text{Pu}}{\text{U}} = \frac{\text{atoms of Pu produced}}{\text{atoms of U burned}}$$

for the heterogeneous natural or low-enrichment uranium reactor, including both thermal and fast fission, and taking account of fast and thermal leakages. (Suggestion: Make use of the critical condition.)

Answer.
$$\frac{\dfrac{(\Sigma_a)_{238}}{(\Sigma_a)_{\mathrm{U}}} + \dfrac{1-p}{pf\mathcal{L}_t} + \eta(\epsilon-1)\left(\dfrac{\sigma_c}{\nu\sigma_f - \sigma_a}\right)_{\mathrm{fast}}}{1 + \dfrac{1-p}{pf\mathcal{L}_t} + \eta(\epsilon-1)\left(\dfrac{\sigma_a}{\nu\sigma_f - \sigma_a}\right)_{\mathrm{fast}}}$$

4.9. Calculate the ratio Pu/U for the ORNL-type reactor, Problems 4.2–4.4, assuming $\eta = 1.327$, $\epsilon = 1.030$, $(\bar\sigma_a)_{238} = 2.44$, $(\bar\sigma_a)_{\mathrm{U}} = 6.74$, $\mathcal{L}_f = 0.950$, and $\mathcal{L}_t = 0.953$.

Answer. 0.424.

4.10. Calculate the maxwellian macroscopic absorption cross section $\bar\Sigma_a$ and inverse diffusion length κ for uranium of density 19.0 gm/cm³ enriched to 1.2 per cent U^{235}, using the transcendental equation (4.17).

Answer. 0.460 cm⁻¹, 0.832 cm⁻¹.

4.11. Calculate the thermal utilization of the U^{235}-$\mathrm{H_2O}$-Al core (Numerical Illustrations, §§ 2.1 and 2.4) taking account of heterogeneity. Assume that the plates are a uniform mixture of U^{235}-Al of width $2w = 0.060$ in., $\Sigma_s = 0.086$ cm⁻¹, and that the water gap is $2(W - w) = 0.090$ in., with diffusion length $L_1 = 1/\kappa_1 = 2.88$ cm. Note that the calculated f is (absorption in *plate*)/(total absorption).

Answer. 0.7747.

4.12. Derive a formula for the average probability p for a neutron to escape collision in an infinite plane slab of width d, total cross section Σ. Suggestion: Make use of the properties of the functions $E_n(x)$ (see § 9.6).

Answer. $\dfrac{\frac{1}{2} - E_3(\Sigma d)}{\Sigma d}$.

4.13. Derive expressions for the fluxes, F, and E for a heterogeneous cell of radius r_1, *hollow* fuel rod with radii r_i (inside) and r_0 (outside). Make use of the functions

$$M_{0b}(r) = K_0(\kappa r) + \frac{K_1(\kappa r_b)}{I_1(\kappa r_b)} I_0(\kappa r)$$

where $b = i$ in the fuel, using κ_0 and $b = 1$ in the moderator, using κ_1.

Answer. $\phi_0(r) = (S_1/\Delta)D_1\kappa_1 M_{11}(r_0)M_{0i}(r)$,

$\phi_1(r) = S_1/\Sigma_1 - (S_1/\Delta)D_0\kappa_0 M_{1i}(r_0)M_{01}(r_0)$,

where $\Delta = \Sigma_1[D_1\kappa_1 M_{0i}(r_0)M_{11}(r_0) + D_0\kappa_0 M_{1i}(r_0)M_{01}(r_0)]$;

$$F = -\frac{\kappa_0(r_0^2 - r_i^2)}{2r_0}\frac{M_{0i}(r_0)}{M_{1i}(r_0)};$$

$$E = \frac{\kappa_1(r_0^2 - r_i^2)}{2r_0}\frac{M_{01}(r_0)}{M_{11}(r_0)}.$$

References

Goodman, Clark, Editor, *The Science and Engineering of Nuclear Power*, Vol. II, Chapter 6, "Calculation of Neutron Distribution in Heterogeneous Piles" by A. M. Weinberg. Addison-Wesley Press, Cambridge (1949).

Guggenheim, E. A., and M. H. L. Pryce, "Uranium Graphite Lattices," *Nucleonics*, February 1953, p. 50.

Houston, R. W. "Calculating Thermal Utilization for Large Thermal Reactors," *Nucleonics*, April 1955, p. 70.

Persson, Rolf, "Criticality of Normal-Water Natural-Uranium Lattices," *Nucleonics*, October 1954, p. 26.

Murray, Raymond L., and A. C. Menius, Jr., "Fast Fission Factor for Hollow Natural Uranium Cylinders," *Nucleonics*, April 1953, p. 21.

Case, K. M., F. De Hoffmann and G. Placzek, *Introduction to the Theory of Neutron Diffusion*, Volume 1. Washington: U. S. Government Printing Office (1953).

McCorkle, W. H., "Using Intermediate Experiments for Reactor Nuclear Design," *Nucleonics*, March 1956, p. 54.

Dopchie, H. et al, "Conducting an Exponential Experiment with a Natural-U Graphite Lattice," *Nucleonics*, March 1956, p. 57.

Weinberg, Isabella Goldin, and E. Richard Cohen, "Neutron Flux Distribution from a Thermal Column Face," *Nucleonics*, July 1955, p. 25.

Atkinson, Ivan C., and Raymond L. Murray, "Optimizing Multiplication Factors in Heterogeneous Reactors," *Nucleonics*, April 1954, p. 50.

Peaceful Uses of Atomic Energy, Volume 5, *Physics of Reactor Design*. New York: Columbia University Press (1956).

  Kaplan, I., and J. Chernick, "Uranium Graphite Lattices—The Brookhaven Reactor," Paper P/606.

  Cohen, E. Richard, "Exponential Experiments on D_2O Uranium Lattices," Paper P/605.

  Kouts, H., G. Price, K. Downes, R. Sher, and V. Walsh, "Exponential Experiments with Slightly Enriched Uranium Rods in Ordinary Water," Paper P/600.

  J. Chernick, "The Theory of Uranium Water Lattices," Paper P/603.

Chapter 5

TWO-GROUP THEORY

One of the most widely used methods for calculating critical conditions in a thermal reactor is the two-group theory. It may be applied to a reflected reactor, and takes account of the slowing process more specifically than does modified one-group theory. The two-group theory incorporates the best available physical logic, short of much more complicated methods that require the application of excessive time or of high-speed computing machines. Because of its great utility in reactor design calculations, a complete chapter will be devoted to its presentation.

5.1. Formulation of differential equations and general solutions

The neutrons in the reactor are classified into two *groups* according to neutron energy. One is the usual *thermal group*, with flux designated by ϕ_2, and obeying the diffusion equation (3.8),

$$D_2 \nabla^2 \phi_2 - \phi_2 \Sigma_2 + S_t = 0 \qquad (5.1)$$

where D_2 is the diffusion coefficient, Σ_2 is the absorption cross section, and S_t is the thermal source. The second is the so-called *fast group*, which is a mathematical composite of all neutrons other than thermals. If $\phi(u,r)$ is the lethargy- and space-dependent flux function, we may define a "fast flux" ϕ_1 as the integral from lethargy zero to thermal value u_t,

$$\phi_1(r) = \int_0^{u_t} \phi(u,r) \, du \qquad (5.2)$$

The fast flux is assumed to be the solution of a second diffusion

110

equation,

$$D_1 \nabla^2 \phi_1 - \phi_1 \Sigma_1 + S_f = 0 \tag{5.3}$$

The fast group diffusion coefficient D_1 is defined as the average of the lethargy-dependent $D(u)$ over the energy region above thermal,

$$D_1 = \frac{\int_0^{u_t} D(u)\phi(u,r) \, du}{\int_0^{u_t} \phi(u,r) \, du} \tag{5.4}$$

The epithermal flux is often approximately separable into a product of space- and lethargy-dependent factors, so that D_1 is not a function of position. In contrast to the thermal case, it is not possible to identify Σ_1 with an *absorption* cross section for two reasons: (a) true absorption of fast neutrons is usually small in practical thermal reactors, (b) the principal mechanism by which fast neutrons are removed is by slowing down into the thermal group. In practice, the true absorption that does occur is included elsewhere by use of a resonance escape probability p, and Σ_1 is interpreted as an effective *removal* cross section, chosen to agree with the calculated rate of thermalization. The connection can be demonstrated very simply by solving the fast group equation for the case of a point source in an infinite medium:

$$D_1 \nabla^2 \phi_1 - \phi_1 \Sigma_1 = 0 \tag{5.5}$$

This is identical in form with Equation (3.45) for the diffusion of thermal neutrons from a point source, where it was found that the mean square displacement from origin to absorption was $\overline{r^2} = 6L^2 = 6D/\Sigma_a$. The corresponding solution of Equation (5.5) will yield, by direct analogy, the mean square displacement from fission to thermal as $\overline{r^2} = 6D_1/\Sigma_1$. According to age theory, § 3.3, $\overline{r^2}$ is equal to 6τ. Thus,

$$\Sigma_1 = \frac{D_1}{\tau} \tag{5.6}$$

This may be considered as a defining relation for the fast "absorption" cross section. In cases where strict age theory is not applicable, τ will be considered to be $\frac{1}{6}$ the mean square displacement, found either by advanced theory or experiment. Note particularly that the two-group formulation of the neutron slowing process consists of replacing the age slowing function $e^{-r^2/4\tau}/(4\pi\tau)^{3/2}$ by a diffusion function $e^{-r/\sqrt{\tau}}/4\pi D_1 r$ having the same $\overline{r^2}$.

We may now turn to the question of sources S_f and S_t. The source of fast neutrons is simply

$$S_f = \phi_2 \Sigma_2 f \eta \tag{5.7}$$

as given in Equation (3.12). The rate at which thermals are created is equal to the rate of removal of fast neutrons from their group by slowing, $\phi_1 \Sigma_1$, except for those taken out by resonance capture. Thus,

$$S_t = p\phi_1 \Sigma_1 = \frac{p\phi_1 D_1}{\tau} \tag{5.8}$$

Equations (5.1) and (5.3) are now rewritten

$$D_1 \nabla^2 \phi_1 - \frac{\phi_1 D_1}{\tau} + \phi_2 \Sigma_2 f \eta = 0 \tag{5.9}$$

$$D_2 \nabla^2 \phi_2 - \phi_2 \Sigma_2 + \frac{p\phi_1 D_1}{\tau} = 0 \tag{5.10}$$

The fluxes in a reflector that contains no fissionable material are given by similar equations except that ηf is automatically zero and p is normally equal to 1. Denoting reflector properties by the subscript r,

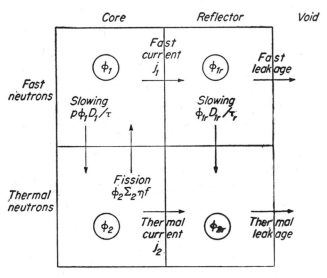

Figure 5.1.   Two-group processes.

$$D_{1r} \nabla^2 \phi_{1r} - \frac{\phi_{1r} D_{1r}}{\tau_r} = 0 \qquad (5.11)$$

$$D_{2r} \nabla^2 \phi_{2r} - \phi_{2r} \Sigma_{2r} + \frac{\phi_{1r} D_{1r}}{\tau_r} = 0 \qquad (5.12)$$

The processes that are to be described are shown schematically in Figure 5.1. The solutions of the core equations (5.9) and (5.10) can be found by proposing that each flux obeys the wave equation (3.17), i.e.,

$$\nabla^2 \phi_1 + B^2 \phi_1 = 0 \qquad (5.13)$$

and

$$\nabla^2 \phi_2 + B^2 \phi_2 = 0 \qquad (5.14)$$

where B^2, a constant to be found, is assumed to be common to both fluxes. (This method can be shown to give the same results as the more conventional operator-approach to the solution of simultaneous linear differential equations.) Combination of Equations (5.9), (5.10), (5.13), and (5.14) gives

$$(1 + B^2\tau)\phi_1 - \frac{\Sigma_2 \tau f \eta \phi_2}{D_1} = 0$$

$$-\frac{p D_1 \phi_1}{\Sigma_2 \tau} + (1 + B^2 L^2)\phi_2 = 0$$

If these simultaneous equations in ϕ_1 and ϕ_2 are to be solved, the determinant formed by the materials-dependent coefficients must be zero. This implies that

$$(1 + B^2\tau)(1 + B^2 L^2) = pf\eta = k \qquad (5.15)$$

This quadratic equation in B^2 has two roots, $B^2 = \mu^2$ and $B^2 = -\nu^2$, where μ^2 and ν^2 are *numerical constants*, analogous to the materials buckling of age-diffusion theory.

Consider the one-dimensional slab reactor, for which Equation (5.13) is now

$$\frac{d^2\phi_1}{dz^2} + \mu^2 \phi_1 = 0 \quad \text{and} \quad \frac{d^2\phi_1}{dz^2} - \nu^2 \phi_1 = 0$$

The solution is the linear combination

$$\phi_1 = a_1 e^{i\mu z} + a_2 e^{-i\mu z} + a_3 e^{\nu z} + a_4 e^{-\nu z}$$

where the a's are arbitrary coefficients. By proper grouping,

$$\phi_1 = b_1 \sin \mu z + b_2 \cos \mu z + b_3 \sinh \nu z + b_4 \cosh \nu z$$

Since the flux must be symmetric about the origin, $d\phi/dz = 0$ at

$z = 0$, the coefficients b_1 and b_3 must be zero. The remaining solutions may be written

$$\phi_1 = AX + CY \qquad (5.16)$$

where $X = \cos \mu z$ and $Y = \cosh \nu z$. A similar solution for ϕ_2 is obtained with a different set of coefficients.

It may be verified by substitution that

$$\phi_2 = S_1 AX + S_2 CY \qquad (5.17)$$

where the core *coupling coefficients* are

$$S_1 = \frac{D_1 p}{\tau D_2} \frac{1}{\mu^2 + 1/L^2} \qquad (5.18)$$

$$S_2 = -\frac{D_1 p}{\tau D_2} \frac{1}{\mu^2 + 1/\tau} \qquad (5.19)$$

It will be well at this point to stop to consider the criticality of a *bare* core, governed by the condition that both ϕ_1 and ϕ_2 must vanish at the extrapolated core boundary. This implies that for a slab of extrapolated height H,

$$A[X] + C[Y] = 0$$
$$S_1 A[X] + S_2 C[Y] = 0$$

where the brackets indicate evaluation at $H/2$. Only if C is zero can these be satisfied, since $[Y] = \cosh \nu H/2$ is never zero and S_1 is never equal to S_2. The bare reactor fluxes are thus merely $\phi_1 = AX$ and $\phi_2 = S_1 AX$, and the critical condition is $[X] = 0$, i.e., $\mu^2 = (\pi/H)^2$. In general, the root μ^2 serves as the materials buckling to be equated to the geometrical buckling, for the bare core.

The one-dimensional form of reflector equation (5.11) is

$$\frac{d^2 \phi_{1r}}{dz^2} - \kappa_{1r}^2 \phi_{1r} = 0 \qquad (5.20)$$

where

$$\kappa_{1r}^2 = \frac{1}{\tau_r} \qquad (5.21)$$

The general solution is

$$\phi_{1r} = c_1 e^{-\kappa_{1r} z} + c_2 e^{+\kappa_{1r} z}$$

In an infinite reflector, ϕ_{1r} must remain finite for indefinitely large z, hence $c_2 = 0$. This leaves

$$\phi_{1r} = F Z_1 \qquad (5.22)$$

where $Z_1 = e^{-\kappa_{1r}z}$, and F is an arbitrary constant. Equation (5.12) for a slab is

$$\frac{d^2\phi_{2r}}{dz^2} - \kappa_{2r}^2\phi_{2r} + \phi_{1r}\frac{D_{1r}}{D_{2r}\tau_r} = 0 \qquad (5.23)$$

where

$$\kappa_{2r}^2 = \frac{1}{L_r^2} \qquad (5.24)$$

Substitution of Equation (5.22) and solution of the resultant inhomogeneous equation in ϕ_{2r} gives

$$\phi_{2r} = GZ_2 + FS_3Z_1 \qquad (5.25)$$

where $Z_2 = e^{-\kappa_{2r}z}$ and the reflector coupling coefficient is

$$S_3 = \frac{D_{1r}}{D_{2r}} \frac{1}{(\tau_r/L_r^2) - 1} \qquad (5.26)$$

The set of flux formulas (5.16), (5.17), (5.22), and (5.25) are in general form that may be used for other geometries, with the proper choice of functions X, Y, Z_1, and Z_2. Table 5.1 tabulates these. The constants S_1, S_2, and S_3, given by Equations (5.18), (5.19), and (5.26), are *independent of geometry*. To complete the tabulation of working formulas, values of μ^2 and ν^2 in terms of fundamental reactor constants are listed below.

$$\mu^2 \simeq \mu_0^2(1 - \epsilon + 2\epsilon^2 - 5\epsilon^3)* \qquad (5.27)$$

where

$$\mu_0^2 = \frac{k-1}{L^2 + \tau} \qquad (5.28)$$

$$a = \frac{1}{L^2} + \frac{1}{\tau} \qquad (5.29)$$

$$\epsilon = \frac{\mu_0^2}{a} \qquad (5.30)$$

$$\nu^2 = \mu^2 + a \qquad (5.31)$$

The slab and cylinder functions of Table 5.1 are applicable as they stand if there is no variation of flux in the other two directions, i.e., in the slab, with x and y going to infinity, and in the cylinder, with infinite length. They are applicable to finite systems also, if the following *modified* constants are used. A buck-

---

* Two or three terms in this approximation are usually sufficient.

Table 5.1. Two-Group Flux Functions

Coordinate	Core	X	Y	Reflector	Z_1	Z_2
r	SPHERE Radius R	$\dfrac{\sin \mu r}{r}$	$\dots$	None	$\dots$	$\dots$
		$\dfrac{\sin \mu r}{r}$	$\dfrac{\sinh \nu r}{r}$	Infinite	$\dfrac{e^{-\kappa_{1r} r}}{r}$	$\dfrac{e^{-\kappa_{2r} r}}{r}$
				Thickness T	$\dfrac{\sinh \kappa_{1r}(R + T - r)}{r}$	$\dfrac{\sinh \kappa_{2r}(R + T - r)}{r}$
z	SLAB Height H	$\cos \mu z$	$\dots$	None	$\dots$	$\dots$
		$\cos \mu z$	$\cosh \nu z$	Infinite	$e^{-\kappa_{1r} z}$	$e^{-\kappa_{2r} z}$
				Thickness T	$\sinh \kappa_{1r}\left(\dfrac{H}{2} + T - z\right)$	$\sinh \kappa_{2r}\left(\dfrac{H}{2} + T - z\right)$
r	CYLINDER Radius R	$J_0(\mu r)^*$	$\dots$	None	$\dots$	$\dots$
		$J_0(\mu r)$	$I_0(\nu r)$	Infinite	$K_0(\kappa_{1r} r)$	$K_0(\kappa_{2r} r)$
				Thickness T	Use κ_{1r} or κ_{2r} in: $K_0(\kappa r) - \dfrac{K_0[\kappa(R + T)]}{I_0[\kappa(R + T)]} \cdot I_0(\kappa r)$	

* ... Bessel function of first kind. See Appendix A.

ling B^2 associated with unreflected dimensions is added or subtracted.

$$\bar{\mu}^2 = \mu^2 - B^2 \qquad (5.32)$$

$$\bar{\nu}^2 = \nu^2 + B^2 \qquad (5.33)$$

$$\bar{\kappa}_{1r}^2 = \kappa_{1r}^2 + B^2 \qquad (5.34)$$

$$\bar{\kappa}_{2r}^2 = \kappa_{2r}^2 + B^2 \qquad (5.35)$$

Table 5.2 lists the appropriate values of B^2 for different finite geometries. Unfortunately, the most important finite systems,

Table 5.2

Bucklings for Modification of Group Constants

B^2

Cylinder, height H:

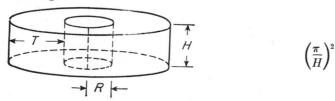

$$\left(\frac{\pi}{H}\right)^2$$

Slab, circular cross section:

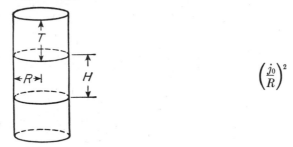

$$\left(\frac{j_0}{R}\right)^2$$

Slab, rectangular cross section:

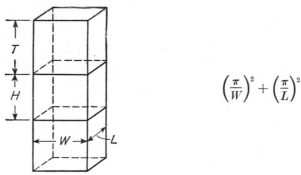

$$\left(\frac{\pi}{W}\right)^2 + \left(\frac{\pi}{L}\right)^2$$

the completely reflected cylinder and parallelepiped, are not amenable to analysis by the methods presented here.

5.2. *Critical condition*

The boundary conditions that connect the core and reflector flux solutions are the continuity of flux and of current [see Equations (3.53) and (3.54)]. We shall let a current be designated generally by $j = -D\phi'$; the proper derivative depends on the coordinate system used. Also, brackets [ ] are used to denote the fact that the functions are to be evaluated at the core-reflector interface.

$$\begin{aligned}
[\phi_1] &= [\phi_{1r}]\\
[\phi_2] &= [\phi_{2r}]\\
-D_1[\phi_1'] &= -D_{1r}[\phi_{1r}']\\
-D_2[\phi_2'] &= -D_{2r}[\phi_{2r}']
\end{aligned} \tag{5.36}$$

Substitute Equations (5.16), (5.17), (5.22), and (5.25) in Equations (5.36) and rearrange to obtain

$$\begin{aligned}
A[X] &+ C[Y] &- F[Z_1] & &= 0\\
S_1A[X] &+ S_2C[Y] &- S_3F[Z_1] &- G[Z_2] &= 0\\
A[X'] &+ C[Y'] &- \rho_1F[Z_1'] & &= 0\\
S_1A[X'] &+ S_2C[Y'] &- \rho_2S_3F[Z_1'] &- \rho_2G[Z_2'] &= 0
\end{aligned} \tag{5.37}$$

where

$$\rho_1 = \frac{D_{1r}}{D_1} \tag{5.38}$$

$$\rho_2 = \frac{D_{2r}}{D_2} \tag{5.39}$$

In order for this homogeneous set of equations to be solvable for A, C, F, and G, the determinant formed by their coefficients must be zero:

$$\Delta = \begin{vmatrix}
[X] & [Y] & -[Z_1] & \\
S_1[X] & S_2[Y] & -S_3[Z_1] & -[Z_2]\\
[X'] & [Y'] & -\rho_1[Z_1'] & \\
AS_1[X'] & S_2[Y'] & -\rho_2S_3[Z_1'] & -\rho_2[Z_2']
\end{vmatrix} = 0 \quad (5.40)$$

This is the *critical condition* for the reflected core. The equation may be rearranged into a convenient calculation form by defining new functions

$$\alpha = \frac{[X']}{[X]}$$

$$\beta = \frac{[Y']}{[Y]}$$

$$\gamma = \frac{[Z_1']}{[Z_1]}$$

$$\delta = \frac{[Z_2']}{[Z_2]}$$

(5.41)

Table 5.3 lists useful expressions for the variables α, β, γ, and

Table 5.3

Computation Functions α, β, γ, δ
for Infinite Reflectors

Geometry		Slab	Sphere	Cylinder
α	=	$-\mu \tan \mu \dfrac{H}{2}$	$\mu \cot \mu R - \dfrac{1}{R}$	$-\mu \dfrac{J_1(\mu R)}{J_0(\mu R)}$
β	=	$\nu \tanh \nu \dfrac{H}{2}$	$\nu \coth \nu R - \dfrac{1}{R}$	$\nu - \dfrac{1}{2R} - \dfrac{1}{8\nu R^2}$ *
γ	=	$-\kappa_{1r}$	$-\kappa_{1r} - \dfrac{1}{R}$	$-\kappa_{1r} - \dfrac{1}{2R} + \dfrac{1}{8\kappa_{1r}R^2}$ *
δ	=	$-\kappa_{2r}$	$-\kappa_{2r} - \dfrac{1}{R}$	$-\kappa_{2r} - \dfrac{1}{2R} + \dfrac{1}{8\kappa_{2r}R^2}$ *

Note: (a) For cores finite in the other directions, modified constants, $\bar{\mu}$, $\bar{\nu}$, $\bar{\kappa}_{1r}$, $\bar{\kappa}_{2r}$ should be used.

    (b) For reflectors of thickness T, use following forms for γ and δ,

Slab	Sphere	Cylinder
$-\kappa \coth \kappa T$	$-\kappa \coth \kappa T - \dfrac{1}{R}$	$\dfrac{-\kappa K_1(\kappa R) - \dfrac{K_0[\kappa(R+T)]}{I_0[\kappa(R+T)]} \kappa I_1(\kappa R)}{K_0(\kappa R) - \dfrac{K_0[\kappa(R+T)]}{I_0[\kappa(R+T)]} I_0(\kappa R)}$

* Approximate.

δ, where certain approximations (designated by *) are presented to avoid some of the tedium of interpolating tables of functions. In this notation the critical equation becomes

$$\alpha = \alpha' \qquad \text{two-group critical equation} \qquad (5.42)$$

where

$$\alpha' = \frac{\rho_2 \delta C_1 + \rho_1 \gamma C_2 + \beta C_3}{C_1 + C_2 + C_3} \qquad (5.43)$$

and

$$C_1 = S_1(\rho_1\gamma - \beta), \quad C_2 = S_2(\beta - \rho_2\delta), \quad C_3 = S_3\rho_2(\delta - \gamma) \quad (5.44)$$

By reference to Tables 5.1 and 5.3, it can be seen that the function α is sensitively related to size and to μ, which in turn is dependent on the dominant factors in the behavior of the reactor, namely k, L^2, and τ. On the other hand, α', the right side of Equation (5.42), is a slowly varying function. Trial and error solutions converge rapidly to the correct value of fuel loading or critical size if α' is computed first. This technique of separating rapidly- and slowly-varying parts is found even more useful in three-group theory, and in the calculation of multi-region reactors.

5.3. *Flux distributions*

The detailed spatial variation of flux in the reactor can be calculated if the arbitrary constants A, C, F, and G in the flux equations (5.16), (5.17), (5.22), and (5.25) are known. It will be presumed that application of the critical relation, Equation (5.42), has yielded a compatible fuel content and size. The four Equations (5.37), with known $[X]$, $[Y]$, $[Z_1]$, and $[Z_2]$ are available for finding A, C, F, and G. As usual in a reactor, one constant remains arbitrary, as a flux or power scale factor. Only three of the equations need be used to find the other three constants (in terms of the reactor power level). The first three of Equations (5.37) are the most readily solved, to obtain the convenient form

$$A = \frac{\Delta_A}{[X]}, \qquad C = \frac{\Delta_C}{[Y]}, \qquad F = \frac{\Delta_F}{[Z_1]}, \qquad G = \frac{\Delta_G}{[Z_2]} \quad (5.45)$$

where

$$\Delta_A = \beta - \rho_1\gamma, \qquad \Delta_F = \beta - \alpha \qquad (5.46)$$
$$\Delta_C = \rho_1\gamma - \alpha, \qquad \Delta_G = S_1\Delta_A + S_2\Delta_C - S_3\Delta_F$$

Several features of this representation are to be noted: (a) the coefficients are expressed in terms of the same auxiliary constants that were used in the critical calculation; (b) when the arbitrary coefficients are inserted in the flux equations, the ratios of functions to values at the core-reflector boundary appear. This is particularly convenient for calculating flux terms that have large values of the variables. The second core function in Equation (5.16) for example, in slab geometry is

$$CY = \frac{\Delta_C Y}{[Y]} = \frac{\Delta_C \cosh \nu z}{\cosh \nu \frac{H}{2}} \simeq \Delta_C e^{-(H/2 - z)\nu}$$

(c) The flux may be scaled uniformly to achieve any normalization, such as unit central flux, $\phi_c = 1$, or unit average flux, $\overline{\phi} = 1$. The latter is readily correlated with total core power by the expression $P = \overline{\phi}\Sigma_f V/c$.

The adequacy of the coolant for the core may be guaranteed by choice of flow rates that provide sufficient heat transfer at the point of highest flux and power density. In some cores this "hot spot" may occur at the center where the thermal flux is ϕ_{2c}, in others at the boundary where the flux is $[\phi_2]$. The flux ratio *boundary to average* surprisingly has the same form for all geometries:

$$\frac{[\phi_2]}{\overline{\phi}_2} = g\left(\frac{S_2 \Delta_C + S_1 \Delta_A}{\Delta_C \beta S_2/\nu^2 - \Delta_A \alpha S_1/\mu^2}\right) \tag{5.47}$$

where $g = R/3$ for sphere, $g = R/2$ for cylinder, $g = H/2$ for slab. Since the average flux $\overline{\phi}_2$ is taken here over one direction only, the variation of flux in the other directions must be considered in determining the averages over the whole core.

5.4. *Reactor design calculation*

The critical U^{235} mass and flux distribution in a specific example reactor is now calculated to illustrate the methods described in §§ 5.1 to 5.3. The Bulk Shielding Facility reactor at Oak Ridge, Tennessee is a useful model, in that it is the prototype of current power reactors. It is a highly enriched heterogeneous reactor consisting of approximately 27 fuel elements, each containing a number of plates of U-Al alloy, clad with Al to prevent fission products from escaping into the light-water moderator. The ratio of aluminum to water in the core is 0.65, with volume fractions approximately $f_{Al} = 0.3935$, $f_{H_2O} = 0.6047$, the rest being uranium. The U^{235} isotopic concentration will be assumed to be 0.93. The overall dimensions for the experimental critical core are taken to be

Height   61.30 cm $= H$
Width   36.85 cm $= W$
Length   46.47 cm $= L$

giving a volume of 105.0 liters. The rectangular parallelepiped is completely surrounded with water, except for an aluminum support structure, the effect of which will be ignored.

Calculation of basic group constants. The assignment of group constants is the most difficult task in the design calculation, largely because several choices are possible. One approach is to calculate all quantities from microscopic constants. For example, η and k can be obtained from basic cross section data. Another is to use the latest experimentally measured value of the composite constant, for example, τ. A third, which is least satisfying but often most expedient, is to use an older and known inaccurate value of a constant on the grounds that its use gave good agreement between theory and experimental critical masses. This choice is often used, with precedent as the only justification. The assignment, below, of constants appearing in Equations (5.9), (5.10), (5.11), and (5.12) will be based primarily on calculations by Oak Ridge National Laboratory, in connection with aluminum-water critical assemblies. Table 5.4 lists the set that will be needed.

Table 5.4

Two-Group Constants

	Fast	*Thermal*
Reflector...............	τ_r	L_r
	D_{1r}	D_{2r}
Core..................	τ	L^2
	D_1	D_2
		k

$\tau_r = 33 \ cm^2$. This age-to-thermal of fission neutrons in water is an early measured value. We shall continue to employ it as an semi-empirical number. It has been remeasured as 31.4 cm², and there is theoretical evidence that it may be even lower. Strictly speaking, the term "age" should not be applied to water, since Fermi's age theory of heavy moderators gives very poor predictions, around 18 cm² for water. Thus τ_r will actually represent the square of an experimental slowing-down length. Ages for moderators as listed in the *Reactor Handbook*, Vol. I (1955) are given in Table 5.5.

Table 5.5

Age-to-Thermal for Fission Neutrons

Moderator	ρ (gm/cm³)	τ (cm²)
H_2O	1.0	31.4
D_2O	1.1	125
Be	1.85	97.2
BeO	3.0	105
C	1.60	364

$L_r = 2.88$ cm. This diffusion length for water is somewhat higher than the more recent figure of 2.85 cm. Table 5.6 gives values of L for common moderators.

Table 5.6

Thermal Diffusion Lengths

Moderator	ρ (gm/cm³)	L (cm)	
H_2O	1.0	2.85	
D_2O	1.1	116	$(0.16\%\ H_2O)$
Be	1.85	20.8	
BeO	2.69	29	
C	1.60	54.4	$(\sigma_a(2200) = 4.4$ mb$)$
		52	$(\sigma_a(2200) = 4.8$ mb$)$

$D_{2r} = 0.162$ cm. To obtain this value, the defining relation $L^2 = D/\Sigma_a$ was employed, using L^2 and the accurate cross section of water. σ_{aH} at 0.0253 ev is 0.330 barns, and room temperature water has $N_H = 0.0668$. Thus Σ_{aH_2O} at 0.025 ev is 0.0220 cm^{-1}, and for a maxwellian distribution is

$$\frac{0.0220}{1.128} = 0.01954 \text{ cm}^{-1} = \overline{\Sigma}_{aH_2O}$$

Table 5.7

Thermal Diffusion Coefficients

Moderator	ρ (gm/cm³)	D_2 (cm)	
H_2O	1.0	0.16	
D_2O	1.1	0.88	$(0.16\%\ H_2O)$
Be	1.85	0.48	
BeO	2.69	0.90	
C	1.60	0.90	

Finally, $D = \Sigma_a L^2 = (0.01954)(8.294) = 0.162$. Standard values given in the *Reactor Handbook* are listed in Table 5.7.

$D_{1r} = 1.143$ *cm.* The fast diffusion coefficient is the flux-weighted average of the energy-dependent D, over the epithermal energy range. The number adopted was obtained by Equation (5.4), where $\phi(u)$ was the epithermal flux per unit lethargy, given by Equation (2.45), but with $q_T = \int_0^u S(u)\, du$:

$$\phi(u) = \frac{\int_0^u S(u)\, du}{\xi \Sigma_s(u)} \qquad (5.48)$$

It will be recalled that this flux formula was correct only for an infinite reactor. A presumably more exact value of the diffusion coefficient can be obtained from an integration over the actual flux distribution, derived with leakage considered. Values of D_1 for the main moderators are shown in Table 5.8.

Table 5.8

Fast Diffusion Coefficients

Moderator	D_1 (cm)
H_2O	1.143
D_2O	1.13
Be	0.63
C	1.11

$\tau = 60.2$ *cm.* Calculations on Al-H_2O mixtures at Oak Ridge, using a transport theory method described by Marshak (see Chapter 10), form the basis for this figure. Their results lie on a straight line.

$$\tau = 33 + 41.8(f_{Al}/f_{H_2O}) \qquad (5.49)$$

An alternate semi-empirical method has been devised by Tittle (see § 10.3) to describe water-metal mixtures without the labor associated with an exact calculation by the transport formula. Discussion of this method and others, such as that of Goertzel and Greuling, is reserved for Chapter 10. For experimental data on mixtures of H_2O with Al or Zr, reference should be made to the *Reactor Handbook*, Vol. I.

$D_2 = 0.2611$ *cm.* Thermal diffusion coefficients for mixtures can be readily estimated by a volume-fraction weighted average of transport cross sections. We assume that

$$\Sigma_t = f_{H_2O}(\Sigma_t)_{H_2O} + f_{Al}(\Sigma_t)_{Al}$$

Now, $(\Sigma_t)_{H_2O} = 1/(3D_{H_2O}) = 2.058$

and

$$(\Sigma_s)_{Al}(1 - \overline{\cos \theta}) = (0.060)(1.40)(0.9753) = 0.0819$$

With $f_{H_2O} = 0.6047$ and $f_{Al} = 0.3935$, it follows that $\Sigma_t = 1.277$ and $D = 0.2611$.

$D_1 = 1.241$ cm. Values of this constant vary slowly with Al/H₂O volume ratio since the high energy cross section of Al is comparable to that of H and O. A straight line was drawn through points computed by ORNL to give

$$D_1 = 1.143 + 0.153(f_{Al}/f_{H_2O}) \tag{5.50}$$

The method described for calculation of D_{1r} is applicable in general to mixtures of elements, but a convenient substitute for more rapid estimates is to assume that the fission neutrons have an energy equal to their average value 2 mev. Equation (2.45), $\phi(u) = q_T/\xi\Sigma_s(u)$, is invoked, but where q_T is taken as constant. D_1 reduces to

$$D_1 \simeq \frac{\int_{1.605}^{u_t} \dfrac{D(u)\, du}{\xi\Sigma_s(u)}}{\int_{1.605}^{u_t} \dfrac{du}{\xi\Sigma_s(u)}} \tag{5.51}$$

L^2 and k. These are the first group constants that depend appreciably on the fuel concentration. If the reactor composition were completely specified, but the size were to be found, these would be computed only once. For our problem the reverse is true; so trial fuel concentrations will be used. The working formulas are (compare § 3.2):

$$\Sigma_2 = f_U(\Sigma_a)_U + f_{H_2O}(\Sigma_a)_{H_2O} + f_{Al}(\Sigma_a)_{Al} \tag{5.52}$$

$$L^2 = \frac{D_2}{\Sigma_2} \tag{5.53}$$

$$f = \frac{f_U(\Sigma_a)_U}{\Sigma_2} \tag{5.54}$$

$$\eta = \frac{(\sigma_f)_{\mathrm{U}}}{(\sigma_a)_{\mathrm{U}}} \nu \qquad (5.55)$$

$$k = pf\eta \qquad (5.56)$$

As shown in § 3.3, the resonance escape probability p for a dilute water-moderated highly-enriched reactor is very close to 1. Maxwellian cross sections for the uranium are

$$(\sigma_a)_{\mathrm{U}} = \frac{(0.93)(687)(0.981) + (0.07)(2.75)}{1.128} = 555.8$$

and

$$(\sigma_f)_{\mathrm{U}} = \frac{(0.93)(580)(0.981)}{1.128} = 469.1$$

Thus $\eta = (469.1)(2.46)/555.8 = 2.076$. For type 2S Al and H_2O, we take maxwellian cross sections $(\Sigma_a)_{\mathrm{Al}} = 0.0123$ cm^{-1} and $(\Sigma_a)_{H_2O} = 0.01954$ cm^{-1}. The part of Σ_2 due to Al and H_2O is 0.01666. From the 105.0-liter volume and uranium density of 18.7 gm/cm^3, the volume fraction of U is $f_{\mathrm{U}} = 0.0005093M$ (kg). Also $(\Sigma_a)_{\mathrm{U}} = (0.0479)(555.8) = 26.62$ cm^{-1}. At this stage, two trial choices of mass of U are made, 3.2 kg and 3.5 kg, and tabular calculations used, with the appropriate equation numbers listed.

Equation No....				(5.52)	(5.53)	(5.54)	(5.56)
Trial	U (kg)	f_{U}	$f_{\mathrm{U}}(\Sigma_a)_{\mathrm{U}}$	Σ_2	L^2	f	k
1	3.2	0.001630	0.04339	0.06005	4.346	0.7226	1.5001
2	3.5	0.001783	0.04746	0.06412	4.070	0.7402	1.5367

Calculation of critical size. A closed solution for the completely reflected rectangular parallelepiped has not been developed. Even the simpler problem of the reflected core of square or rectangular cross section can be solved only by difference equation methods. Therefore, it is necessary to invent systems believed to be equivalent. The proper choice is ambiguous, lacking extensive experimental data and exact calculations by machine methods. One may obtain a few logical conclusions by inspection of graphs of the mass and dimensions of critical reactors as they vary with fuel concentration. Figure 5.2(a) shows a characteristic plot of critical mass of a reflected thermal spherical core as a function of fuel concentration. Proceeding to the left, the increased absorption by moderator requires that the reactor be made rapidly larger, and M_c increases; proceeding to the right, the loss of core moderation again causes M_c to increase. It is safe to assume that the critical mass of a *cube* at every concentration

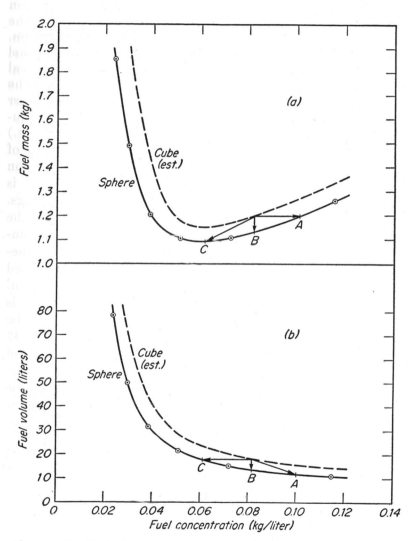

Figure 5.2. Variation of critical mass and size with fuel concentration. (Based on water sphere, two-group theory.)

would be higher than for the sphere.   In Figure 5.2(b), we plot the critical spherical and (assumed) cubical core volumes.   There are two possible methods of effecting a transition to an equivalent system—equal mass, and equal fuel concentration.   Assume first that the size of the cube has been specified, and that it has been found by calculations with a sphere of comparable size that the applicable region of Figure 5.2(a) is to the right of the minimum. The sphere containing the *same critical mass* (A) has a higher fuel concentration and a smaller volume.   The sphere that is critical at the same concentration (B) also has a smaller volume.   The sphere that is critical with the same volume will have a lower concentration and mass than the cube (C).   (Note that the arguments are reversed on the left side of the minimum mass point.)

For the present problem, the dimensions are far from those of a cube, and it is necessary to take account of the long dimension separately.   First, the effect of top and bottom reflector is equated to that of an additional fuel volume, the reflector savings. Estimates of the appropriate layer can be made by solving the two-group problem of an end-reflected, bare-sided core and comparing heights of the two, as was done in § 3.5 by modified one-group theory.   Separate calculations not reproduced here yielded a value of H' of 77.34, a total saving of $77.34 - 61.30 = 16.04$ cm. Thus the buckling used to modify constants (see Table 5.2) is $B^2 = (\pi/H')^2 = 0.001650$.   Of the several criteria that can be used to "convert" the rectangular cross section 36.85 cm by 46.47 cm into an equivalent circle of radius R, the easiest to picture and apply would be that of *equal area*, i.e., $WL = \pi R^2$.   It is clear, however, that the chance of leakage from a circular array will be considerably smaller than for the actual rectangular configuration.   Such a criterion would yield a critical mass that is too small.   A more logical choice would be the equal ratio of surface area to volume (perimeter to cross-sectional area), on the basis that neutron leakage is a surface phenomenon while neutron production is related to volume.   This gives the relation

$$\frac{1}{R} = \frac{1}{W} + \frac{1}{L}$$

and $R = 20.55$ cm.   For comparison, the equal area conversion predicts 23.35 cm.   By use of equations displayed in §§ 5.1 and 5.2, we now proceed to the calculation of critical mass.

Reflector Constants

Eq. No.	(5.38)	(5.39)	(5.26)	(5.21)	(5.34)		(5.24)
	ρ_1	ρ_2	S_3	κ_{1r}^2	$\bar{\kappa}_{1r}^2$	$\bar{\kappa}_{1r}$	κ_{2r}^2
	0.9210	0.6204	2.369	0.03030	0.03195	0.1787	0.1206

Eq. No.	(5.35)					Table 5.3	
	$\bar{\kappa}_{2r}^2$	$\bar{\kappa}_{2r}$	$\dfrac{1}{8\bar{\kappa}_{1r}R^2}$	$\dfrac{1}{8\bar{\kappa}_{2r}R^2}$	$\dfrac{1}{2R}$	γ	δ
	0.1222	0.3496	0.0016	0.0008	0.0243	-0.2014	-0.3731

Eq. No.		(5.44)
	$\rho_1\gamma$	$\rho_2\delta$	C_3
	-0.1855	-0.2315	-0.2522

Core Constants

Eq. No.			(5.29)	(5.28)	(5.30)		(5.27)
Trial	$1/L^2$	$1/\tau$	a	μ_0^2	ϵ	$1-\epsilon+2\epsilon^2$	μ^2
1	0.2301	0.01661	0.2467	0.007748	0.0314	0.9706	0.007520
2	0.2457	0.01661	0.2623	0.008351	0.0318	0.9702	0.008102

Eq. No.	(5.31)		(5.18)		(5.19)
Trial	ν^2	μ^2+1/L^2	S_1	μ^2+1/τ	S_2
1	0.2542	0.2376	0.3323	0.02413	-3.272
2	0.2704	0.2538	0.3110	0.02471	-3.195

Coupled Constants

Eq. No.	(5.33)		Table 5.3			(5.44)	
Trial	$\bar{\nu}^2$	$\bar{\nu}$	$\dfrac{1}{8\bar{\nu}R^2}$	β	$\rho_1\gamma-\beta$	C_1	$\beta-\rho_2\delta$
1	0.2558	0.5058	0.0006	0.4809	-0.6664	-0.2214	0.7124
2	0.2720	0.5215	0.0006	0.4966	-0.6821	-0.2121	0.7281

Eq. No.	(5.44)	(5.43)				(5.43)	(5.43)
Trial	C_1	Denom.	$\rho_2\delta C_1$	$\rho_1\gamma C_2$	βC_3	Numer.	α'
1	-2.331	-2.805	0.0513	0.4324	-0.1213	0.3624	-0.1292
2	-2.326	-2.790	0.0491	0.4315	-0.1252	0.3554	-0.1274

Eq. No.	(5.32)			Fig. 5.3	Table 5.3
Trial	$\bar{\mu}^2$	$\bar{\mu}$	$\bar{\mu}R$	$\dfrac{J_1(\bar{\mu}R)}{J_0(\bar{\mu}R)}$	α
1	0.005870	0.07662	1.575	1.208	-0.0926
2	0.006452	0.08032	1.651	1.348	-0.1083
3	(new)	0.08402	1.727	1.515	-0.1273

A convenient graphical solution is demonstrated in Figures 5.3 and 5.4. The first of these is a plot of $J_1(x)/J_0(x)$, which may be used for any cylindrical system. The second includes M, α, and α' vs. $\bar{\mu}$. The quantity α' is assumed to be linear in the region of interest, and α is computed for trial $\bar{\mu}$, since it varies more sensitively.

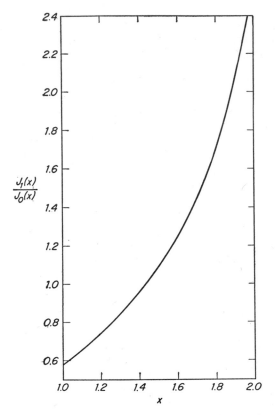

Figure 5.3. $J_1(x)/J_0(x)$ for use with cylindrical reactor cores.

Intersection occurs at $\bar{\mu} = 0.0836$ or at a mass of $U = 3.78$ kg. The experimental value is approximately 3.6 kg of U^{235}, 3.87 kg of uranium, implying an error of 2 per cent. This is probably more accurate than expected from the two-group theory in such geometries. An estimate may be made of the core radius that would correspond to a given mass, e.g., 3.5 kg, by solving Equation (5.42) in the form

$$\frac{\bar{\mu} J_1(\bar{\mu} R)}{J_0(\bar{\mu} R)} = \alpha'$$

using the $\bar{\mu}$ and α' computed for that mass. This approach is based on the observation that α' varies slowly with core radius. Carrying out this operation, $\bar{\mu} R$ is found to be 1.754 and $R = 21.84$ cm.

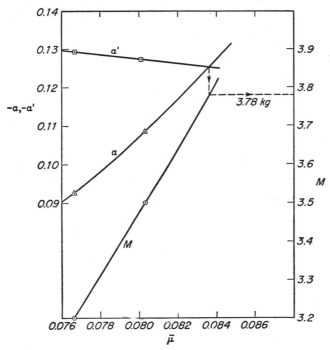

Figure 5.4. Graphical solution for critical mass by two-group theory.

Flux plot. A calculation of radial flux distribution will be made for the case of a core with radius $R = 21.84$ cm, 3.5 kg mass, since all constants are readily available.

Constant	Value	Constant	Value
$\bar{\mu}$	0.08032	Δ_G	-1.0806
$\bar{\nu}$	0.5215	S_1	0.3110
$\bar{\mu} R$	1.754	S_2	-3.195
$\bar{\nu} R$	11.39	$\bar{\kappa}_{1r}$	0.1787
Δ_A	0.6821	$\bar{\kappa}_{2r}$	0.3496
Δ_C	-0.0581	S_3	2.369
Δ_F	0.6240		

The flux functions for cylindrical geometry according to Table 5.1 are $X = J_0(\bar{\mu}r)$, $Y = I_0(\bar{\nu}r)$, $Z_1 = K_0(\bar{\kappa}_1r)$ and $Z_2 = K_0(\bar{\kappa}_{2r}r)$. The last three become very large at the core boundary. Use of the series approximation for large argument of Bessel functions given in Appendix A gives the ratios

$$\frac{Y}{[Y]} = \frac{I_0(\bar{\nu}r)}{I_0(\bar{\nu}R)} \simeq \sqrt{\frac{R}{r}}\, e^{-\bar{\nu}(R-r)}$$

and

$$\frac{Z}{[Z]} = \frac{K_0(\bar{\kappa}r)}{K_0(\bar{\kappa}R)} \simeq \sqrt{\frac{R}{r}}\, e^{-\bar{\kappa}(r-R)}$$

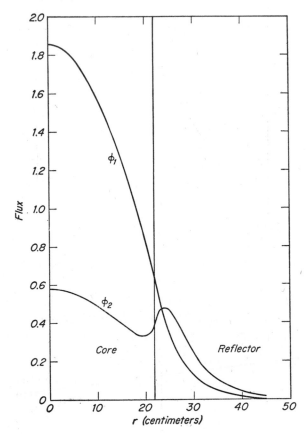

Figure 5.5. Flux distributions in water-moderated and reflected cylinder.

The radial flux solutions are thus approximately:
  Core:

$$\phi_1 \simeq \frac{\Delta_A J_0(\bar{\mu}r)}{J_0(\bar{\mu}R)} + \Delta_C \sqrt{\frac{R}{r}}\, e^{-\bar{\nu}(R-r)}$$

$$\phi_2 \simeq S_1\Delta_A \frac{J_0(\mu r)}{J_0(\mu R)} + S_2\Delta_C \sqrt{\frac{R}{r}}\, e^{-\bar{\nu}(R-r)}$$

Reflector:

$$\phi_{1r} \simeq \Delta_F \sqrt{\frac{R}{r}}\, e^{-\bar{\kappa}_{1r}(r-R)}$$

$$\phi_{2r} \simeq S_3\Delta_F \sqrt{\frac{R}{r}}\, e^{-\bar{\kappa}_{1r}(r-R)} + \Delta_G \sqrt{\frac{R}{r}}\, e^{-\bar{\kappa}_{2r}(r-R)}$$

The calculation is straightforward from this point and only the results will be displayed in Figure 5.5. Of note is the thermal flux peak just outside the core boundary. Fast neutrons created in the core escape from it, and are slowed down in the reflector. The resulting thermals are absorbed there less rapidly than in the core, and tend to "pile up" near the interface. This effect is particularly pronounced in a beryllium-reflected water-moderated reactor such as the MTR, where the peak flux in the reflector is several times the peak in the core.

5.5. *Modified two-group theory*

Reactors with an appreciable amount of epithermal absorption and fission should be calculated in general by the use of more than two groups, in order to represent the processes properly. It has been shown by Edlund that a two-group theory that is *modified* to include resonance effects is equivalent to a three-group approach, if the energy range for the resonance region is not too large. Assume that a reactor is to be built that will operate steadily without refueling for many months. During this operating period, fuel will be consumed at the rate of approximately 1.3 gm/megawatt-day. In order for the system to be critical at the end of the cycle, considerable excess of fuel must be loaded initially, compensated and controlled by absorbing elements. The total absorption cross section under these conditions will be unusually high, and there will be a tendency for neutrons to be

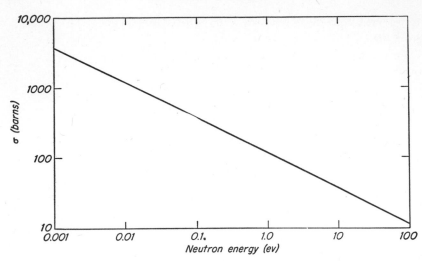

Figure 5.6. Boron cross section for low-energy neutrons.

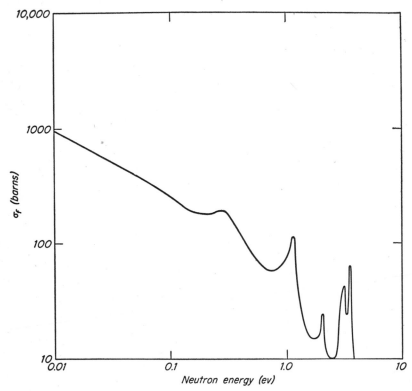

Figure 5.7. U²³⁵ fission cross section.

removed before they slow down to thermal energy.   The $1/v$ poison boron, for example, still has a cross section of 100 barns at 1.5 ev, which energy is well above that for the room temperature maxwellian peak (see Figure 5.6).   The fission cross section of uranium varies rapidly in this region also, as shown in Figure 5.7, and the fission rate cannot be correlated with thermal neutron fluxes.

The complete energy range is divided into three groups: thermal, resonance, and fast.   Fluxes will be assigned only for the thermal (ϕ_2) and fast (ϕ_1) groups, but the neutron balance will include all three, as sketched in Figure 5.8.   Of the neutrons removed from the fast group, $\phi_1\Sigma_1$, the number escaping capture in the resonance region is $p\phi_1\Sigma_1$, while those absorbed therein, $(1 - p)\phi_1\Sigma_1$, produce fission neutrons at a rate of $f_r\eta_r(1 - p)\phi_1\Sigma_1$. These are added to the fast neutrons from thermal fission $f\eta\phi_2\Sigma_2$.

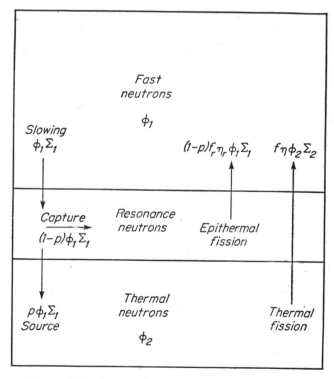

Figure 5.8.   Neutron processes, modified two-group
theory.

The familiar two-group diffusion equations (see § 5.1) may be applied, but with a new fast source,

$$S_f = f\eta\phi_2\Sigma_2 + f_r\eta_r(1 - p)\phi_1\Sigma_1 \qquad (5.57)$$

and the usual thermal source

$$S_t = p\phi_1\Sigma_1 \qquad (5.58)$$

The fast group equation becomes

$$D_1 \nabla^2\phi_1 - \phi_1\Sigma_1[1 - (1 - p)f_r\eta_r] + \phi_2\Sigma_2 f\eta = 0 \qquad (5.59)$$

Now define a modified age for mathematical convenience,

$$\tau' = \frac{\tau}{1 - (1 - p)f_r\eta_r} \qquad (5.60)$$

and a modified multiplication factor,

$$k' = \frac{k}{1 - (1 - p)f_r\eta_r} \qquad (5.61)$$

where the thermal k is $pf\eta$. The quadratic equation analogous to Equation (5.15) is

$$(1 + B^2L^2)(1 + B^2\tau') = k' \qquad (5.62)$$

which is of exactly the same *form* used in conventional two-group theory.

The whole calculation structure of two-group theory may be applied, with one exception, that S_1 and S_2 (Equations 5.18 and 5.19) read with $D_1p/\tau D_2$ and $\mu^2 + (1/\tau')$. A composite multiplication factor of the system, including both thermal and resonance fission is

$$K = pf\eta + (1 - p)f_r\eta_r \qquad (5.63)$$

by an argument based on neutron economy. For each fast neutron, p arrive at thermal and each of these gives rise to $f\eta$ fission neutrons; $1 - p$ are absorbed in the resonance region, and each gives $f_r\eta_r$ fission neutrons. The sum is thus the composite multiplication factor. The smallest buckling root μ^2 for a heavily poisoned reactor with $L^2 \ll \tau$, will be approximately $(K - 1)/\tau$, which shows how K takes the place of the usual k.

The resonance multiplication factor $f_r\eta_r$ is

$$f_r\eta_r = \frac{\int \phi(u)\Sigma_{aU}(u)\eta(u)\,du}{\int \phi(u)\Sigma_a(u)\,du} \qquad (5.64)$$

which, if we take η as essentially constant, and let the resonance flux be $\phi(u) = q_T/(\xi\Sigma_s)$ is

$$f_r\eta_r = \frac{\eta\Sigma_{rU}}{\Sigma_r} \tag{5.65}$$

where the quotient of *resonance integrals* appears.

Numerical Illustration: A homogeneous U^{235}-fueled, beryllium oxide moderated reactor is of such size that it is critical with a thermal utilization of 0.8. It is desired to *double* the fuel concentration for future burn-up, and to control the reactor with boron rods. Assuming that the rods are equivalent to enough distributed boron to reduce f to 0.8 again, calculate the resonance multiplication factor $f_r\eta_r$, the resonance escape probability p, and the composite multiplication factor K.

Solution. The initial BeO and U amounts are determined from the condition

$$\frac{1}{f} - 1 = \frac{(\Sigma_a)_{BeO}}{(\Sigma_a)_U} = 0.25$$

First assume that U displaces a negligible volume of BeO, density 2.8 gm/cm³. Then $N_{BeO} = 0.0675$ and with a maxwellian cross section of BeO 0.0089 barns, $(\Sigma_a)_{BeO} = 6.01 \times 10^{-4}$ cm⁻¹. Thus $(\Sigma_a)_U = 24.0 \times 10^{-4}$ cm⁻¹, and with $(\sigma_a)_U = 597.5$ barns, $N_U = 4.02 \times 10^{-6}$ (in units of 10^{24}). At the heavier loading,

$$\frac{1}{f} - 1 = \frac{(\Sigma_a)_{BeO} + (\Sigma_a)_B}{2(\Sigma_a)_U} = 0.25$$

and

$$(\Sigma_a)_B = 6.01 \times 10^{-4} \text{ cm}^{-1}$$

Since $(\sigma_a)_B = 669$ barns, $N_B = 8.98 \times 10^{-7}$. Also, the new value of N_U is 8.04×10^{-6}. The resonance integral between any two energies E_1 and E_2 in boron, since it is a $1/v$ absorber, may be written $(\sigma_r)_B = 2[\sigma_a(E_1) - \sigma_a(E_2)]$. We take the energy range from 0.15 ev to 5 ev as that where most of the important resonance absorption exists. Rigorously, the integrations should be extended to a higher energy, but the error will not be serious in this illustration. The value of $(\sigma_r)_B$ is found to be 518 barns. Thus $(\Sigma_r)_B = (8.98 \times 10^{-7})(518) = 4.65 \times 10^{-4}$ cm. Numerical integration of Figure 5.7 gives $(\sigma_r)_U = \int (\sigma_a)_U \, dE/E = 336$ barns, and $(\Sigma_r)_U = (8.04 \times 10^{-6})(336) = 27.0 \times 10^{-4}$. Applying Equation (5.65),

$$f_r \eta_r = \frac{(2.08)(27.0 \times 10^{-4})}{31.65 \times 10^{-4}} = 1.77$$

The resonance escape probability may be written $p = e^{-\Sigma_r/\overline{\xi\Sigma}_s}$, where the scattering of BeO appears only in $\overline{\xi\Sigma}_s$. Since $\xi_{Be} = 0.208$, $\xi_O = 0.121$, $(\bar{\sigma}_s)_{Be} = 5.9$, and $(\bar{\sigma}_s)_O = 3.75$, we find $\overline{\xi\Sigma}_s = 0.114 \text{ cm}^{-1}$. The resonance escape probability is $p = e^{-0.003165/0.114} = e^{-0.0278} = 0.973$. The thermal multiplication factor is $pf\eta = (0.973)(0.8)(2.08) = 1.62$, and the composite from Equation (5.63) is $K = 1.62 + (0.027)(1.77) = 1.67$, which is seen to be sensibly higher than the multiplication factor computed as if the reactor were strictly thermal.

5.6. *Matrix-method solution for multiple reflectors*

For purposes of economy of neutrons and materials, it is often desirable to use two or more reflectors outside the core. The MTR, for example, has a layer of Be near the core, with graphite beyond; the CP-5 reactor has a D_2O reflector surrounded by graphite. The mathematical complication in calculating critical conditions and flux distributions for such systems may be reduced by the use of a matrix method devised by Garabedian and Householder.

The method of analysis will be outlined for the simplest case: a parallelepiped of half-width h, reflected by two layers. The outer reflector we take as infinite; the middle layer ends at a distance l from the origin.

The two-group flux solutions for the core (c) and outer reflector (r) are conventional,

$$\phi_{1c} = A \cos \mu z + C \cosh \nu z$$
$$\phi_{2c} = S_1 A \cos \mu z + S_2 C \cosh \nu z$$
$$\tag{5.66}$$

$$\phi_{1r} = F e^{-\kappa_{1r}z}$$
$$\phi_{2r} = S_3 \phi_{1r} + G e^{-\kappa_{2r}z}$$
$$\tag{5.67}$$

Those for the middle layer (m) are

$$\phi_{1m} = H \cosh \kappa_{1m}z + I \sinh \kappa_{1m}z$$
$$\phi_{2m} = S_m \phi_{1m} + J \cosh \kappa_{2m}z + K \sinh \kappa_{2m}z$$
$$\tag{5.68}$$

Application of the continuity equations on flux and current would result in an unwieldy 8×8 critical determinant. Let us devise a (4×1) matrix,* which will be called the general flux vector,

$$\Phi = \begin{bmatrix} \phi_1 \\ \phi_2 \\ J_1 \\ J_2 \end{bmatrix}$$

where J_1 and J_2 are the *negatives* of the usual currents. Each flux vector may be represented as a product of two matrices, one depending on the flux functions, the other involving only arbitrary coefficients. Thus Equations (5.66) are written compactly as

$$\Phi_c = M_c(z)a_c \qquad (5.69)$$

where

$$M_c(z) = \begin{bmatrix} \cos \mu z & \cosh \nu z \\ S_1 \cos \mu z & S_2 \cosh \nu z \\ -D_1\mu \sin \mu z & D_1\nu \sinh \nu z \\ -D_2\mu S_1 \sin \mu z & D_2 S_2 \nu \sinh \nu z \end{bmatrix} \qquad (5.70)$$

and

$$a_c = \begin{bmatrix} A \\ C \end{bmatrix} \qquad (5.71)$$

---

* A summary of those aspects of matrix algebra that are needed in the following discussion is given below.

(a) A matrix is an array of numbers or *elements* of the form

$$A = [A_{ij}] = \begin{bmatrix} A_{11} & A_{12} & \cdots & A_{1m} \\ A_{21} & A_{22} & \cdots & A_{2m} \\ \cdot & \cdot & & \cdot \\ \cdot & \cdot & & \cdot \\ \cdot & \cdot & & \cdot \\ A_{n1} & A_{n2} & \cdots & A_{nm} \end{bmatrix}$$

(b) The *order* of the matrix is indicated by the symbol $(n \times m)$ i.e., (rows $\times$ columns). The square matrix having an equal number of rows and columns is the only one for which a determinant may be found.

(c) The product AB of two matrices A and B is the matrix C if the number of columns in A is equal to the number of rows in B. If A is of order $(n \times h)$ and B is of order $(h \times m)$, then C is of order $(n \times m)$.

(d) The elements of C are

$$C_{pq} = \sum_{s=1}^{n} A_{ps}B_{sq}$$

with $p = 1, 2, 3, \cdots, n; q = 1, 2, 3, \cdots, m$.

(e) The inverse of a matrix A, denoted A^{-1}, has the property that $AA^{-1} = E$, where the unit matrix E has unity for the diagonal running from upper left to lower right, and zeros elsewhere. A matrix multiplied by E remains the same as it was. The elements A_{pq}^{-1} are formed by dividing the cofactor of A_{qp} by the determinant of A.

Application of the multiplication rule for matrices will verify this result.   Similarly, Equation (5.68) becomes

$$\Phi_m = M_m(z)a_m \qquad (5.72)$$

where

$$M_m(z) = \begin{bmatrix} \cosh \kappa_{1m}z & \sinh \kappa_{1m}z & 0 & 0 \\ S_m \cosh \kappa_{1m}z & S_m \sinh \kappa_{1m}z & \cosh \kappa_{2m}z & \sinh \kappa_{2m}z \\ D_1\kappa_{1m} \sinh \kappa_{1m}z & D_1\kappa_{1m} \cosh \kappa_{1m}z & 0 & 0 \\ D_2 S_m\kappa_{1m} \sinh \kappa_{1m}z & D_2 S_m\kappa_{1m} \cosh \kappa_{1m}z & D_2\kappa_{2m} \sinh \kappa_{2m}z & D_2\kappa_{2m} \cosh \kappa_{2m}z \end{bmatrix}$$

$$(5.73)$$

and

$$a_m = \begin{bmatrix} H \\ I \\ J \\ K \end{bmatrix} \qquad (5.74)$$

Also, Equation (5.67) becomes

$$\Phi_r = M_r(z)a_r \qquad (5.75)$$

where

$$M_r(z) = \begin{bmatrix} e^{-\kappa_{1r}z} & 0 \\ S_3 e^{-\kappa_{1r}z} & e^{-\kappa_{2r}z} \\ -D_{1r}\kappa_{1r}e^{-\kappa_{1r}z} & 0 \\ -D_{2r}S_3\kappa_{1r}e^{-\kappa_{1r}z} & -D_{2r}\kappa_{2i}e^{-\kappa_{2r}z} \end{bmatrix} \qquad (5.76)$$

and

$$a_r = \begin{bmatrix} F \\ G \end{bmatrix} \qquad (5.77)$$

The condition of continuity of flux and current at l, the interface of middle region and reflector, may be expressed by

$$\Phi_m(l) = \Phi_r(l) \qquad (5.78)$$

or

$$M_m(l)a_m = M_r(l)a_r \qquad (5.79)$$

The vector a_m can be found by multiplying both sides of the last equation by the inverse $M_m^{-1}(l)$, to obtain

$$a_m = M_m^{-1}(l)M_r(l)a_r \qquad (5.80)$$

Now the core-middle region continuity condition at h may be applied, as

$$\Phi_c(h) = \Phi_m(h) \qquad (5.81)$$

or

$$M_c(h)a_c = M_m(h)a_m \qquad (5.82)$$

Substituting the value of a_m from Equation (5.80),

$$M_c(h)a_c = M_m(h)M_m^{-1}(l)M_r(l)a_r \qquad (5.83)$$

This is a set of four simultaneous equations in the familiar arbitrary coefficients of the core and reflector A, C, F, and G, analogous to Equations (5.37). The determinant of the coefficients is set equal to zero, and gives the critical condition, as in Equation (5.40). It can be shown by application of the matrix rules already listed that the product $M_m(h)M_n^{-1}(l)$, which we label $M(t)$, turns out to be a (4×4) matrix dependent only on a difference $l - h$, which is the thickness t of the middle layer. It is

$$M(t) = \begin{bmatrix} C_1 & 0 & -\dfrac{S_1}{S_{1m}\kappa_{1m}} & 0 \\[2mm] S_m(C_1 - C_2) & C_2 & \dfrac{S_m}{D_{1m}}\left(\dfrac{S_2}{\kappa_{2m}} - \dfrac{S_1}{\kappa_{1m}}\right) & -\dfrac{S_2}{D_{2m}\kappa_{2m}} \\[2mm] -D_{1m}\kappa_{1m}S_1 & 0 & C_1 & 0 \\[2mm] D_{2m}S_m(\kappa_{2m}S_2 - \kappa_{1m}S_1) & -D_{2m}\kappa_{2m}S_2 & \dfrac{D_{2m}}{D_{1m}}S_m(C_1 - C_2) & C_2 \end{bmatrix} \quad (5.84)$$

where $C_1 = \cosh \kappa_{1m}t$, $C_2 = \cosh \kappa_{2m}t$, $S_1 = \sinh \kappa_{1m}t$, $S_2 = \sinh \kappa_{2m}t$. Now letting the remaining matrix product be

$$N = M(t)M_r(l) \qquad (5.85)$$

and inserting it in Equation (5.83) along with the definitions of M_c, a_c, and a_r in Equations (5.70), (5.71), and (5.77), we obtain the critical determinant

$$\begin{vmatrix} 1 & 1 & N_{11} & 0 \\ S_1 & S_2 & N_{21} & N_{22} \\ D_1\alpha & D_1\beta & N_{31} & 0 \\ D_2S_1\alpha & D_2S_2\beta & N_{41} & N_{42} \end{vmatrix} = 0 \qquad (5.86)$$

where α and β are standard abbreviations (Table 5.3). The matrix N is best evaluated numerically by use of Equation (5.85).

Problems

5.1. A homogeneous thermal breeder reactor consists of a spherical core, with a higher enriched U^{235} fuel in water solution, $N_H/N_{235} = 450$, surrounded by a 6-in. thick reflector-blanket of thorium salt dissolved in water, $N_H/N_{Th} = 40$. At the outset, no U^{233} is present in the reflector. Assume the following basic constants for core and reflector: $\tau = 33$ cm², $D_1 = 1.143$ cm, $D_2 = 0.162$ cm. Values of 0.025-ev absorption cross sections are: $U^{235} = 687$ barns, (not-1/v factor $= 0.981$); H $= 0.330$ barns; Th $= 7$ barns. Also, disregard poisoning or displacement due to structural materials and fuel molecules.

(a) Calculate the infinite multiplication factor for maxwellian neutrons at room temperature.

Answer. $k = 1.7043$.

(b) Find the roots μ^2 and ν^2 for the core.

Answer. $\mu^2 = 0.01986$, $\nu^2 = 0.7181$.

(c) Find the coupling coefficients S_1, S_2, and S_3.

Answer. $S_1 = 0.3108$, $S_2 = -4.262$, $S_3 = 1.386$.

(d) Find L^2 for the core and reflector.

Answer. $L^2 = 1.497$ cm^2, $L_r^2 = 5.418$ cm^2.

5.2. Find the critical core radius and critical mass of U^{235} for the reactor in Problem 5.1.

Answer. $R = 16.44$ cm, $M_{235} = 1.08$ kg.

5.3. Calculate and plot the absolute thermal flux distribution in the core and reflector for a core power level of 1 kw.

Answer:

$$\phi_2(r) = 10^{11} \left[2.825 \frac{\sin 0.1409r}{r} + \frac{1.271 e^{-0.8474(16.44 - r)}}{r} \right] \Big/ \text{cm}^2\text{-sec}$$

$$\phi_{2r}(r) = 10^{11} \left[1.252 \frac{\sinh 0.1741(31.68 - r)}{r} - 0.01576 \right.$$
$$\left. \frac{\sinh 0.4296(31.68 - r)}{r} \right] \Big/ \text{cm}^2\text{-sec}$$

5.4. Derive a formula for the integral $\int_R^{R+T} Z \, dV$, needed in the evaluation of average thermal flux in a reflector of thickness T, surrounding a spherical core of radius R.

Answer. $\dfrac{4\pi}{\kappa^2} [\kappa R \cosh \kappa T + \sinh \kappa T - \kappa(R + T)]$

5.5. Ignoring intermediate steps in the decay chain, find the initial production rate of U^{233} in the blanket, per kilowatt of core power, for the reactor in Problems 5.1–5.3. Find also the conversion ratio, (atoms of U^{233} produced)/(atoms of U^{235} burned).

Answer. 2.9×10^{-5} gm/day; 0.223.

5.6. Investigate the nature of the fluxes in a reflector that contains fuel, so that its multiplication factor is greater than zero. Consider three cases $k < 1$, $k = 1$, and $k > 1$. List and examine solutions for all of the combinations of core and reflector, with the possibilities for $k = 0$, <1, $=1$, >1.

5.7. Show that the total fast neutron leakage per unit area on the reactor surface defined as the integral over lethargy of the current per unit lethargy range, is equal to $-D_1 d\phi_1/dz$.

5.8. An MTR-type reactor is constructed with a thin beryllium reflector in order to achieve a high epithermal and fast neutron radiation source. Derive a formula relating fast current density at the outside surface of this reflector and the total core power, assuming a spherical core, of the form $j_1 = aP$.

5.9. Show, using expansions of Bessel functions for large argument (Appendix A), that the flux functions Z_1 and Z_2 in Table 5.1 for a cylinder with finite reflector are approximately

$$K_0(\kappa r)[1 - e^{-2\kappa(R+T-r)}]$$

5.10. What is the nature of the solution for the flux in the reflector if τ_r happens to be equal to L_r^2, and according to Equation (5.26), S_3 would appear to be infinite?

5.11. Verify the two-group critical Equation (5.43) and the form for the arbitrary coefficients in Equations (5.45) and (5.46).

5.12. (a) Calculate the modified two-group τ' and K from the following data: $p = 0.90$, $f_r = 0.85$, $\eta_r = \eta = 2.08$, $f = 0.75$, $L^2 = 625$, $\tau = 350$. (b) Find the values of the radii of a bare sphere by modified two-group and standard two-group theory.

Answer. (a) 425 cm², 1.581, (b) 129 cm, 159 cm.

References

Glasstone, Samuel, and Milton C. Edlund, *The Elements of Nuclear Reactor Theory.* New York: D. Van Nostrand Co. (1952).

The Reactor Handbook, Volume 1, *Physics*, AECD-3645. Washington: U. S. Government Printing Office (1955).

Breazeale, W. M., "The Swimming Pool, A Low Cost Research Reactor," *Nucleonics*, November 1952, p. 56. (See also ORNL-1105.)

Murray, R. L., M. R. Keller, and D. E. Hostetler, "How to Use the Fission Spectrum Formula in Reactor Calculations," *Nucleonics*, September 1954, p. 64.

Fieno, Daniel, Harold Schneider, and Robert B. Spooner, "Lumped Reflector Parameters for Two-Group Reactor Calculations," *Nucleonics*, August 1953, p. 16.

Spinrad, B. I., and Dieter Kurath, *Computation Forms for Solution of Critical Problems by Two-Group Diffusion Theory*, ANL-4352 (1952).

Garabedian, H. L., and A. S. Householder, *Two-Group Theory of Piles with Multiple Reflectors*, AECD-3585 (1946).

Peaceful Uses of Atomic Energy, Volume 2, *Physics; Research Reactors.* New York: Columbia University Press (1956).

Weinberg, A. M., Thomas E. Cole, and Marvin M. Mann, "The Materials Testing Reactor and Related Research Reactors," Paper P/490.

Radkowsky, A., and S. Krasik, "Physics Aspects of the Pressurized Water Reactor (PWR)," Paper P/604.

Greuling, E., B. Spinrad, and A. V. Masket, *Critical Mass and Neutron Distribution Calculations for the H_2O Moderated Reactor with D_2O, H_2O and Be Reflectors*, Mon P-402 (1947).

Chapter 6

THE TIME-DEPENDENT REACTOR

||||||||||||||||||||||||||||||||||||||||||||||||||||||||||||||||||||||||||||||||||||||||||||||||||||||||||||||||||||||||||||||||||

A variation of reactor power with time will result from a change in the amount of neutron absorption or leakage. There are two important situations of interest. First, in order to raise or lower the power to a new steady value, a temporary adjustment in the neutron balance must be made, and a transient is experienced. Second, the rapid rise in reactor power with time, resulting from an accidental disturbance of the system, must be avoided by proper design and operation. In this chapter, the differential equations that govern the time-dependent neutron density will be derived and solved. The role that delayed neutrons play in providing inherent safety in reactor control will be developed.

6.1. *Neutron accumulation*

In the critical reactor, the typical fission neutron must produce another neutron by the end of the slowing, diffusion, and absorption cycle. The amounts of fuel, moderator, and poison are compatible with the shape and size of the core and reflector. An accidental or deliberate adjustment of any of these factors can result in an *accumulation* of neutrons. This corresponds to an increase in flux and power level. The analogy to compound interest may be instructive. At 6 per cent interest per year, a principal will increase in 20 years by a factor $(1.06)^{20} = 3.2$. In a reactor, with a 6 per cent increase in neutrons *per cycle* and a time for the neutron to complete its cycle of 10^{-3} seconds, the number present after one second would be increased by a factor of $(1.06)^{1000} = 10^{25}$. A power increase of this amount would cer-

145

tainly do violence to the reactor. One concludes that the gain in neutrons per cycle must be kept very low, or if there should be a large change in multiplication, automatic and inherent safety devices must operate.

The rate of neutron accumulation depends mutually on the time required for one cycle and on the gain of neutrons per cycle. In the thermal reactor, the cycle time consists of two parts—the time to slow down from fission to thermal, and the time for diffusion as thermals until absorption (or leakage).

Slowing-down time. The time between collisions is λ_s/v, and the average change in lethargy per collision is ξ. For an infinitesimal change in u with corresponding time interval, we have

$$\frac{du}{\xi} = \frac{dt}{\lambda_s/v}$$

However, $du = -2dv/v$, and for the range fission to thermal the total time elapsed is

$$l_f = \int_{v_t}^{v_f} \frac{2\lambda_s \, dv}{\xi v^2}$$

If an average mean free path is assigned, the integral becomes

$$l_f = \frac{2\overline{\lambda}_s}{\xi}\left(\frac{1}{v_t} - \frac{1}{v_f}\right) \simeq \frac{2\overline{\lambda}_s}{\xi v_t} \qquad \text{slowing-down time} \qquad (6.1)$$

Neutron leakage from the reactor has not been included in this derivation. Because of the low neutron speed near the end of the slowing process, the time the neutron spends in this energy range is relatively long. The scattering cross section near thermal is usually representative of the average $\overline{\Sigma}_s$.

Numerical Illustration: Find the slowing-down time in graphite.

Solution. The epithermal cross section of carbon is 4.8 barns. With $N_C = 0.083$, $\overline{\Sigma}_s$ is 0.40 and $\lambda_s = 2.5$ cm. Also, $\xi = 0.159$ and v_t, the average thermal speed, is 2.5×10^5 cm/sec. Thus from Equation (6.1),

$$l_f = \frac{(2)(2.5)}{(0.159)(2.5 \times 10^5)} = 1.3 \times 10^{-4} \text{ sec}$$

It will be found that the slowing-down times in Be, D_2O and H_2O are progressively shorter, primarily because of the larger values of ξ. For example, in H_2O, $\bar{\lambda}_s = 1.1$ cm and l_f is approximately 10^{-5} sec.

The fast reactor, having no moderator, has no true slowing-down time. The cycle time between fissions is approximately 10^{-7} sec.

Thermal lifetime. The time neutrons exist as *thermals* in a critical reactor is given in general by

$$l_t = \text{thermal lifetime} = \frac{\text{number of thermals present}}{\text{rate of supply of thermals}}$$

or $\qquad l_t = \dfrac{n}{k\phi\Sigma_a\mathcal{L}_f} = \dfrac{\mathcal{L}_t}{v\Sigma_a}$ $\qquad\qquad\qquad$ (6.2)

where the local n and ϕ are representative of the whole reactor, and the criticality condition $1 = k\mathcal{L}_f\mathcal{L}_t$ has been invoked. For an infinite reactor medium with no thermal leakage, this reduces to

$$l_0 = \frac{1}{v\Sigma_a} \qquad\qquad (6.3)$$

The total cycle time is $l = l_f + l_t$. When l is much larger than the slowing-down time l_f, the latter can be ignored, and $l \simeq l_t$.

Numerical Illustration: In the "Borax" experiments at Arco, Idaho, an MTR type reactor with water volume fraction 0.613, $B^2 = 0.010$, $D = 0.21$ cm, and $\Sigma_a = 0.076$ cm^{-1}, was subjected to a large excess multiplication. Estimate the total cycle time l for this system.

Solution. The slowing-down time will be taken as $1/0.613$ times that for water, 10^{-5} sec, on the assumption that the aluminum acts essentially as a void. Thus $l_f = 1.6 \times 10^{-5}$ sec. The value of L^2 is $D/\Sigma_a = 2.8$ and $\mathcal{L}_t = 1/(1 + B^2L^2) = 0.97$. Thus from Equation (6.2),

$$l_t = \frac{0.97}{(2.48 \times 10^5)(0.076)} = 5.1 \times 10^{-5} \text{ sec}$$

and the total cycle time is 6.7×10^{-5} sec.

Delayed neutrons. The fact that a small fraction of the fission neutrons are emitted by certain fission products according to the laws of radioactive decay is a valuable protective feature for reactors. Excesses in multiplication factors up to about 0.7 per cent can be introduced without catastrophic rise in power. Of the ν neutrons per fission, a fraction β are *delayed*, a fraction $1 - \beta$ are *prompt*. For example, in U^{235}, β is 0.0073, which means that $(0.0073)(2.46) = 0.02$ neutron is delayed, and 2.44 appear immediately. The individual fractions associated with the ith emitter are labeled β_i, where i runs from 1 to 5, and

$$\sum_{i=1}^{5} \beta_i = \beta \qquad (6.4)$$

Table 6.1 shows the half-lives of the principal emitters and percentages of each for U^{235}, Pu^{239}, and U^{233} upon thermal fission.

Table 6.1

Properties of Delayed Neutron Emitters

Emitter i	Half-Life $(t_H)_i$ (sec)	Neutron Energy (kev)	Percent of All Neutrons from Fission		
			U^{235}	Pu^{239}	U^{233}
1	0.43	250	0.085	0.119	0.018
2	1.52	570	0.241	$\cdots$	0.062
3	4.51	412	0.213	0.126	0.086
4	22.0	670	0.166	0.105	0.058
5	55.6	400	0.025	0.014	0.018
		Total	0.730	0.364	0.242

Average lifetime of reactor. The presence of delayed neutrons tends to give the reactor a very long effective cycle time, as is now demonstrated. A radioactive atom disintegrates, on the average, after a time $\tau = t_H/0.693$, labeled the *mean life*. Visualize the ith emitter as "withholding" its neutrons for a time τ_i, so that the total time from fission to fission is $l + \tau_i$ for these delayed neutrons. The prompt neutrons require the usual time l. The average lifetime, with weighting according to numbers of each variety is

$$\bar{l} = (1 - \beta)l + \sum_{i=1}^{5} \beta_i(l + \tau_i) \qquad (6.5)$$

Introduce the average of the emitter mean lives,

$$\bar{\tau} = \frac{\sum_i \beta_i \tau_i}{\beta} \tag{6.6}$$

Equation (6.5) becomes

$$\bar{l} = l + \beta\bar{\tau} \qquad \text{average neutron lifetime in reactor} \tag{6.7}$$

From Table 6.1 and Equation (6.6), $\bar{\tau}$ for U^{235} is found to be 12.7 sec. Thus if $l = 0.0001$ sec, then $\bar{l} = 0.0001 + (0.0073)(12.7) = 0.0928$ sec. The extension of cycle time by delayed neutron effects is seen to be so large that the actual physical lifetime is negligible. It must be pointed out, however, that the foregoing analysis refers to accumulations that are slow enough to allow all the delayed neutrons time enough to contribute to the average lifetime. We shall see later that the actual lifetime becomes more important for sudden power changes.

The rate of growth of neutron density in the case of a small disturbance may be derived using $\bar{l}$. Let the *effective multiplication factor* be denoted by k_e, the number of neutrons resulting from one initial thermal absorption. Equation (3.31) may be generalized to read

$$k_e = k\mathcal{L}_f\mathcal{L}_t \tag{6.8}$$

When k_e is 1, the reactor is critical; when $k_e > 1$, the reactor is super-critical and there will be a gain in the number of neutrons each cycle of amount

$$\delta k_e = k_e - 1 \tag{6.9}$$

which will serve as a definition of "delta-k-effective." If the whole reactor contains n neutrons, the gain per cycle will be $n\, \delta k_e$. The rate of increase of n with time is clearly

$$\frac{dn}{dt} = \frac{n\, \delta k_e}{\bar{l}} \tag{6.10}$$

If δk_e is not dependent on time

$$n = n_0 e^{(\delta k_e/\bar{l})t} \qquad \begin{array}{l}\text{approximate response} \\ \text{to small } \delta k_e\end{array} \tag{6.11}$$

where n_0 is the number at the instant the reactor was changed from critical to super-critical. The time for n to increase by a factor $e = 2.718$ is designated by the *period* T, which for this case is

$$T = \frac{\bar{l}}{\delta k_e} \qquad \text{period, small } \delta k_e \qquad (6.12)$$

A more general definition appears in the *reciprocal period*,

$$\frac{1}{T} = \frac{1}{n}\frac{dn}{dt} \qquad (6.13)$$

which may vary with time, since n is in general never exactly exponential in character.

> **Numerical Illustration:** A U^{235} mass of 100 grams is added to a homogeneous water-moderated reactor with a critical mass of 2.5 kg, thermal utilization 0.9, $\bar{l} = 0.093$. Calculate δk_e and the period of the resulting transient.
>
> *Solution.* The principal effect of small fuel changes in a reactor of this type is to change the infinite multiplication factor k, rather than the leakage factors. A useful recipe for relating small changes in fuel mass m, k, and k_e is derived.
>
> $$\frac{1}{f} - 1 = \frac{\eta}{k} - 1 = \frac{\Sigma_{am}}{\Sigma_{aU}} \qquad (6.14)$$
>
> Differentiating,
>
> $$-\frac{\eta}{k^2}\,dk = -\frac{\Sigma_{am}}{(\Sigma_{aU})^2}\,d\Sigma_{aU} \qquad (6.15)$$
>
> Combining Equations (6.8), (6.14), and (6.15), and letting $d\Sigma_{aU}/\Sigma_{aU} = dm/m$,
>
> $$\frac{\delta k_e}{k_e} = \frac{dk}{k} = (1 - f)\frac{dm}{m} \qquad (6.16)$$
>
> Thus for $dm/m \simeq 0.1/2.5$, $k_e \simeq 1$, and $f = 0.9$, δk_e is found from Equation (6.16) to be 0.004, and from Equation (6.12), $T = 0.093/0.004 = 23.2$ sec.

6.2. *Factors affecting transient response*

Before embarking on the detailed analysis of transient behavior, an outline of the factors that affect the responses is presented.

(a) *Source of impressed* δk_e. The multiplication constant may be changed from unity by a variety of physical changes, such as

Control element position adjustments
Fuel, moderator, coolant, poison, or reflector addition, adjustment or removal.

Temperature increase or decrease
Core size or shape variations

A particular functional relation exists between the δk_e and physical changes.

(b) *Magnitude of δk_e.* This is a sensitive index of the neutron response, in that a value of $\delta k_e \gg \beta$ gives very rapid reactions, while a $\delta k_e \ll \beta$ is quite safe.

(c) *Time dependence of δk_e.* Without further analysis, it can be anticipated that the introduction of a certain δk_e in a very gradual manner over a period of many minutes would result in a slow rise in neutron level. An abruptly impressed δk_e of the same final value would be expected to give a more vigorous reaction. The two most common forms of excess multiplication are the *step function* and *ramp*, as sketched in Figure 6.1. No actual physical process ever can duplicate the rise with infinite slope as specified in the step; seldom will the change in k_e be strictly linear. The justification for concentration on these two forms lies in the fact that mathematical solutions are easily obtained.

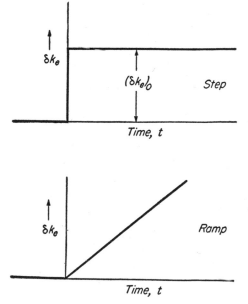

Figure 6.1. Excess multiplication functions.

(d) *Compensating effects.* A change in power level will normally result in a physical response that tends to stop the reaction. For instance, in most reactors a rise in temperature results in a negative δk_e that tends to balance out any impressed δk_e, usually in amount proportional to temperature. The temperature, in turn, is dependent on the method and rate of heat removal. In a boiling reactor, the volume of steam voids that reduce δk_e is *power*-dependent. The reaction may, instead, consist of a mechanical adjustment of control rod location as dictated by an electric signal from a neutron detector. We shall reserve consideration of temperature and power effects until Chapter 7.

6.3. *Differential equations of time-dependent reactor*

Reactor kinetics can be described by a modified version of Equation (3.8). If the thermal neutron absorption rate per unit volume is A, the leakage rate is L, the source is S, and there is an unbalance, the neutron density will change according to

$$\frac{\partial n}{\partial t} = S - A - L$$

or

$$\frac{\partial n}{\partial t} = D \nabla^2 \phi - \phi \Sigma_a + S \tag{6.17}$$

The partial derivative of n is used because n is a function of both position and time. It will be presumed that the reactor is near critical and the *shape* of the flux distribution remains constant, even though it rises in *amplitude* with time. Thus $\nabla^2 \phi = -B^2 \phi$. This eliminates the space dependence, and allows use of dn/dt in place of $\partial n/\partial t$. We also simplify by invoking several relations:

$$\phi = nv$$

$$D/\Sigma_a = L^2$$

and from Equation (6.2) as applied to a bare reactor,

$$l_t = l_0/(1 + B^2 L^2) = \mathcal{L}_t l_0 \tag{6.18}$$

With these substitutions, Equation (6.17) becomes

$$\frac{dn}{dt} = -\frac{n}{l_t} + S \tag{6.19}$$

It is necessary now to examine the nature of the source S, which has two parts S_p and S_d, referring to prompt and delayed neutrons, respectively. The rate of *fission* is $\phi\Sigma_f$. However, only a fraction $1 - \beta$ of the eventual ν neutrons are available immediately. The *prompt* neutron generation rate is thus

$$\phi\Sigma_f(1 - \beta)\nu$$

and if a fraction $\mathcal{L}_f p$ of these get to thermal without escaping by leakage, the *prompt* thermal source is

$$S_p = k\phi\Sigma_a(1 - \beta)\mathcal{L}_f \tag{6.20}$$

The rest of the neutrons, in number $\phi\Sigma_f\nu\beta$, are *potential* neutrons, still associated with the particular fission fragments that emit delayed neutrons. At any time, there will be a number c_1 (concentration) of type 1 emitter present in a unit volume of the core, c_2 of type 2, etc. It is by decay of the emitters that the delayed neutrons finally get back in the cycle. See Figure 6.2 for a diagram of this chain. Being radioactive, each of the emitters obeys the radioactive law

$$\frac{dc_i}{dt} = -\lambda_i c_i + g_i \tag{6.21}$$

where g_i is the generation rate of type i and λ_i is its decay constant $0.693/(t_{\mathrm{H}})_i$. Since each emitter "contains" one potential neutron, the production rate is

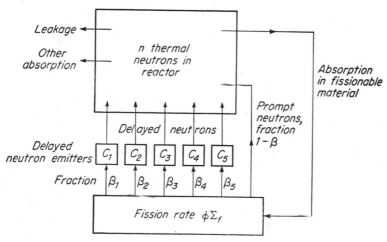

Figure 6.2. Neutron flow chart for transient reactor.

$$g_i = \phi\Sigma_f\beta_i\nu = \eta f\phi\Sigma_a\beta_i = \frac{k\beta_i n\mathcal{L}_t}{pl_t} \tag{6.22}$$

The rate at which the delayed neutrons are supplied to the reactor is

$$S_d = \sum_{i=1}^{5} \lambda_i c_i \mathcal{L}_f p \tag{6.23}$$

where it is assumed that the fast leakage factor for delayed and prompt neutrons is the same. Since the concentration of delayed emitters is only of incidental interest, we shall invent a modified concentration

$$C_i = c_i\mathcal{L}_f p \tag{6.24}$$

and define the prompt excess multiplication,

$$\delta k_{ep} = k_e(1 - \beta) - 1 = \delta k_e - \beta k_e \tag{6.25}$$

Now insert Equations (6.20) and (6.23) in (6.19), and use Equations (6.8), (6.24), and (6.25); also combine Equations (6.21), (6.22), and (6.24). The results are

$$\frac{dn}{dt} = \frac{n\,\delta k_{ep}}{l} + \sum_i \lambda_i C_i \qquad \text{transient} \tag{6.26}$$
$$\text{equations}$$
$$\frac{dC_i}{dt} = -\lambda_i C_i + \frac{k_e\beta_i n}{l} \tag{6.27}$$

where l_t has been replaced by the total cycle time l for greater rigor.* These coupled equations of the time-dependent reactor are widely used for reactors other than the unreflected case for which they were derived.

6.4. *Accident conditions*

We may temporarily sidestep the solution of this set of six equations by applying them to the case of a very large δk_e, as in a reactor accident.

Examination of the structure of Equation (6.26) reveals that

---

*The reader may observe that the slowing-down time never appears in Equations (6.26) and (6.27) *as derived*. Mr. Gene A. Baraff has kindly pointed out that, rigorously, the source S in Equation (6.19) must be evaluated at a time earlier than t by the slowing-down time. A solution by Laplace transform methods, taking this fact into account, demonstrates that the *total cycle time should be used in place of the thermal lifetime* in these equations.

the first term on the right is of the same form as Equation (6.10) except that l, the cycle time, appears in place of $\bar{l}$ the average lifetime. This one term would completely represent the response if its time scale were very short compared with the half-life of the shortest delayed neutron emitter. The delayed neutron contribution, described by the second term, would be negligible. This situation exists when the prompt excess multiplication δk_{ep} is very large. For this special case, $\delta k_{ep} \gg \beta$,

$$\frac{dn}{dt} = \frac{n \, \delta k_{ep}}{l} \tag{6.28}$$

This equation describes the "prompt critical" reactor, one which multiplies without need for delayed neutron contribution. It would be applicable in a serious reactor accident, or to the atomic bomb. With a *step* δk_e, the rise would be rapidly exponential:

$$n = n_0 e^{(\delta k_{ep}/l)t} \qquad \text{response to large step } \delta k_{ep} \tag{6.29}$$

with period

$$T = \frac{l}{\delta k_{ep}} = \frac{l}{\delta k_e - \beta k_e} \tag{6.30}$$

Note that the excess of δk_e above βk_e determines the period.

The reactor power may be used interchangeably with average or total neutron density because of the proportionality of P and n. The total energy release

$$W = \int_0^t P \, dt \tag{6.31}$$

is usually of greater interest than power level, since W determines core heating effects and the total nuclear radiation. A power flashup due to a large step, using Equations (6.29) and (6.30) in (6.31), will give

$$W \text{ (step)} = [P(t) - P(0)]T \tag{6.32}$$

Now $P(t)$ is very much larger than $P(0)$; so $W \simeq P(t)T$, which means that the total energy produced by the time the power reaches P is the same as if the power had been constant for *one period*.

Numerical Illustration: Control rods are suddenly removed from a U^{235} reactor with cycle time 2×10^{-4} sec operating at 1 watt. This event results in a step δk_e of 5 per cent. Find the average release in kilowatt-hours up to a time 0.1 sec.

Solution. The effective multiplication factor is $k_e = 1.05$ and δk_{ep} from Equation (6.25) is $1.05(1 - 0.0073) - 1 = 0.042$. The period T is $2 \times 10^{-4}/0.042 = 0.0048$ sec, and $P(t) = 1 \times e^{0.1/0.0048} = e^{21} = 1.3 \times 10^9$ watts or 1300 megawatts. The energy release from Equation (6.32) is $W = (1.3 \times 10^9)(0.0048) = 6.2 \times 10^6$ watt-sec $= 1.7$ kwh. This is a surprisingly small total heat, considering the very high power level, but the time interval is very short.

The rise in level due to the ramp function may also be developed. For the time during which δk_e is approaching βk_e, the response is relatively slow, as described by Equation (6.11). Thereafter, there will be a rapid increase. Let the excess of δk_e above βk_e be labeled γt, i.e.,

$$\delta k_{ep} = \delta k_e - \beta k_e = \gamma t$$

Again ignoring the delayed neutron effects, the solution of Equation (6.28) is

$$n = n_0 e^{\gamma t^2/2l} \tag{6.33}$$

where n_0 is the neutron density at the time the ramp reaches βk_e.

6.5. *Inhour equation*

A general solution of Equation (6.26) in conjunction with the set implied by Equation (6.27) for a step δk_e is now displayed. The trial solution method is applied to these coupled equations, i.e.,

$$n \sim e^{t/T} \tag{6.34}$$

$$C_i \sim e^{t/T} \tag{6.35}$$

where T plays the role of an unknown parameter and the constants of proportionality are arbitrary. Thus

$$\frac{dn}{dt} = \frac{n}{T} \tag{6.36}$$

and

$$\frac{dC_i}{dt} = \frac{C_i}{T} \tag{6.37}$$

Substitution of Equation (6.37) into Equation (6.27) yields

$$C_i = \frac{k_e \beta_i n}{l(1/T + \lambda_i)} \tag{6.38}$$

If this result and Equation (6.36) are put into Equation (6.26), n cancels out. Rearranging by several manipulations, we find

$$\frac{\delta k_e}{k_e} = \frac{l}{k_e T} + \sum_{i=1}^{5} \frac{\beta_i}{1 + \lambda_i T} \qquad (6.39)$$

This is called the *inhour* equation.

Several features of the equation will be listed:

(a) It is an algebraic equation in T of 6th degree, which implies six roots, each of which can be used in Equation (6.34) to give a solution of the original differential equations. The sum of the six solutions, with arbitrary coefficients, is the most general one, i.e.,

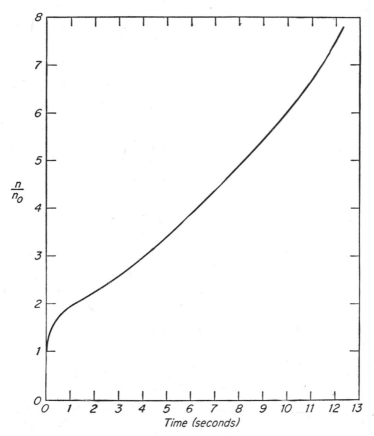

Figure 6.3. Neutron level rise resulting from $\delta k_e/k_e$ of 0.003, $l = 10^{-3}$ sec.

$$n = \sum_{j=1}^{6} a_j e^{t/T_i} \qquad \begin{array}{l}\text{general solution of}\\ \text{inhour equation}\end{array} \qquad (6.40)$$

Figure 6.3 shows a response for the case of $\delta k_e/k_e = 0.003$ and $l = 10^{-3}$ sec. Note the characteristic rapid rise at the start, the "prompt jump," followed by a more gradual increase.

(b) A new quantity $\delta k_e/k_e$ appears. It is given the name *reactivity*, symbolized by ρ.

$$\rho = \frac{\delta k_e}{k_e} \qquad \text{reactivity} \qquad (6.41)$$

For small δk_e, it is almost the same as δk_e itself.

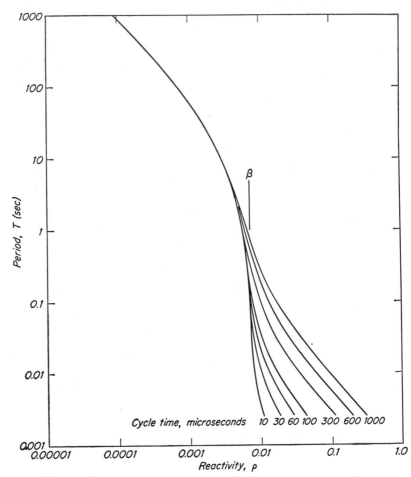

Figure 6.4. Relation of reactivity and period for various cycle times.

(c) It may be shown that for a positive δk_e, all of the roots T_j of Equation (6.39) are *negative* except one. Therefore five terms in Equation (6.40) decrease toward zero as time goes on, leaving only one important solution of the form $e^{+t/T}$. The corresponding *period* is the one dominating neutron response for long times after δk_e is applied. In order to find the value of ρ that will yield a given dominant period, one may substitute the latter in Equation (6.39). Figure 6.4 shows a graph of ρ as it depends on T for particular values of l.

(d) The use of the term "inhour" can be justified, by inserting a period of T of 3600 sec in Equation (6.39). According to the graph, the reactivity is 2.62×10^{-5}. This amount of reactivity is called the inhour (inverse hour) since it gives a period of 1 hr. Two other specialized units of reactivity are defined. The *dollar* is equal to a reactivity of $\beta = 0.0073$, and the *cent* is $1/100$ of that reactivity.

(e) If δk_e and ρ are very small, $\ll \beta$, the dominant period will be very large compared with any of the half-lives of the delayed emitters, and $\lambda_i T_i$ is much larger than the 1 in the denominator of the second term of Equation (6.39). The inhour equation becomes

$$\delta k_e \simeq \frac{l + \beta \bar{\tau}}{T} = \frac{\bar{l}}{T}$$

The fact that this is identical to Equation (6.12) serves to show that the simple analysis using the average lifetime is applicable only for a small δk_e.

(f) If δk_e and ρ are large, $\gg \beta$, the dominant period will be very short and $\lambda_i T_i \ll 1$. Equation (6.39) reduces then to

$$\rho \simeq \frac{l}{k_e T} + \beta$$

which simplifies to

$$T = \frac{l}{\delta k_{ep}}$$

which is exactly the same as Equation (6.30). The last two conclusions are of great significance. For ρ much less than β, the response is slow and safe, and primarily governed by delayed neutrons; for ρ much greater than β, the response is violent, governed by prompt neutrons. Thus it is of utmost importance to design and operate to guarantee that the reactor remains below the "β-point."

(g) The effect of a negative δk_e, as in a reactor shut-down, is to make all solutions T_j of Equation (6.34) negative, so that the neutron density drops rapidly. Eventually, however, the rate of decline is determined by the emitter of longest half-life, 55.6 sec. The period after a long time is $55.6/0.693 = 80.2$ sec.

6.6. *One–delayed-neutron group approximation*

The task of solving the sixth-degree inhour equation can be avoided by the strategem of assuming that the set of delayed neutron emitters is replaceable by a single emitter. It will be admitted at the outset that the transient response will be only qualitatively correct and applicable only to *small changes in* k_e. The solution is easy to obtain, however, and serves to display the distinction between behavior at short and long times after the disturbance in k_e is applied.

Suppose that the equivalent single emitter has a mean life $\bar\tau = 1/\lambda$, given by the average of Equation (6.6), the modified concentration is simply C, and the fraction of delayed neutrons is β. The transient equations that replace (6.26) and (6.27) are

$$\dot n(t) = \frac{n(t)\,\delta k_{ep}}{l} + \lambda C(t) \tag{6.42}$$

$$\dot C(t) = -\lambda C(t) + \frac{k_e\beta n(t)}{l} \tag{6.43}$$

where the quantities that are time-dependent have been so designated. These simultaneous equations may be solved by conventional methods. Because of its wide utility, we shall instead apply the *Laplace transform* method which is summarized in Appendix C. Using the tables of transforms, the equations become

$$s\,\bar n(s) - \bar n(0) = \bar n(s)\,\frac{\delta k_{ep}}{l} + \lambda\bar C(s) \tag{6.44}$$

$$s\,\bar C(s) - \bar C(0) = -\lambda\bar C(s) + \frac{k_e\beta\bar n(s)}{l} \tag{6.45}$$

These equations are solved algebraically for $\bar n(s)$ with some rearrangement:

$$\bar{n}(s) = \frac{A(s)}{B(s)} \tag{6.46}$$

where

$$A(s) = \bar{n}_0 + \frac{\lambda \bar{C}_0}{s + \lambda} \tag{6.47}$$

and

$$B(s) = s\left[1 + \frac{k_e \beta}{l(s + \lambda)}\right] - \frac{\delta k_e}{l} \tag{6.48}$$

Now $\bar{n}(s)$ goes to infinity for s values λ_1 and λ_2, which are the roots of the equation $B(s) = 0$. Referring again to the table of transforms in Appendix C,

$$n(t) = \mathcal{L}^{-1}\left\{\frac{A(s)}{B(s)}\right\} = a_1 e^{\lambda_1 t} + a_2 e^{\lambda_2 t} \tag{6.49}$$

where

$$a_k = \frac{A(\lambda_k)}{\dfrac{dB}{ds}(\lambda_k)} \quad (k = 1,2) \tag{6.50}$$

The coefficients a_1 and a_2 are computed as follows. The function $B(s)$ may be written* as

$$B(s) = \frac{(s - \lambda_1)(s - \lambda_2)}{s + \lambda} \tag{6.51}$$

whence the values of its derivatives at λ_1 and λ_2 are

$$B'(\lambda_1) = \frac{\lambda_1 - \lambda_2}{\lambda_1 + \lambda} \tag{6.52}$$

$$B'(\lambda_2) = \frac{\lambda_2 - \lambda_1}{\lambda_2 + \lambda}$$

Combining Equations (6.47), (6.50), and (6.52), and noting in Equation (6.43) that at $t = 0$, $\dot{C}$ is zero and the initial emitter concentration is $C_0 = n_0 k_e \beta / l\lambda$,

$$a_1 = \frac{A(\lambda_1)}{B'(\lambda_1)} = n_0\left(\frac{\lambda_1 + \lambda + k_e\beta/l}{\lambda_1 - \lambda_2}\right) \simeq \frac{n_0}{1 - \delta k_e/\beta} \tag{6.53}$$

$$a_2 = \frac{A(\lambda_2)}{B'(\lambda_2)} = n_0\left(\frac{\lambda_2 + \lambda + k_e\beta/l}{\lambda_2 - \lambda_1}\right) \simeq \frac{-n_0\,\delta k_e/\beta}{1 - \delta k_e/\beta} \tag{6.54}$$

(The approximations may be justified by use of Equations (6.56)

---

* A polynomial $y(x)$ that has roots x_i and infinities x_j can be expressed as $y(x) = \dfrac{\Pi_i(x - x_i)}{\Pi_j(x - x_j)}$ where Π_i and Π_j indicate products.

and (6.57) below.)   The roots λ_1 and λ_2 of the equation $B(s) = 0$ are obtained from Equation (6.48), i.e.,

$$s[l(s + \lambda) + k_e\beta] - \delta k_e(s + \lambda) = 0$$

or
$$\frac{\delta k_e}{k_e} = \frac{ls}{k_e} + \frac{\beta s}{s + \lambda} \qquad (6.55)$$

The two roots of this quadratic equation, to good approximation for l small, are

$$\lambda_1 \simeq \frac{\lambda\, \delta k_e}{\beta k_e - \delta k_e} \qquad (6.56)$$

$$\lambda_2 \simeq -\frac{\beta k_e - \delta k_e}{l} \qquad (6.57)$$

Since λ_2 is large and negative, the exponential term $e^{\lambda_2 t}$ decreases rapidly with time, and is important only at time near zero.   The dominant term is $e^{\lambda_1 t}$, corresponding to λ_1 small and positive, which for small δk_e has a period $T = 1/\lambda_1 \simeq \beta\bar{\tau}/\delta k_e$, approximating that found earlier (see Equation 6.12).

Numerical Illustration: Calculate the ratio n/n_0 for a thermal reactor with neutron lifetime $l = 10^{-4}$ sec for a step δk_e of 0.001 by the one-delayed-emitter model.

Solution.   Additional numbers needed are $\beta = 0.0073$, $\bar{\tau} = $ 12.7 sec, and $\lambda = 0.0787$.

$$\lambda_1 = \frac{(0.0787)(0.001)}{(0.0073)(0.001) - 0.001} = 0.0125$$

$$\lambda_2 = -\frac{(0.0073)(1.001) - 0.001}{10^{-4}} = 63$$

From Equations (6.53) and (6.54)

$$a_1 = \frac{n_0}{1 - 0.137} = 1.158\, n_0$$

$$a_2 = \frac{-n_0\, 0.137}{0.863} = -0.158\, n_0$$

The complete solution is

$$n/n_0 = 1.158 e^{0.0125t} - 0.158 e^{-63t}$$

There is a rapid initial rise, associated with the second term, which in turn is governed by the prompt neutrons.   It dies out quickly, in about 0.1 sec, leaving the dominant exponential of period 80 sec.

6.7. *Response to the ramp function*

The linearly increasing $\delta k_e = \gamma t$ is a fair representation of the effect of a control element moving with constant speed. Thus the solution of the transient equations (6.26) and (6.27) for the ramp function has importance in the problem of reactor control and regulation. For simplicity, we shall solve the one-delayed-group version of § 6.6. First, differentiate Equation (6.42) and substitute $\dot{C}$ from Equation (6.43) and C from Equation (6.42):

$$\ddot{n} + \left(\lambda - \frac{\delta k_{ep}}{l}\right)\dot{n} - \left(\frac{\delta \dot{k}_{ep}}{l} + \frac{\lambda \, \delta k_e}{l}\right)n = 0 \qquad (6.58)$$

In order to solve conveniently, two slight approximations will be made as needed, namely $\beta \ll 1$ and $\lambda \ll \beta/l$. Now for a ramp function $\delta k_e = \gamma t$, $\delta k_{ep} = \gamma(1 - \beta)t - \beta$ and $\delta \dot{k}_{ep} = \gamma(1 - \beta)$. Substituting and simplifying,

$$l\ddot{n} + (\beta - \gamma t)\dot{n} - (\lambda t + \gamma)n = 0$$

Changes of dependent and independent variable are made:

$$n(t) = N(t)e^{-\lambda t} \qquad (6.59)$$

and

$$s = \frac{\beta - \gamma t}{\sqrt{\gamma l}} \qquad (6.60)$$

Substitution yields

$$\frac{d^2N}{ds^2} + s\frac{dN}{ds} - N\left(1 + \frac{\beta\lambda}{\gamma}\right) = 0 \qquad (6.61)$$

This equation admits a simple solution for *integral* values of $\beta\lambda/\gamma$. The condition $m = \beta\lambda/\gamma$, where $m = 0, 1, 2, \cdots$, implies that the rate of increase of δk_e is such that it reaches β in an integral multiple of the mean life $\bar{\tau} = 1/\lambda$.

The general solution of Equation (6.61) according to Kamke (see References) is

$$N(s) = \frac{d^m}{ds^m}\left[e^{s^2/2}\left(C_1 + C_2 \int_{s_0}^{s} e^{-s^2/2}\,ds\right)\right] \qquad (6.62)$$

where C_1 and C_2 are arbitrary constants and s_0 is the value of s at time zero, $\beta/\sqrt{\gamma l}$. The case $m = 1$ is considered as the simplest realistic example. Differentiating as indicated in Equation (6.62),

$$N(s) = C_1 s e^{s^2/2} + C_2\left(1 + s e^{s^2/2} \int_{s_0}^{s} e^{-s^2/2} \, ds\right) \qquad (6.63)$$

Initial conditions taken are $n(0) = n_0$, i.e., $N(s_0) = n_0$, and $n(0) = 0$ or $\dfrac{dN(s_0)}{ds} = \lambda n_0$. The constants are thus

$$C_1 = -n_0(s_0 - \lambda)e^{-s_0^2/2} \qquad (6.64)$$

$$C_2 = n_0[1 + s_0(s_0 - \lambda)]$$

and finally,

$$\frac{n(t)}{n_0} = e^{-\lambda t}\left\{-s\left(s_0 - \lambda\right)e^{(s^2-s_0^2)/2} + \left[1 + s_0\left(s_0 - \lambda\right)\right]\right.$$
$$\left.\left[1 + s e^{s^2/2} \int_{s_0}^{s} e^{-s^2/2} \, ds\right]\right\} \qquad (6.65)$$

Tables of the normal probability function

$$P(x) = \frac{1}{\sqrt{2\pi}} \int_{-x}^{x} e^{-\alpha^2/2} \, dx$$

are very useful, along with asymptotic values of the function, in calculating $n(t)$. Of particular interest is the strong dependence in each case on the new variable s, which is seen to be proportional to the difference between δk_e and β. Shortly after δk_e passes β, s^2 becomes very large and $n(t)$ increases rapidly.

Numerical Illustration: Find the time response of a reactor with neutron lifetime 3×10^{-5} sec, when a control rod is removed at such a rate that $\gamma = 0.000575$/sec.

Solution. The time to reach $\beta = 0.0073$ is 12.7 sec, which puts the problem in the class $m = 1$, Equation (6.65). Now $s_0 = \beta/\sqrt{\gamma l} = 0.0073/\sqrt{(5.75 \times 10^{-4})(3 \times 10^{-5})} = 55.6$, $\lambda = 1/12.7 = 0.0787$ sec^{-1}, and $s = s_0 - t\sqrt{\gamma/l} = 55.6 - 4.38t$. Substitution and use of the $P(x)$ tables is straightforward. Figure 6.5 shows the response on logarithmic scale. The rapid rise near the time δk_e approaches β is noted.

6.8. *Sub-critical multiplication—reactor startup*

During the initial fuel loading process for a new reactor and restarting one that has been shut down, it is necessary to make repeated observations of the neutron level. Such levels are appreciable only if a continual supply of neutrons from a non-fission source is provided. Typical sources used for this purpose are usually based on the liberation of neutrons from beryllium or boron, by bombardment by alpha particles or gamma rays. Reactions employed are

$$\gamma + {}_4Be^9 \longrightarrow 2\ {}_2He^4 + {}_0n^1$$
$${}_2He^4 + {}_4Be^9 \longrightarrow {}_6C^{12} + {}_0n^1$$
$${}_2He^4 + {}_5B^{11} \longrightarrow {}_7N^{14} + {}_0n^1$$

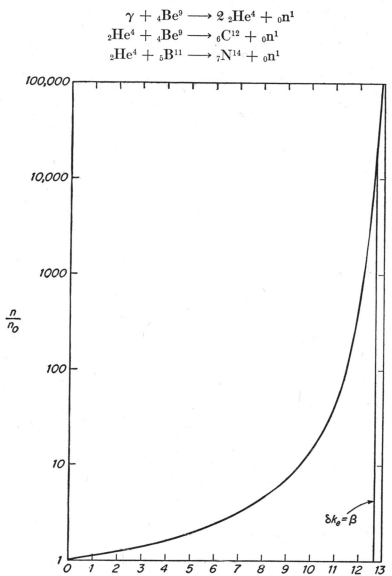

Figure 6.5. Response to ramp with $\gamma = 0.000575/\text{sec}$.

The origin of the gamma rays may be fission products, radium, or the decay of 60-day antimony Sb^{124}, which incidentally is produced by neutron absorption in Sb^{123}. Alpha particles may be provided by decay of radium and its decay products or polonium, Po^{210}.

The thermal neutron level in a sub-critical reactor with $k_e < 1$ and an artificial fast source of strength S neutrons/sec can be obtained by an extension of Equation (6.26):

$$\frac{dn}{dt} = \frac{n \, \delta k_{ep}}{l} + \sum_i \lambda_i C_i + S \mathcal{L}_f \qquad (6.66)$$

The time-dependent response may be obtained by solution in conjunction with Equation (6.27). The steady-state neutron density can be derived by setting both dn/dt and dC/dt equal to zero. Forming the sum $\lambda_i C_i$ over all emitters and inserting in Equation (6.66) gives

$$n = \frac{S \mathcal{L}_f l}{1 - k_e} \qquad (6.67)$$

The number of neutrons in the reactor, and hence the leakage flux to a detector, increases as k_e is increased toward unity by addition of fuel or removal of absorber.

The choice and location of neutron detectors may be based on the knowledge of neutron fluxes, emission rates, or power. A simple neutron balance can be applied to determine the total rate of fast neutron emission S_T, which is the sum of that due to artificial sources S, and that due to fission S_F. The number of neutrons *lost* from the system each second, $S_T(1 - k_e)$, must equal the artificial supply rate S. Therefore,

$$S_T = \frac{S}{1 - k_e} \qquad (6.68)$$

The source due to *fission only* must then be

$$S_F = \frac{S k_e}{1 - k_e} \qquad (6.69)$$

As a check, if one lets $S_F = nvk\Sigma_a$ and $k_e = k\mathcal{L}_f\mathcal{L}_t$, solution for n gives Equation (6.67).

Numerical Illustration: Estimate the average thermal neutron flux, the total fast neutron emission rate, and the power equivalent for a 100-liter sub-critical core with $k_e = 0.98$, $l =$

6.7×10^{-5} sec, $\mathcal{L}_f = 0.7$, and an artificial source of strength of 10^8 neutrons/sec.

Solution. From Equation (6.67), the total number of thermals in the core is

$$n = \frac{(10^8)(0.7)(6.7 \times 10^{-5})}{0.02} = 2.3 \times 10^5$$

The average velocity of a maxwellian distribution at room temperature is $(2.2 \times 10^5)(1.128) = 2.48 \times 10^5$ cm/sec. The flux is thus

$$\bar{\phi} = \frac{(2.3 \times 10^5)(2.48 \times 10^5)}{10^5} = 5.7 \times 10^5/\text{cm}^2\text{-sec}$$

The total fast neutron emission rate from Equation (6.68) is $10^8/0.02 = 5 \times 10^9$/sec. For each watt of fission power, $(3.3 \times 10^{10})(2.46) = 8.1 \times 10^{10}$ neutrons are emitted. Thus the equivalent power is $(5 \times 10^9)/(8.1 \times 10^{10}) = 0.062$ watts.

6.9. *Reactor transient simulators*

The differential equations (6.26) and (6.27) of neutron density and delayed emitter concentration bear a close resemblance to those of current or voltage in certain electric networks. This analogy is exploited by use of a *kinetic simulator* circuit, which performs the integrations electrically. A simulator designed by Pagels (see References) will illustrate the connection.

Rewrite these equations, making use of the definition of δk_{ep} (Equation 6.25) and returning to a lower case c to represent modified emitter concentration, to avoid confusion with electric capacitance C.

$$\frac{dn}{dt} = \frac{\bar{n}(\delta k_c - k_e\beta)}{l} + \sum_i \lambda_i c_i$$

$$\frac{dc_i}{dt} = \frac{k_e\beta_i n}{l} - \lambda_i c_i$$

Add all six equations to obtain

$$\dot{n} = \frac{n\,\delta k_e}{l} - \sum_i \dot{c}_i \tag{6.70}$$

It will be convenient to use as parameters the reactivity,

$\rho = \delta k_e/k_e$, and a modified lifetime $l_1 = l/k_e$. Equations (6.70) and (6.27) then become

$$n = \frac{l_1\dot{n}}{\rho} + \frac{l_1}{\rho}\sum_i \dot{c}_i \qquad (6.71)$$

$$\dot{c}_i = \frac{\beta_i n}{l_1} - \lambda_i c_i \qquad (6.72)$$

Equation (6.72) is analogous to the equation governing voltage, charge, and current in the RC circuit sketched in Figure 6.6(a).

$$V = R_i I_i + \frac{Q_i}{C_i} \qquad (6.73)$$

or since $I_i = dQ_i/dt$,

$$\frac{dQ_i}{dt} = \frac{V}{R_i} - \frac{Q_i}{R_i C_i} \qquad (6.74)$$

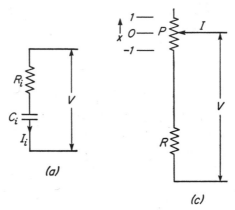

(a)

(c)

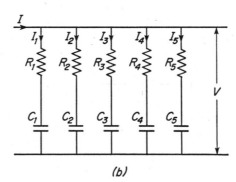

(b)

Figure 6.6. Circuit components of simulator: (a) one-delayed-neutron emitter, (b) five delayed emitters, (c) reactivity potentiometer.

The following table shows the comparison:

Reactor	Electric
n	V
c_i	Q_i
l_1/β_i	R_i
$\beta_i/l_1\lambda_i$	C_i

Thus the charge on the capacitor is proportional to delayed emitter concentration, and the current in the circuit is $I_i = \dot{c}_i$. This correspondence suggests that the sum $\sum_{i=1}^{5} \dot{c}_i$ in Equation (6.70) may be simulated by five RC networks connected in parallel, as shown in Figure 6.6(b).

If we choose the resistances R_i in such a way that all products $R_i\beta_i$ are the same, then the total current is

$$I = \frac{1}{R_i\beta_i} \sum_{i=1}^{5} l_1\dot{c}_i = \sum_{i=1}^{5} I_i$$

The term $l_1\dot{n}$ in Equation (6.71) requires a current proportional to the derivative of a voltage if the previous analogy is followed. The charging current of a capacitor, $I = dQ/dt = C(dV/dt)$ in parallel with the 5 emitter circuits, has the proper form if we let $C = l_1/R_i\beta_i$. A current of adjustable magnitude ρn can be produced by the potentiometer circuit sketched in Figure 6.6(c), having resistance P that is small compared with R. Let x be the fractional displacement of the tap from the center toward one end. The maximum current I_m is given by

$$I_m = \frac{V}{R(1 + R/P)}$$

when $x = 1$. Let this correspond to a maximum reactivity ρ_m. At any other setting, the current will be

$$\frac{I}{I_m} = x = \frac{\rho}{\rho_m}$$

Thus

$$I = \left[\frac{1}{R(1 + R/P)\rho_m}\right]n\rho$$

Now if the scale factor, in brackets, is chosen as

$$\frac{1}{R(1 + R/P)\rho_m} = \frac{1}{R_i\beta_i}$$

Equation (6.71) becomes

$$I + \sum_{i=1}^{5} I_i + I_6 = 0$$

as required for the potentiometer to be used as the proper current supply for the delayed neutron circuits, currents I_1, I_2, $\cdots$, I_5,

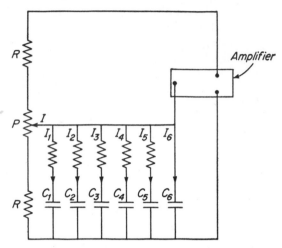

Figure 6.7.   Completed analogue circuit, schematic.

and the differentiating line, current I_6.   The final circuit shown in Figure 6.7 incorporates a high-gain DC amplifier in a feedback

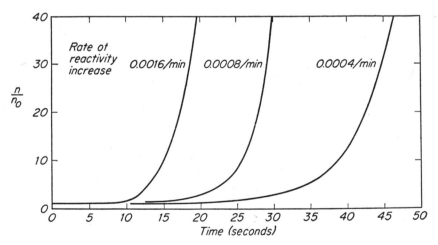

Figure 6.8.   Simulator responses to ramp functions: $l = 3.2 \times 10^{-4}$ sec.
(After Nemsek.)

system that varies the output voltage V to maintain the sum of the input currents essentially zero. A switch is used to introduce a pre-set step function ρ. To simulate a ramp function, a motor-driven potentiometer is used. Figure 6.8 shows a number of ramp responses obtained by Nemsek (see References) with a modified Pagels simulator.

Problems

6.1. Calculate the neutron slowing-down time l_f for 2 mev to 0.025 ev and the thermal neutron diffusion time l_0 for beryllium oxide, density 2.69 gm/cm³. The cross sections are $(\sigma_s)_{Be} = 6.0$ barns, $(\sigma_s)_O = 3.8$ barns, $(\bar{\sigma}_a)_{BeO} = 0.0089$ barns.

Answer. $l_f = 8.2 \times 10^{-5}$ sec, $l_0 = 7.0 \times 10^{-3}$ sec.

6.2. (a) Show that the mean delayed neutron emitter lifetime $\bar{\tau}$ for U^{235} is 12.7 sec. (b) Compare the average neutron lifetimes l of reactors fueled with U^{235}, Pu^{239}, and U^{233}. Let $l = 0.001$.

Answer. (b) U^{235} 0.0937 sec; Pu^{239} 0.0545 sec; U^{233} 0.0409 sec.

6.3. Derive a formula for the reactivity effect of an infinitesimal change in absorption cross section, $d\Sigma_a$, due to the insertion of a uniform poison in a homogeneous bare core by *one-group* theory.

Answer. $\dfrac{\delta k_e}{k_e} = \dfrac{-d\Sigma_a}{k\Sigma_a} k_e.$

6.4. A safety capsule containing 2 gm of B^{10}, $\bar{\sigma}_a = 3555$ barns for a maxwellian distribution, is broken into the 50-liter core of a homogeneous reactor for which $\bar{\Sigma}_a = 0.12$ cm⁻¹, $k = 1.4$. Find the reactivity value of this control device using the answer to Problem 6.3.

Answer. $-0.048.$

6.5. An instantaneous δk_e of 0.015 is applied to a heterogeneous reactor of the swimming pool type when it is at 1-watt power level. Assume the core volume 105 liters, with aluminum/water ratio 0.65, core $\bar{\Sigma}_a = 0.066$ cm⁻¹, a thermal leakage factor $\mathcal{L}_t = 0.9$, and a slowing-down time $l_f = 1.4 \times 10^{-5}$ sec. Calculate the period and the total energy released by the time the power has increased to 500 megawatts. If most of this energy goes into heating the aluminum of specific heat 0.2 cal/gm-°C, what metal temperature increase is experienced?

Answer. Period 0.0091 sec, energy 4.55 megawatt-sec, temperature 48.7°C.

6.6. For a reactor with $l = 10^{-4}$ sec, compare the predictions of reactivity required to give a stable period of 1000 sec, 100 sec, and 10 sec according to the general inhour equation (6.39) and the average lifetime formula, Equation (6.12). Repeat for 10 sec, 1 sec, and 0.1 sec, according to Equation (6.39) and the accident formula (6.30).

Answer.

		ρ *According to Equation:*	
T (sec)	(6.12)	(6.39)	(6.30)
1000	9.3×10^{-5}	8.9×10^{-5}	$\cdots$
100	9.3×10^{-4}	7.0×10^{-4}	$\cdots$
10	9.2×10^{-3}	2.8×10^{-3}	7.3×10^{-3}
1	$\cdots$	5.8×10^{-3}	7.4×10^{-3}
0.1	$\cdots$	8.0×10^{-3}	8.3×10^{-3}

6.7. (a) Determine the variation of n/n_0 with time with step $\delta k_e = 0.010$, $l = 10^{-4}$ sec, by the one-delayed-group approximation. (b) How does the value of the stable period compare with that obtained from the accident formula (6.30)?

Answer. (a) $-2.74e^{-0.30t} + 3.74e^{26.5t}$; (b) one–delayed-group, 0.0377 sec; accident, 0.0381 sec.

6.8. A control rod is withdrawn from a reactor with cycle time 6×10^{-5}, in such a way as to give a constant rate of increase of δk_{ep} of 0.008/sec. By what factor will the power increase from its value when $\delta k_e = k_e\beta$ if the time lag from then until the rod drops is 100 milliseconds?

Answer. 1.07.

6.9. Draw a schematic graph of $\rho = \delta k_e/k_e$ versus the reciprocal period $\nu = 1/T$, using the general inhour equation, by noting where infinities occur. Then demonstrate that (a) for positive ρ, all roots of Equation (6.39) are negative but one; (b) for negative ρ, all roots are negative; (c) for large negative ρ, the solution at large times goes into $e^{-\lambda_5 t}$, where λ_5 is the decay constant of the 55.6-sec emitter.

6.10. Show that $k_e = \dfrac{pf\eta}{(1 + \mu^2 L^2)(1 + \mu^2\tau)} + \dfrac{(1 - p)f_r\eta_r}{1 + \mu^2\tau}$ for a bare reactor according to modified two-group theory (see § 5.5), by a detailed analysis of the neutron cycle.

References

The Reactor Handbook, Volume 1, *Physics*, AECD-3645 (1955), Chapter 1.6.

Luckow, William K., and Lawrence C. Widdoes, "Predicting Reactor Temperature Excursions by Extrapolating Borax Data," *Nucleonics*, January 1956, p. 23.

Schultz, M. A., *Control of Nuclear Reactors and Power Plants.* New York: McGraw-Hill Book Co. (1955).

Isbin, H. S., and J. W. Gorman, "Applications of Pile-Kinetic Equations," *Nucleonics*, November 1952, p. 68.

Hurwitz, H. Jr., "Safeguards Considerations for Nuclear Power Plants," *Nucleonics*, March 1954, p. 57.

Rumsey, V. H., "Kinetics of Piles with Reflectors," *Journ. Appl. Phys.* **25**, 1395 (1954).

Coveyou, R., and T. W. Mulliken, *Solution of Equation* $\ddot{N} + (a + bt)\dot{N} + (c + dt)N = 0$, AECD-2407 (1948).

Wallach, S., *Solutions of Pile-Kinetic Equations When the Reactivity is a Linear Function of the Time*, WAPD-13 (1950).

Harrer, J. M., R. E. Boyar, and Darwin Krucoff, "Transfer Function of the Argonne CP-2 Reactor," *Nucleonics*, August 1952, p. 32.

Nemsek, Thomas A., *A Nuclear Reactor Simulator*, Master's Thesis, North Carolina State College, Raleigh (1953).

Dynamics and Control of Thermal Reactors, Nuclear Engineering Project M. I. T., AECD-3658 (1953).

Tables of Normal Probability Functions. National Bureau of Standards Applied Mathematics Series 23. Washington: U. S. Government Printing Office (1953).

Chapter 7

TEMPERATURE EFFECTS
ON MULTIPLICATION

The primary function of a power reactor core is to transfer heat energy to a circulating coolant at elevated temperature. Under this condition, the nuclear properties are different from those in the critical reactor at room temperature, for three reasons:

(a) The density of reactor materials and thus the number of nuclei per unit volume change with thermal expansion.

(b) The neutron temperature (in a thermal reactor) is correlated with that of the medium.

(c) The interaction between neutrons and nuclei varies with nuclear agitation.

A complex coupling exists between the neutron flux, the power density resulting from fission by neutrons, the temperature distribution established by heat generation rates and coolant flows, and the local poisoning of the core.

7.1. Temperature coefficient and thermal expansion

Consider a rise in reactor power due to an increase in the effective multiplication factor. Qualitatively, if the subsequent increase in temperature of a reactor medium causes an expansion, the number of scattering nuclei per unit volume is reduced, the mean free path for neutrons is longer, and an increase in neutron leakage results. Therefore, the effective multiplication factor is automatically reduced, which tends to compensate for the initial disturbance. Most thermal reactors are designed to contain this self-regulation feature. Unfortunately, the problem is not quite this simple because of several conflicting effects. First, if the core volume can expand, neutron leakage is reduced for purely geometrical reasons. Second, if the reactor is cooled with fluid that has a higher absorption cross section than the moderator, its expansion or expulsion may increase the multiplication.

Two different approaches to the effect of temperature are used. (a) To compute two separate critical assemblies at room and operating temperatures and to express their difference in terms of the mass of fuel or core size. This method is most useful in providing a certain amount of safety factor in core design loading. (b) To evaluate the fractional rate of change in effective multiplication factor or reactivity with temperature. As a derivative, this has reference only to infinitesimal changes at a particular temperature. A temperature coefficient may then be defined. We shall use

$$\frac{1}{k_e}\frac{dk_e}{dT} = \alpha \tag{7.1}$$

as the fractional change in effective multiplication factor per degree, and call it a temperature coefficient.*

Reactors with large thermal expansion coefficients will have large values of temperature coefficient. The rates of absorption, scattering, and fission, per unit volume, represented by the macroscopic cross section $\Sigma = N\sigma$, are directly proportioned to the number of nuclei per unit volume, N. In a homogeneous medium with volume expansion coefficient α_T given by

$$\frac{1}{V}\frac{dV}{dT} = \alpha_T \tag{7.2}$$

a change in temperature will thus result in a decrease in atom and mass density. In differential form,

$$\frac{1}{N}\frac{dN}{dT} = -\frac{1}{V}\frac{dV}{dT} = -\alpha_T \tag{7.3}$$

---

* A variety of usages are found in the literature in this connection. In terms of effective multiplication k_e and the reactivity $\rho = (k_e - 1)/k_e$, one finds the same meaning attached to $\dfrac{dk_e}{dT}$, $\dfrac{d\rho}{dT}$, and $\dfrac{1}{k_e}\dfrac{dk_e}{dT}$ as temperature coefficients. Since the three differ from one another only by factors $1 - \rho$ and $(1 - \rho)^2$, where ρ is small, the distinction is not normally important.

The changes in other parameters of the core are readily determined by dimensional analysis. Variations for the bare homogeneous reactor, in which an age and a diffusion length may be
defined, are listed in Table 7.1. Should the reactor core be

Table 7.1

**Rates of Change with
Temperature Due to Expansion**

Basic relation: $\dfrac{1}{x}\dfrac{dx}{dT} = a\alpha_T$

$\underline{x}$	$\underline{a}$
V	1
$\Sigma, \Sigma_a, \Sigma_s, \Sigma_t$	-1
N	-1
D, λ_t	1
L^2	2
τ	2
k	0
B^2	$-\frac{2}{3}$
R	$\frac{1}{3}$
$B^2\tau$	$\frac{4}{3}$
B^2L^2	$\frac{4}{3}$

heterogeneous, with different expansion coefficients of the components, for example in a water-moderated metal structure, a
proper weighting of effects must be made.   (See answers to Problems 7.1, 7.2, and 7.3.)

The variation with temperature of the effective multiplication
factor,

$$k_e = k\mathcal{L}_f\mathcal{L}_t \tag{7.4}$$

may be written in general as

$$\frac{1}{k_e}\frac{dk_e}{dT} = \frac{1}{k}\frac{dk}{dT} + \frac{1}{\mathcal{L}_f}\frac{d\mathcal{L}_f}{dT} + \frac{1}{\mathcal{L}_t}\frac{d\mathcal{L}_t}{dT} \tag{7.5}$$

The effects on the different factors in Equation (7.4) are seen
to be additive. The formulas in Table 7.1 facilitate evaluation of temperature coefficients associated with thermal expan-
sion. If the *age-diffusion theory* is applied, with $\mathcal{L}_f = e^{-B^2\tau}$ and
$\mathcal{L}_t = (1 + B^2L^2)^{-1}$, the temperature coefficient due to density
changes only is, by the use of Table 7.1,

$$\alpha = \frac{1}{k_e}\frac{dk_e}{dT} = -\frac{4}{3}\alpha_T\left(B^2\tau + \frac{B^2L^2}{1 + B^2L^2}\right) \tag{7.6}$$

As expected, α is *negative*, i.e., the reactor has a negative temperature coefficient.   An unexpected increase in power will result in heating that tends to stop the reaction.

Numerical Illustration: Find the temperature coefficient associated with density at 20°C for a water-moderated reactor with $\tau = 33$ cm², $L^2 = 2.4$ cm², $k = 1.5$.

Solution.   The critical buckling is found by Equation (3.25) to be 0.0113; at 20°C, α_T for water is 2.07×10^{-4}/°C.   Thus

$$\alpha = -\tfrac{4}{3}(2.07 \times 10^{-4})(0.373 + 0.026) = -1.10 \times 10^{-4}/°C.$$

The relative importance of effects on fast leakage and on thermal leakage is displayed by these numbers.   In the water-moderated system, thermal leakage is small, hence the contribution to α is small.

7.2. *Cross section variations*

An increase in temperature of reactor moderator will be shared by the neutrons in equilibrium with it.   The effective microscopic absorption cross section for a $1/v$ absorber in a maxwellian distribution, according to Equation (2.20), is $\bar{\sigma}_a = \sigma_{ap} v_p/\bar{v}$.   Now since $\bar{v} = \sqrt{8kT/(\pi m)}$ from Equation (2.16), the ratio of σ_a values at any two temperatures is

$$\frac{(\bar{\sigma}_a)_2}{(\bar{\sigma}_a)_1} = \sqrt{\frac{T_1}{T_2}} \tag{7.7}$$

Thus for infinitesimal changes at a temperature T,

$$\frac{1}{\bar{\sigma}_a}\frac{d\bar{\sigma}_a}{dT} = -\frac{1}{2T} \tag{7.8}$$

The absolute temperature, °K, must of course be used in any relation involving T itself.

To a first approximation, the thermal utilization $f = \Sigma_{aU}/\Sigma_a$ of a homogeneous uranium system is independent of temperature, because of the approximate $1/v$ character of all absorbers.   The scale factor $\sqrt{T_1/T_2}$ will be common to the numerator and denominator.   However, the average fluxes in the different media of a heterogeneous reactor will vary differently with temperature, and f will change.   For refined calculations, especially in high-temperature systems, the variation of the not-1/v factor (see § 2.4) for the fuel should be included.

The scattering cross section for thermal neutrons cannot readily be expressed by a simple function of energy, but fortunately, the variation with energy is rather small.   Inspection of curves for light and heavy water reveals that the scattering cross section is roughly

$$\sigma_s \sim \frac{1}{E^n}$$

where for H_2O, $n = 0.225$, and for D_2O, $n = 0.112$.

Thus at two temperatures in these moderators,

$$\frac{(\sigma_s)_2}{(\sigma_s)_1} = \left(\frac{T_1}{T_2}\right)^n \tag{7.9}$$

and for infinitesimal changes at a temperature T,

$$\frac{1}{\sigma_s}\frac{d\sigma_s}{dT} = -\frac{n}{T} \tag{7.10}$$

We may now compound the effects of density and cross section changes in quantities such as the diffusion length.   Noting that $L^2 = \frac{1}{3}\lambda_a\lambda_t = (3\Sigma_a\Sigma_t)^{-1}$ and using Equations (7.8) and (7.10), we may form the cross section effect as

$$\frac{1}{L^2}\frac{dL^2}{dT} = -\frac{1}{\bar{\sigma}_a}\frac{d\bar{\sigma}_a}{dT} - \frac{1}{\sigma_s}\frac{d\sigma_s}{dT} = \frac{1}{2T} + \frac{n}{T} \tag{7.11}$$

The same result could have been obtained from the relation between diffusion lengths at any two temperatures:

$$\frac{(L^2)_2}{(L^2)_1} = \left(\frac{T_2}{T_1}\right)^{\frac{1}{2}+n} \tag{7.12}$$

According to Table 7.1, for expansion, $\dfrac{1}{L^2}\dfrac{dL^2}{dT} = 2\alpha_T$.   The complete temperature coefficient for L^2 is thus

$$\frac{1}{L^2}\frac{dL^2}{dT} = \frac{\frac{1}{2} + n}{T} + 2\alpha_T \tag{7.13}$$

Numerical Illustration: Calculate the fractional rate at which L^2 for a water reflector varies with temperature at 20°C.

Solution. For H_2O, $n = 0.225$; $T = 293°K$, and $\alpha_T = 2.07 \times 10^{-4}/°C$. Substituting in Equation (7.13),

$$\frac{1}{L^2}\frac{dL^2}{dT} = 0.00247 + 0.00042 = 0.00289$$

The cross section effect is seen to be dominant at this temperature.

The age is essentially unchanged by temperature effects other than density changes. The lower limit of the age integral is increased only slightly.

Nuclear velocity changes: Doppler effect. By the definition of temperature as a measure of molecular agitation, it can be seen that an increase in reactor temperature will change the relative motion of neutrons and nuclei. For neutrons of energy in the vicinity of resonance cross section peaks, the interaction rate with nuclei is appreciably distorted. The phenomenon is termed Doppler effect, by analogy with observed frequency changes due to relative motion of sources and receivers of light and sound. A temperature coefficient of multiplication arises from the fact that the Doppler effect is a temperature phenomenon.

The resonance cross sections of many reactor materials may be fairly well represented by the Breit-Wigner formula,

$$\sigma(E) = \frac{\sigma_0}{1 + [(E - E_r)/(\Gamma/2)]^2} \tag{7.14}$$

where E is the energy of the neutron *relative* to the nucleus, whose peak cross section at energy E_r is σ_0, and the total width of the resonance peak at half-maximum is Γ. Figure 7.1 shows the cross section peak of U^{238} at 6.70 ev fitted to this function, with $\Gamma = 0.0025$ ev. The cross section $\sigma(E)$ is the sum of two terms

$$\sigma_a = \frac{\Gamma_\gamma}{\Gamma}\sigma_0, \qquad \sigma_s = \frac{\Gamma_n}{\Gamma}\sigma_0 \tag{7.15}$$

where Γ_γ/Γ and Γ_n/Γ are the relative capture (n,γ) and resonance scattering (n,n) rates. The total cross section is $\sigma + \sigma_p$, where σ_p is an additional non-resonance potential scattering.

Consider an individual neutron, mass m, moving with a speed v, energy E_0, and a nucleus with mass M, speed v_N in the same direction. The relative energy of the neutron is $E = \frac{1}{2}m(v - v_N)^2$.

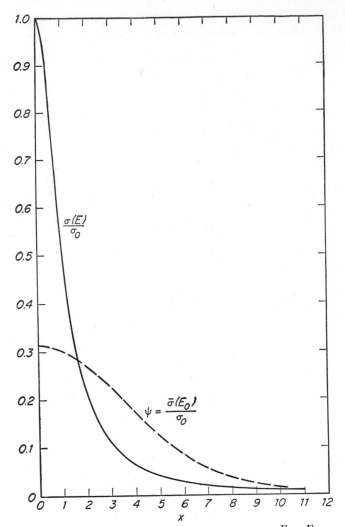

Figure 7.1. Resonance at 6.7 ev in U^{238}: $x = \dfrac{E - E_r}{\Gamma/2}$.

For a maxwellian distribution of nuclear speeds, of temperature T, it can be shown that the probability that the relative energy is E is approximately

$$w(E) \, dE \simeq \frac{1}{\sqrt{\pi} \, \Delta} \, e^{-(E - E_0)^2/\Delta^2} \, dE$$

where $\Delta = 2\sqrt{(m/M)E_0 kT}$ is called the Doppler width.   The effective cross section for reaction of neutrons of energy E_0 is

$$\bar{\sigma}(E_0) = \int \sigma(E) w(E) \, dE = \sigma_0 \psi(\xi, x) \qquad (7.16)$$

where

$$\psi(\xi, x) = \frac{\xi}{2\sqrt{\pi}} \int_{-\infty}^{\infty} \frac{e^{-[\xi(x-y)/2]^2}}{1 + y^2} \, dy \qquad (7.17)$$

$$\xi = \frac{\Gamma}{\Delta}$$

$$x = \frac{(E_0 - E_r)}{\Gamma/2}$$

The function $\psi(\xi, x)$ has been calculated by Rose et al. (see References). The effective cross section as a function of neutron energy is a broader, flatter curve than the resonance curve itself, as shown in Figure 7.1.

We may now consider the consequences of this Doppler broadening. The simplest case is a dilute homogeneous mixture of uranium and moderator, where the total scattering cross section far exceeds the total resonance absorption. The exponent in the resonance escape probability (see § 3.3) is

$$-\frac{N_U}{\xi \Sigma_s} \int \sigma_{aU} \frac{dE}{E}$$

where the integral is the familiar resonance integral. We may evaluate the contribution of a given narrow resonance peak from the effective capture cross section, using Equations (7.15), (7.16), and (7.17), assuming that E is constant at E_r.

$$\int_{-\infty}^{\infty} \sigma_a \frac{dE}{E} \simeq \frac{\pi \Gamma_\gamma \sigma_0}{2 \Gamma E_r} \qquad (7.18)$$

This is *independent of temperature*, since it involves only the properties of the resonance peak. We thus conclude that the resonance escape probability of a dilute homogeneous mixture does not change appreciably with temperature.

Next, we examine qualitatively the case in which the scattering is less important, and the exponent in p must be written

$$-\int \frac{\Sigma_a}{\xi(\Sigma_a + \Sigma_s)} \frac{dE}{E} = -\frac{N_U}{\xi \Sigma_D} \int \frac{\sigma_{aU}}{\dfrac{\sigma_{aU} + \sigma_{sU}}{\sigma_D} + 1} \frac{dE}{E}$$

where Σ_D is the sum of the macroscopic moderator scattering and uranium potential scattering cross sections; $\sigma_D = \Sigma_D/N_U$; $\sigma_{aU} + \sigma_{sU}$ are resonance components.

The effective resonance integral exhibits a temperature dependence through ψ and Δ, in the form

$$\sigma_{re} = \frac{\Gamma_\gamma \sigma_D}{\Gamma} \int \frac{\psi}{\psi + \sigma_D/\sigma_0} \frac{dE}{E}$$

For a natural-U reactor, the Doppler effect results in a negative temperature coefficient.

A few experimental data on temperature effects for natural-U graphite reactors are presented.

(a) The effective resonance integral may be written

$$\sigma_r \simeq \sigma_{r0} + 10^{-4}T$$

where T is in degrees centigrade above room temperature.

(b) The "metal" temperature coefficients of multiplication for the Oak Ridge and Brookhaven reactors are $-1.04 \times 10^{-5}/°C$ and $-1.95 \times 10^{-5}/°C$ respectively.

An argument to confirm the negative coefficient can be advanced. We may accept the fact that the flux at energy corresponding to a high resonance peak is depressed, and the product $\phi\Sigma_a$ is diminished, relative to the case with a more uniform cross section. An increase in metal temperature broadens the resonances, and reverses this effect, i.e., causes *increased* absorption. The resonance escape probability is lower, and the temperature coefficient of the reactor is negative.

However, in a fast reactor composed of U^{235}, the Doppler effect increases *fission*, which results in a positive coefficient. The increased absorption is not sufficient to counteract the effect. A hazardous condition is avoided by restricting the isotopic concentration of U^{235}, i.e., retaining enough U^{238} (with its negative coefficient) to make the coefficient of the reactor negative. The limiting enrichment of U^{235} is theoretically about 35 per cent, according to Goertzel.

7.3. *Power and temperature distributions*

Two types of temperature distributions in a reactor are considered: The first has to do with the internal structure of the fuel elements and the neutron and heat flux distributions in them. The second refers to the over-all reactor temperature pattern, including its dependence on the cooling system.

Temperature drop in plate-type fuel elements. The fuel in many heterogeneous enriched-uranium reactors is contained in thin metal plates, as shown in Figure 7.2. If the surface is maintained at temperature T_s by the coolant flow, we should like to find the maximum temperature T_0 at the center of the plate and the temperature drop $T_0 - T_s$. In a volume element of unit area, thickness dx, the rate of release of fission energy is $\dfrac{\phi \Sigma_f}{c}\, dx$, where c is the number of fissions per watt-second. The total rate of heat generation from the center of the plate out to x is

$$q = \int_0^x \frac{\phi \Sigma_f}{c}\, dx \qquad (7.19)$$

In steady state, this must be equal to the heat flux per unit area at x:

$$q = -k\frac{dT}{dx} \qquad (7.20)$$

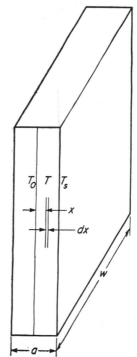

Figure 7.2. Geometry for deriving temperature distribution in fuel plates.

where k is the metal conductivity. For thin plates, the thermal neutron flux is approximately uniform in the x-direction; hence integration of Equation (7.19) and combination with Equation (7.20) gives

$$\frac{\phi \Sigma_f x}{c} = -k\frac{dT}{dx}$$

Integrating again,

$$T_0 - T = \frac{\phi \Sigma_f x^2}{2kc} \qquad \begin{array}{l}\text{temperature distribution}\\ \text{in plate}\end{array} \qquad (7.21)$$

and the maximum temperature drop to the surface is

$$T_0 - T_s = \frac{\phi \Sigma_f a^2}{8kc} \qquad \begin{array}{l}\text{metal temperature}\\ \text{drop}\end{array} \qquad (7.22)$$

where a is the total plate thickness. The thermal flux will vary in general in the z direction, parallel to the long axis of the plates. For a plate of width w, the total power per unit length in the z-direction is

$$P(z) = \frac{aw\phi\Sigma_f}{c} \tag{7.23}$$

and if we define a conduction resistance,

$$R_c = \frac{a}{8kw} \tag{7.24}$$

Equation (7.22) may be written

$$T_0 - T_s = R_c P(z) \tag{7.25}$$

Temperature drop in cylindrical fuel element. Consider

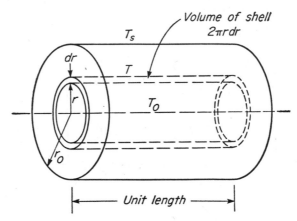

Figure 7.3. Geometry of cylindrical fuel element.

a unit length of a rod-type fuel element, as shown in Figure 7.3. The heat flux per unit area at a radius r is

$$q = \frac{1}{2\pi r} \int_0^r \frac{\phi\Sigma_f}{c} 2\pi r \, dr = -\frac{k \, dT}{dr}$$

Assuming ϕ to be essentially independent of r, and integrating,

$$\frac{\phi\Sigma_f r}{2c} = -k\frac{dT}{dr}$$

or

$$T_0 - T = \frac{\phi\Sigma_f r^2}{4kc}$$

The maximum temperature drop is

$$T_0 - T_s = \frac{\phi \Sigma_f r_0^2}{4kc} = R_c P(z) \tag{7.26}$$

where the conduction resistance is

$$R_c = \frac{1}{4\pi k} \tag{7.27}$$

and the power per unit length is

$$P(z) = \frac{\pi r_0^2 \phi \Sigma_f}{c} \tag{7.28}$$

Temperature distribution in the reactor. As a coolant passes over the surface of the fuel element or its jacket, the rate of increase of coolant temperature with distance along the channel is

$$\frac{dT_c}{dz} = \frac{P}{cM} \tag{7.29}$$

where c is the specific heat and M is the mass flow rate associated with one channel between neighboring plates. Let the origin of z be at the coolant inlet. Then at any position z from the inlet,

$$T_c(z) = T_c(0) + \frac{1}{cM} \int_0^z P(z)\, dz \tag{7.30}$$

A temperature drop exists in the film between fuel element and coolant of amount

$$T_s - T_c = R_f P(z) \tag{7.31}$$

where the film resistance is

$$R_f = \frac{1}{hS}$$

Here, h is the heat transfer coefficient and S is the total surface area per unit length. Using Equations (7.30), (7.31), and either (7.25) or (7.26), the center temperature of the fuel elements as a function of position in the reactor is

$$T_0(z) = T_c(0) + (R_c + R_f)P(z) + \frac{1}{cM} \int_0^z P(z)\, dz \tag{7.32}$$

The maximum temperature occurs where $dT_0(z)/dz = 0$, i.e., where

$$\frac{P(z)}{P'(z)} = -(R_c + R_f)cM \tag{7.33}$$

The most likely power distribution to be encountered in reactor design is the "chopped sine," sketched in Figure 7.4, and given by

$$P(z) = P_0 \sin \frac{\pi(z + d)}{H} \qquad (7.34)$$

where P_0 is the peak power per unit length. This formula will fit a bare core with $d = 0$, a large reflected core with $d \simeq L_r$ (see

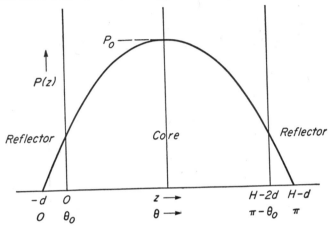

Figure 7.4.   Chopped-sine power distribution.

§ 3.5), or a two-group solution (Chapter 5) if there is not too large a rise in neutron flux near the core-reflector boundary. The point at which the peak temperature occurs and the temperature itself can readily be obtained from Equations (7.32) and (7.33). The results are listed in convenient form in Table 7.2.

Numerical Illustration: Find the outlet coolant temperature and the maximum metal temperature in a liquid-sodium-cooled, natural-uranium, graphite-moderated reactor of core height 20 ft, operating with a central channel power of 0.5 mw. Assume a coolant flow rate of 10 ft/sec in an annulus of area 1.5 sq in. surrounding a slug of 1-in. diameter. Use the following metal and coolant properties. The latter are obtained from the *Liquid Metals Handbook* (see References).

$$T_c(0) = 300°F$$
$$\rho = 56 \text{ lb/ft}^3$$
$$c = 0.32 \text{ BTU/lb-}°F$$
$$h = 10,250 \text{ BTU/hr-}°F\text{-ft}^2$$
$$k_U = 19 \text{ BTU/hr-}°F\text{-ft}$$

Solution. The mass flow rate is $M = \rho v A = (56 \text{ lb/ft}^3)$ $(3.6 \times 10^4 \text{ ft/hr})(1.5/144 \text{ ft}^2) = 2.1 \times 10^4 \text{ lb/hr}$, and the product cM is $6.72 \times 10^3 \text{ BTU/hr-°F}$. With a rate of heat production of $(500 \text{ kw})(3413 \text{ BTU/hr-kw}) = 1.71 \times 10^6 \text{ BTU/hr}$ $= P_T$, the maximum coolant temperature rise from Table 7.2 is

$$\frac{1.71 \times 10^6 \text{ BTU/hr}}{6.72 \times 10^3 \text{ BTU/hr-°F}} = 255°F \text{ and the outlet temperature is}$$

555°F. With a surface area per unit length of $S = \pi/12 = 0.262 \text{ ft}^2$, the film resistance is $R_f = 1/hS = 0.00037$ and the conduction resistance is $R_c = 1/(4\pi k_U) = 0.00419$. The distance d is taken as the diffusion length in graphite, $L = 50 \text{ cm}$ $= 1.64 \text{ ft}$, and H is the core height augmented by a distance $2d$, i.e., 23.28 ft. Now $-(\pi/H)(R_c + R_f)cM = -(\pi/23.28)$ $(0.00456)(6.72 \times 10^3) = -4.135$, and from Table 7.2, $\theta_m = 1.808$, whence the corresponding z-value is 11.76 ft, or 1.76 ft beyond the center of the core. From $P_T = 1.71 \times 10^6$ BTU/hr, and $\cos \theta_0 = 0.976$, the maximum metal temperature is

$$T_0(\theta_m) = 300 + \frac{1.75 \times 10^6}{2(6.72 \times 10^3)}(1 + 4.26) = 985°F$$

Table 7.2

Temperatures for Chopped Sine Distribution

Angles.............. $\theta = \dfrac{\pi(z + d)}{H}$, $\quad \theta_0 = \dfrac{\pi d}{H}$ (when $z = 0$)

Power
  distribution........ $P(z) = P_0 \sin \theta$

Total
  channel power...... $P_T = \dfrac{2HP_0}{\pi} \cos \theta_0$

Coolant
  temperature........ $T_c(\theta) = T_c(\theta_0) + \dfrac{P_T}{2cM}\left(1 - \dfrac{\cos \theta}{\cos \theta_0}\right)$

Metal
  temperature........ $T_0(\theta) = T_c(\theta_0) + P_T\left[\dfrac{1 - \dfrac{\cos \theta}{\cos \theta_0}}{2cM} + \dfrac{\pi(R_c + R_f)}{2H}\dfrac{\sin \theta}{\cos \theta_0}\right]$

Point of
  maximum metal
  temperature........ $\theta_m = \tan^{-1}\left[\dfrac{-\pi}{H}(R_c + R_f)cM\right]$

Maximum metal
  temperature........ $T_0(\theta_m) = T_c(\theta_0) + \dfrac{P_T}{2cM}(1 - \sec \theta_m \sec \theta_0)$

7.4. *Distributed fuel and coolant*

The previous analysis was restricted to variations of flux and temperature *along the axis* of the reactor, parallel to the direction of coolant flow. Since the neutron flux drops off radially from this axis, the heat generation rate and rise in coolant temperature will drop off correspondingly. In a bare cylindrical reactor, for example, if $P(z)$ is the power distribution and T_{c1} is the outlet coolant temperature for a channel on the axis, then, at a distance r out, each of these quantities will be $J_0(2.405r/R)$ times as large. In order to improve thermal efficiency and reduce the maximum fuel temperature, it is desirable to have a common coolant outlet temperature. This may be achieved in one of several ways.

(a) Adjust the *flow velocity* in each constant-dimension passage to match the power developed, by the use of orifices. This implies a maximum velocity at the axis of the core and a minimum at the core boundary.

(b) Design cooling passages of *varying sizes*, to allow a larger mass flow rate in the regions of high heat generation, with constant pressure difference between inlet and outlet.

(c) *Distribute fuel* in such a way that the power density is constant over the core with coolant passages of uniform size.

Case (a) is simply a problem in fluid flow, since the neutron flux distribution will not be affected by the speed of the coolant. Cases (b) and (c) involve a re-analysis of the neutron diffusion problem.

Coolant passages of varying sizes. The criterion for choosing passage sizes is easily understood. The coolant temperature rise per unit length of channel, dT/dz, according to Equation (7.29) is $P(z)/cM$, where $P(z)$ is the heat generation rate per unit length, c is the specific heat, and M is the mass flow rate. Now if the volume fractions of fuel-bearing material and coolant are f_U and f_c respectively, then two proportions may be written

$$P(z) \sim \phi \Sigma_{fU} f_U$$

and

$$M \sim \rho v A \sim f_c$$

Thus if dT/dz is to be constant,

$$\phi f_U = g f_c \tag{7.35}$$

where g is a proportionality constant. Both f_U and f_c may vary with location in the reactor, at least in directions perpendicular to the direction of coolant flow. In the critical calculations, non-linear differential equations often arise which must be solved numerically or approximately. Estimates of effects on critical size and flux distribution may be made from the simple models presented below.

Slab thermal reactor with absorbing coolant. Let us apply modified one-group theory to a bare homogeneous slab in which a coolant of relatively high cross section $\Sigma_p(z)$ is distributed to achieve heat removal proportional to heat generation, and follow the procedure developed by Banister (see References). If very little fuel volume is displaced by the coolant, f_U in Equation (7.35) is approximately constant. Thus f_c is directly proportional to ϕ, which we take to be a cosine function as a first approximation. We shall ascertain the differences in composition and flux distribution between this case and the original critical unpoisoned slab. If we propose to keep the core *size fixed*, it will be necessary to reduce the moderator or structure absorption by a (uniform) amount $\Delta\Sigma_m$, to compensate for the increased coolant poison. Now assume the coolant flow to be in the x-direction, parallel to the sides of the slab, reserving z for the transverse coordinate. The wave equation (3.17) becomes

$$\frac{d^2\phi}{dz^2} + B^2(z)\phi = 0 \tag{7.36}$$

where the buckling, by modified one-group theory, is

$$B^2(z) = \frac{k(z) - 1}{L^2 + \tau} \tag{7.37}$$

Now assume that $M^2 = L^2 + \tau$ does not vary appreciably with z, which will be true if L^2 is much smaller than τ. The new multiplication factor will be given by

$$\frac{1}{k(z)} = \frac{1}{k_0} + \frac{\Sigma_p(z) - \Delta\Sigma_m}{\Sigma_U\eta} \tag{7.38}$$

where k_0 is the original critical value, and Σ_U is the fuel absorption cross section. Combining Equations (7.36), (7.37), and (7.38) and rearranging,

$$\frac{d^2\phi}{dz^2} + \frac{k_0 - 1}{M^2}\phi = \frac{k_0}{\Sigma_{\mathrm{U}}\eta}(\Delta\Sigma_m - \Sigma_p)\left(\frac{d^2\phi}{dz^2} - \frac{\phi}{M^2}\right) \quad (7.39)$$

The right side of Equation (7.39) includes all the perturbations. In it, let

$$\frac{d^2\phi}{dz^2} \simeq -B_0^2\phi$$

where

$$B_0^2 = \frac{k_0 - 1}{M^2} = \left(\frac{\pi}{H}\right)^2$$

is the original buckling. Also, assume

$$\phi \simeq \phi_c \cos \pi \frac{z}{H}$$

$$\Sigma_p(z) = \Sigma_{pc} \cos \frac{\pi z}{H}$$

where Σ_{pc} is the coolant cross section at the center of the reactor, chosen to satisfy heat transfer requirements. Equation (7.39) becomes

$$\frac{d^2\phi}{dz^2} + B_0^2\phi \simeq \alpha\Sigma_p \cos^2 B_0 z - \alpha\Delta\Sigma_m \cos B_0 z$$

where $\alpha = k_0\phi_c/(\Sigma_{a0}M^2)$ and Σ_{a0} is the initial total core absorption. This differential equation may be solved by standard methods to give the flux distribution

$$\phi(z) \simeq A \cos B_0 z + \frac{\phi_c k_0}{2\Sigma_{a0}(k_0 - 1)}$$

$$(\Sigma_{pc} - \tfrac{1}{3}\Sigma_{pc}\cos 2B_0 z - \Delta\Sigma_m B_0 z \sin B_0 z) \quad (7.40)$$

By application of the boundary conditions $\phi(0) = \phi_c$ and $\phi(H/2) = 0$, we obtain the value of the arbitrary constant,

$$A = \phi_c\left[1 - \frac{k_0\Sigma_{pc}}{3\Sigma_{a0}(k_0 - 1)}\right] \quad (7.41)$$

and the amount of moderator reduction needed,

$$\Delta\Sigma_m = \frac{8\Sigma_{pc}}{3\pi} \quad (7.42)$$

This states that the total amount of moderator absorption that must be removed is $\frac{4}{3}$ of the *total* coolant poison cross section that has been added, a result that can also be derived by perturbation theory.   Figure 7.5 shows that the distortion of the flux distribution from a cosine function consists of a flattening.   This suggests

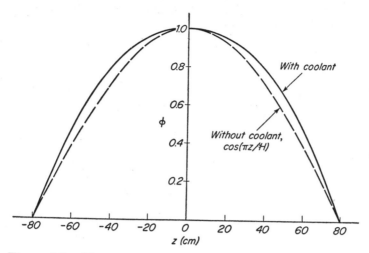

Figure 7.5.   Thermal neutron flux with cosine-distributed coolant.

that one should actually introduce coolant in a distribution somewhat different from the cosine function.

Fast reactor, with liquid metal coolant.   This example is based on the work of Goertzel and Loeb (see References).   In the fast reactor, the scattering and absorption cross sections of the coolant are negligible compared with those of the fuel.   Let the uranium metal be in the form of plates of varying thickness and spacing in the z-direction, while the coolant flows in the x-direction.   No structure is included, and the coolant merely displaces fuel.   Thus the local absorption cross section is $\Sigma_U f_U$ and the diffusion coefficient is D_U/f_U, where $f_U(x)$ is as yet unknown.   Making use of Equations (3.4) and (3.48), the new diffusion equation for a slab geometry becomes

$$\frac{d}{dz}\left(\frac{D_U}{f_U}\frac{d\phi}{dz}\right) + (k - 1)\Sigma_U f_U \phi = 0 \qquad (7.43)$$

Now introduce a new variable defined by

$$dw = f_U\,dz \quad \text{or} \quad w = \int_0^z f_U\,dz$$

and let $B^2 = (k - 1)\Sigma_U/D_U$. Equation (7.43) becomes the familiar wave equation

$$\frac{d\phi^2}{dw^2} + B^2\phi = 0 \qquad (7.44)$$

the solution of which is

$$\phi = \phi_c \cos Bw \qquad (7.45)$$

Now invoke Equation (7.35) in the form

$$\phi f_U = g(1 - f_U) \qquad (7.46)$$

The constant g may be evaluated in terms of the flux ϕ_c and the uranium volume fraction f_{Uc} at $z = 0$.

$$g = \frac{\phi_c f_{Uc}}{1 - f_{Uc}} \qquad (7.47)$$

Combining equations (7.45), (7.46), and (7.47), the fuel distribution becomes

$$f_U = \frac{1}{\left(\dfrac{1}{f_{Uc}} - 1\right) \cos Bw + 1} \qquad (7.48)$$

Returning to the definition of w, we obtain

$$z = \int_0^w \frac{dw}{f_U} = w + \left(\frac{1}{f_{Uc}} - 1\right)\frac{\sin Bw}{B} \qquad (7.49)$$

The boundary condition $\phi = 0$ at $z = H/2$ (ignoring extrapolation distances) implies that no coolant is needed at $H/2$ and $f_U = 1$; hence from Equation (7.48), $\cos Bw_1 = 0$, where w_1 is the surface value of w. Thus $w_1 = \pi/2B$ and from Equation (7.49), the critical condition is

$$\frac{BH}{2} = \frac{\pi}{2} + \frac{1}{f_{Uc}} - 1 \qquad (7.50)$$

Numerical Illustration: Find the critical width of a fast reactor slab with $f_{Uc} = 0.5$ and the constant B^2 is 0.102 cm^{-2} (as in the numerical illustration of § 3.4). Calculate and plot the fuel and flux distributions.

Solution. From Equation (7.50), $\frac{1}{2}BH = \frac{1}{2}\pi + 1$ and $H = 16.1$ cm. A tabular correlation gives the fuel and flux.

Bw	$\phi/\phi_c =$ $\cos Bw$	$\sin Bw$	f_U	w	$\dfrac{\sin Bw}{B}$	z
0	1	0	0.500	0	0	0
$\pi/12$	0.966	0.259	0.509	0.82	0.81	1.63
$\pi/6$	0.866	0.500	0.536	1.64	1.57	3.21
$\pi/4$	0.707	0.707	0.586	2.46	2.22	4.68
$\pi/3$	0.500	0.866	0.667	3.28	2.71	5.99
$5\pi/12$	0.259	0.966	0.794	4.10	3.03	7.13
$\pi/2$	0	1	1.000	4.92	3.13	8.05

Figure 7.6 shows the results.   The dashed line is the simple cosine function.

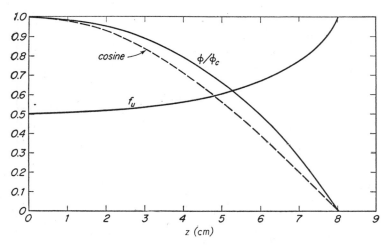

Figure 7.6.   Fuel and flux distribution in fast reactor slab to give uniform outlet coolant temperature.

Uniform power density in a reflected reactor.   The effect of a reflector on a homogeneous core is to give a more favorable ratio of average to central thermal flux than in the unreflected case, but the power distribution still retains a sinusoidal shape. By introducing the fuel non-uniformly, with a high concentration toward the core-reflector boundary, the *power density* $\phi\Sigma_f/c$ *can be made constant* even though the flux varies.   Consider an infinite medium containing a fuel slab of width H, of such composition that the slowing properties of the core and reflector are essentially the same and are governed by age theory.   The neutron balance in this system is governed by the volcano kernel, as discussed in § 3.6.   The thermal flux, by comparison with Equations (3.84) and (3.85) is

$$\phi(z) = \int_{-H/2}^{H/2} \phi(z')\Sigma_f(z')\nu G_v(z,z')\ dz' \qquad (7.51)$$

Since the integration is rather tedious, we treat the problem with a simpler logic, applicable if the diffusion length in the core is short compared with the slowing-down length, i.e., if $L^2 \ll \tau$. Thermal neutrons are absorbed almost immediately after becom-

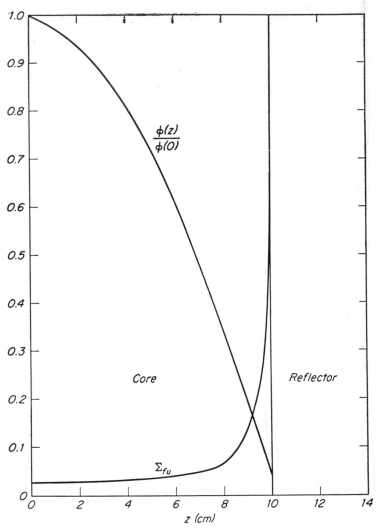

Figure 7.7.   Fuel distribution to achieve uniform power density.

ing thermal, and in the limit, the rate of appearance is equal to the rate of absorption, $q_t = \phi \Sigma_a$.* Now from Equation (3.76)

$$q_t(z) = \int_{-H/2}^{H/2} \phi(z') \Sigma_f(z') \nu G_f(z,z') \, dz' = \phi(z) \Sigma_a(z) \quad (7.52)$$

However, since the product $\phi \Sigma_f$ is constant, we may take it outside the integral and cancel ϕ, to give the cross section

$$\Sigma_a = \Sigma_f \int_{-H/2}^{H/2} G_f(z,z') \, dz' \quad (7.53)$$

or the *local* multiplication factor

$$k = \eta f = \frac{\Sigma_f \nu}{\Sigma_a} = \int_{-H/2}^{H/2} \frac{e^{-|z-z'|^2/4\tau}}{(4\pi\tau)^{1/2}} \, dz' \quad (7.54)$$

Integration yields

$$k(z) = \frac{\Sigma_f \nu}{\Sigma_a} = \frac{2}{\text{erf}\left(\dfrac{\frac{1}{2}H + z}{2\sqrt{\tau}}\right) + \text{erf}\left(\dfrac{\frac{1}{2}H - z}{2\sqrt{\tau}}\right)} \quad (7.55)$$

where the error function is defined by Equation (3.83). The general trend may be seen in the limiting case of a relatively large core, with H appreciably larger than $4\sqrt{\tau}$. Then when $z = 0$, $\text{erf}\,\dfrac{H/2}{2\sqrt{\tau}} \simeq 1$ and $k \simeq 1$; when $z = H/2$, one term drops out, leaving $\text{erf}\,\dfrac{H}{2\sqrt{\tau}} \simeq 1$ and $k \simeq 2$.

Numerical Illustration: Find the approximate fuel and flux distributions for a water-moderated reactor with U^{235} fuel fixed in very thin metal plates. Assume the slab core width to be 20 cm, and an infinite reflector.

Solution.   A tabular calculation of $k(z)$ is performed, using $\tau = 33 \text{ cm}^2$, $\sqrt{\tau} = 5.74$.

z	$\frac{1}{2}H+z$	$\frac{1}{2}H-z$	$x_1 = \dfrac{\frac{1}{2}H+z}{2\sqrt{\tau}}$	$x_2 = \dfrac{\frac{1}{2}H-z}{2\sqrt{\tau}}$	$\text{erf } x_1$	$\text{erf } x_2$	$k(z)$
0	10	10	0.871	0.871	0.782	0.782	1.28
2	12	8	1.045	0.697	0.861	0.675	1.30
4	14	6	1.219	0.523	0.915	0.540	1.37
6	16	4	1.394	0.348	0.951	0.377	1.51
8	18	2	1.568	0.174	0.973	0.194	1.71
10	20	0	1.742	0	0.986	0	2.03

* Mathematically, this means that the diffusion kernel is approximated by a delta-function.

The product $\phi\Sigma_{fU}$ is everywhere constant at its value at the plane $z = 0$, i.e., $\phi(0)\Sigma_{fU}(0)$. Thus $\dfrac{\phi(z)}{\phi(0)} = \dfrac{\Sigma_{fU}(0)}{\Sigma_{fU}(z)}$. It can be shown that

$$\Sigma_{fU} = \frac{\Sigma_{aH_2O}/\nu}{\dfrac{1}{k} - \dfrac{1}{\eta}}$$

Letting $\Sigma_{aH_2O} = 0.0195$, $\nu = 2.46$ and $\eta = 2.08$, we obtain

z	Σ_{fU}	$\phi(z)/\phi(0)$
0	0.026	1.00
2	0.028	0.93
4	0.032	0.81
6	0.044	0.59
8	0.076	0.34
10	0.67	0.04

From the tables and Figure 7.7 we see that the fuel concentration must be increased sharply within a centimeter or so of the core boundary.

Although we have properly described the effect of the reflector in maintaining a finite value of slowing-down density at the edge of the core, the diffusion into the core has not been correctly evaluated. The more general solution of Equation (7.51), removing $\phi\Sigma_f$ from the integral, is

$$\Sigma_f(z) = \frac{1}{\nu \int G_v(z,z')\,dz'} = \frac{1}{\nu \int \left[G_{ft}(z,z') - \dfrac{1}{\eta}\,G_t \right] dz'} \tag{7.56}$$

where the right side of the equation is integrable, using Equations (3.80) and (3.82).

7.5. *Temperature-reactivity-power coupling*

The power response of a reactor upon the introduction of an excess multiplication at time zero $(\delta k_e)_0$ is ultimately governed by the temperature changes in the reactor, which are due, in turn, to the heat generated. Let us examine the general cycle sketched in Figure 7.8. Coolant is circulated through the core and the primary side of a heat exchanger. Energy is dissipated in a load in the secondary loop, for example by a steam turbine. The coupling between the nuclear behavior and the thermal effects will be demonstrated by simple idealized models.

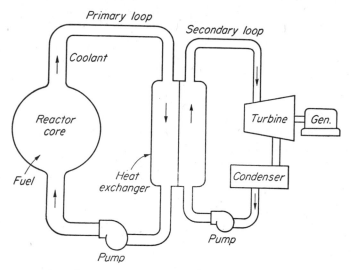

Figure 7.8.   Nuclear-thermal cycle.

Zero power extraction.   The simplest response is that corresponding to approximately zero heat removal, as if the secondary loop were suddenly emptied of fluid, or the primary coolant did not circulate.   A small-step function δk_e of amount $(\delta k_e)_0$ is applied, for example by a sudden shift in control rod position.   The power level will rise from its initial value P_0; fission heat will raise the core temperature from its initial value by an amount T; the moderator will expand and induce a negative multiplication, of amount approximately $-|\alpha|T$, where $|\alpha|$ is the absolute value of the negative temperature coefficient of the core.   Assuming $\delta k_e \ll \beta$, the power level of the reactor will increase according to Equation (6.10), where power has been substituted for neutron density.

$$\frac{1}{P}\frac{dP}{dt} = \frac{\delta k_e}{\bar{l}} \tag{7.57}$$

The use of the effective lifetime $\bar{l}$ has been shown by Soodak (see References) to be valid in the case of a variable δk_e, if the δk_e is such that the response is slow compared with the mean delayed emitter lifetimes.   The *net* excess multiplication factor is

$$\delta k_e = (\delta k_e)_0 - |\alpha| T \qquad (7.58)$$

The rate of temperature increase with time will be

$$\frac{dT}{dt} = \frac{P}{C} \qquad (7.59)$$

where C is the total heat capacity of the core. Eliminating time by dividing Equations (7.57) and (7.59), we obtain

$$\frac{dP}{dT} = \frac{C[(\delta k_e)_0 - |\alpha| T]}{l} \qquad (7.60)$$

The first observation is that the power reaches a maximum, $dP/dT = 0$, when the temperature is

$$T = \frac{(\delta k_e)_0}{|\alpha|}$$

i.e., when the negative temperature effect cancels the initial δk_e. Integrating Equation (7.60), the power response is

$$P = P_0 + \frac{C[(\delta k_e)_0 T - |\alpha| T^2/2]}{l} \qquad (7.61)$$

Upon substitution of the "cancellation temperature," we find the peak power to be

$$P_{max} = P_0 + \frac{C(\delta k_e)_0^2}{2|\alpha|l}$$

By the time P again crosses the starting level P_0, the temperature has risen to

$$T = \frac{2(\delta k_e)_0}{|\alpha|}$$

or twice the temperature to balance $(\delta k_e)_0$. This characteristic temperature appears in many similar problems. Combining Equations (7.59) and (7.61) and integrating, we obtain the δk_e at any time, and hence the temperature

$$\delta k_e = (\delta k_e)_0 - |\alpha| T = by$$

where

$$b = \sqrt{(\delta k_e)_0^2 + \frac{2|\alpha| P_0 \bar{l}}{C}} \qquad (7.62)$$

$$y = \frac{y_0 - x}{1 - y_0 x} \qquad y_0 = \frac{(\delta k_e)_0}{b}$$

$$x = \tanh \frac{bt}{2\bar{l}}$$

An examination of these functions shows that the temperature continues to approach a steady state value,

$$T_{max} = \frac{(\delta k_e)_0 + b}{|\alpha|}$$

implying a final net negative δk_e of amount $-b$. The power must thus decline to zero.

Numerical Illustration: Determine the behavior of a homogeneous reactor of mass 50 kg operating initially at 20 kw when an initial excess multiplication $(\delta k_e)_0 = 0.0015$ is applied. Assume $l = 0.0928$, a specific heat of 1.035 cal/gm-°C, and a temperature coefficient $\alpha = -10^{-4}/°C$.

Solution. The heat capacity of the core is readily found to be 217 kw-sec/°C. The cancellation temperature rise is $0.0015/10^{-4} = 15°C$, and from Equation (7.62), $b = 0.0020$. Thus the maximum temperature is $(0.0015 + 0.0020)/10^{-4} = 35°$ above the initial value. The peak power is

$$P_{max} = 20 + \frac{(217)(2.25 \times 10^{-6})}{(2)(10^{-4})(0.0928)} = 46.3 \text{ kw}$$

The time required for the power excursion is computed from Equation (7.62) to be 183 sec. The power, temperature, and δk_e as a function of time are plotted in Figure 7.9.

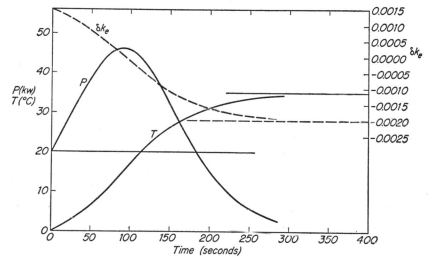

Figure 7.9. Response to step δk_e with zero power extraction.

Power extraction proportional to temperature. This is a somewhat more realistic model than the insulated case. The rate of heat transfer from the coolant is proportional to the temperature drop to the surroundings, which may be considered as an infinite reservoir. Let an initial δk_e be applied so that the power rises and the reactor heats up. If the core were originally at ambient temperature, then the rate of extraction of energy would be

$$P_e = KT \tag{7.63}$$

The rate of increase of temperature is an extension of Equation (7.59),

$$\frac{dT}{dt} = \frac{P - KT}{C} \tag{7.64}$$

where P is governed by

$$\frac{1}{P}\frac{dP}{dt} = \frac{(\delta k_e)_0 - |\alpha|T}{\bar{l}} \tag{7.65}$$

These coupled equations cannot be solved in closed form by the simple methods of differential equations, a situation that is met frequently in transient analysis. The problem must be solved numerically. The following qualitative argument may be made, however. The core temperature will rise more slowly than in the zero extraction case, by virtue of the heat loss to the surroundings. The power will rise higher, and after its peak, decline more slowly.

Step-function increase in power demand. We now turn to the practical problem of a sudden increase in power requirement by the load. For instance, the throttle valve on the steam turbine is opened to increase the demand from previous steady level P_0 to a new level P_1. Instead of attempting to formulate the details of the effect on the primary loop, the simple assumption is made that the moderator-coolant tends to decrease in temperature at a rate $(P - P_1)/C$, where C is the heat capacity of the core. The reactor power level will increase because of the δk_e due to the temperature effect, to a value P. The net rate of change of temperature is

$$\frac{dT}{dt} = \frac{P - P_1}{C} \tag{7.66}$$

Instead of employing the average neutron lifetime $\bar{l}$, we shall include effects of one delayed-neutron group explicitly. In the expectation that δk_e varies with time, we may start with Equation (6.58), in terms of power rather than neutron density.

$$\ddot{P} + \left(\lambda - \frac{\delta \dot{k}_{ep}}{l}\right)\dot{P} - \left(\frac{\dot{\delta k}_{ep}}{l} + \frac{\lambda \delta k_e}{l}\right)P = 0 \qquad (7.67)$$

For this problem, however,

$$k_e = 1 - |\alpha|T$$
$$\dot{k}_e = -|\alpha|T$$
$$k_{ep} = -[\beta + |\alpha|T(1 - \beta)]$$
$$\dot{k}_{ep} = -|\alpha|\dot{T}(1 - \beta)$$

Since the differential equation is non-linear, a restriction to small power changes is made, which allows several approximations:

(a) δk_e is small, and can be ignored in comparison with β.
(b) The function P in the last term of Equation (7.67) is equal to P_0 and the product $\ddot{P}l$ is negligible.
(c) The lifetime l is short, so that $l\lambda$ is negligible compared with β.
(d) $1 - \beta$ can be replaced by 1.

Combining Equations (7.66) and (7.67) with several rearrangements, we are led to

$$\frac{1}{a}P'' + P' + P = P_1 \qquad (7.68)$$

where $a = \alpha P_0/(\beta \lambda C)$, and the prime signifies differentiation with respect to λt. This is the equation of harmonic motion with damping. The complete solution is

$$P = (P_0 - P_1)e^{-at/2}\left(\cos \omega t + \frac{a}{2\omega} \sin \omega t\right) + P_1 \qquad (7.69)$$

where t is measured in units of the mean delayed lifetime $\bar{\tau}$, the angular frequency of the oscillations is $\omega = \sqrt{a - a^2/4}$ and the time for the amplitude to decrease by a factor of e is $2/a$.

Numerical Illustration: Find the power response for a reactor of heat capacity 500 kw-sec/°C, temperature coefficient -10^{-4}/°C, lifetime 10^{-4} sec, upon experiencing a change in power demand from 2000 kw to 2500 kw.

Solution. The parameter a is computed to be 0.6964, the value of ω is 0.7584, which implied a period of oscillation of 105.2 sec. However, the time for the exponential function to reduce its amplitude by a factor of e is $2/a = 2.87$ mean lives or 36 sec. The transient is thus strongly damped, as shown in Figure 7.10.

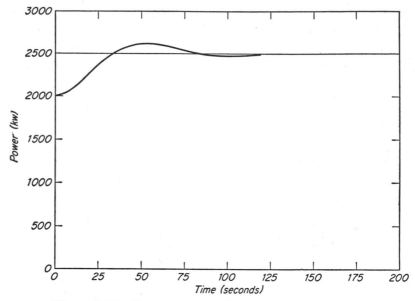

Figure 7.10. Response to step increase in power demand.

Circulating fuel reactor. It was tacitly assumed in the foregoing cases that the fuel remained fixed in the core. If the fuel circulates, two differences appear. First, some delayed neutrons are emitted outside the core and fail to contribute their share of the multiplication process. Second, and probably more important, fuel is continually flowing out of the core and carrying with it heat energy previously generated. Consider a unit mass of fuel that leaves the core at time t, when the reactor power is $P(t)$. At a time earlier by amount s, the power was $P(t - s)$; the energy gain in time interval ds was $P(t - s)\, ds$. If the mass takes a time θ to get through the core, then the average rate of removal of heat energy is

$$\frac{1}{\theta} \int_0^\theta P(t - s)\, ds$$

which is directly proportional to the fuel outlet temperature (if the inlet temperature is constant).   The rate of core temperature change, instead of being given by Equations (7.59), (7.64), or (7.66) is now

$$\frac{dT}{dt} = \frac{P(t) - \frac{1}{\theta} \int_0^\theta P(t - s)\, ds}{C} \qquad (7.70)$$

where the temperature response is seen to depend on the past history of the reactor.   Evidence is presented by Ergen (see References) that the response of the system to a disturbance for this case also consists of damped oscillations.

Power-dependent reactivity—the boiling reactor.   The negative reactivity induced by heating in certain reactors is principally dependent on the power rather than the temperature.   For instance, in a reactor with *boiling water moderator*, the rate of steam bubble production and the consequent void volume fraction are proportional to the local power density.   The age and neutron leakages increase with the void fraction, reducing the multiplication factor.   The complete description of transient behavior includes the usual temperature coefficient for temperatures up to the boiling point, plus a *void coefficient* defined as the δk_e for each per cent of steam voids.   A typical number is -0.24 per cent/per cent steam.   The amount of steam void reactivity that can be tolerated without experiencing power oscillations is strongly dependent on the operating pressure.   Experiments at Argonne National Laboratory show that at 300 psi, steady operation with 3.2 per cent void reactivity can be obtained.   Another parameter of importance is the ratio of power density to δk_e; a typical value is 4 kw/liter-per cent δk_e.

General dynamic problem.   The set of equations that more completely and rigorously define the time-dependent behavior of the nuclear-thermal system sketched in Figure 7.8 will now be presented.   Consider a heterogeneous reactor with metal fuel elements, with coolant flowing past them.   Heat and neutron balance equations are written, using the following notation:

UA: over-all heat transfer coefficient
C: heat capacity of a given component
c: specific heat of coolant
M: mass flow rate of coolant
T: temperature

Subscripts for inlet (i) and outlet (o), secondary (s), primary coolant (c), coolant-moderator for the reactor (r), and fuel elements (e) are also used.

Nuclear power (compare Equations 6.26 and 6.27).

$$\frac{dP}{dt} = \frac{\delta k_{ep}P}{l} + \sum_i \lambda_i C_i$$

$$\frac{dC_i}{dt} = -\lambda_i C_i + \frac{k_e \beta_i P}{l}$$

Reactor fuel elements (e):

heat loss to coolant: $-(UA)_r(T_e - T_r)$
heat supply from fission: P

rate of temperature change: $\dfrac{dT_e}{dt} = \dfrac{P - (UA)_r(T_e - T_r)}{C_e}$

Reactor coolant (r):

heat loss to exchanger: $-cM(T_{ci} - T_{co})$
heat supply from fuel elements: $(UA)_r(T_e - T_r)$

rate of temperature change: $\dfrac{dT_r}{dt} = \dfrac{(UA)_r(T_e - T_r) - cM(T_{ci} - T_{co})}{C_r}$

Primary coolant loop (c):

heat loss to secondary: $-UA(T_c - T_s)$
net rate of heat supply from reactor: $cM(T_{ci} - T_{co})$

rate of temperature change: $\dfrac{dT_c}{dt} = \dfrac{cM(T_{ci} - T_{co}) - UA(T_c - T_s)}{C_c}$

Secondary loop (s):

heat supply from exchanger: $UA(T_c - T_s)$
energy extracted by turbine: $-P_1$

rate of temperature change: $\dfrac{dT_s}{dt} = \dfrac{UA(T_c - T_s) - P_1}{C_s}$

In these equations, the mean temperatures are logically taken as the averages of inlet and outlet values. It should be noted that a finite time Δt is required for the coolant to go from the core to the heat exchanger. Thus the inlet temperature $T_{ci}(t)$ for the exchanger is equal to the outlet temperature for the core at an earlier time, $T_{ci}(t - \Delta t)$. A similar delay should be applied for the return line.

A solution in closed form is impractical, and use of an analog computer is indicated.

A qualitative description of the sequence of events after a disturbance such as increasing the steam flow to the turbine, is given to supplement the equations.

(a) Temperature of secondary drops.
(b) Heat transfer rate to secondary increases.
(c) Temperature of exchanger outlet coolant drops.
(d) Inlet reactor moderator temperature falls.
(e) Reactor power increases because of lower average core temperature.
(f) Fuel element temperature increases.
(g) Heat transfer rate from elements to coolant increases.
(h) Temperature of reactor outlet (and exchanger inlet) increases
(i) Heat transfer rate to secondary rises to balance new demand.

A new steady state is approached, of course, only after the coolant makes a number of complete cycles through the system.

Problems

7.1. Derive a formula for $\dfrac{1}{k}\dfrac{dk}{dT}$ for a bare heterogeneous reactor, volume fractions f_m moderator and f_U fuel, in which only the moderator expands appreciably. Does the effect increase or decrease the multiplication?

Answer.

$$\frac{1}{k}\frac{dk}{dT} = \alpha_T \frac{f_m \Sigma_{am}}{(\Sigma_a)_{core}} \qquad \text{increase}$$

7.2. Derive an approximate formula for $\dfrac{1}{\tau}\dfrac{d\tau}{dT}$ for the heterogeneous reactor of Problem 7.1, assuming that τ is representable by $1/\Sigma^2$ where Σ is an effective "cross section for slowing," i.e., a volume-fraction weighted composite of values for metal and moderator.

Answer.

$$\frac{1}{\tau}\frac{d\tau}{dT} = 2\alpha_T f_m \sqrt{\frac{\tau}{\tau_m}}$$

where τ_m is the age in pure moderator.

7.3. Derive a formula for $\dfrac{1}{L^2}\dfrac{dL^2}{dT}$, due to density changes, for the heterogeneous reactor of Problem 7.1, assuming that the absorption and transport cross sections of the core are volume-weighted composites.

Answer.

$$\frac{1}{L^2}\frac{dL^2}{dT} = \alpha_T f_m \left(\frac{\Sigma_{tm}}{\Sigma_t} + \frac{\Sigma_{am}}{\Sigma_a} \right)$$

7.4. Calculate the temperature coefficients at room temperature of k, τ, and L^2, due to density changes in a bare, heterogeneous, water-moderated reactor, using the following data:

Properties of moderator: $f_m = 0.7$, $\Sigma_{am} = 0.02 \text{ cm}^{-1}$,

                                  $\Sigma_{tm} = 2.0 \text{ cm}^{-1}$, $\tau_m = 33 \text{ cm}^2$

Properties of core: $\Sigma_a = 0.07 \text{ cm}^{-1}$, $\Sigma_t = 1.5 \text{ cm}^{-1}$,

                                   $\tau = 50 \text{ cm}^2$

Expansion coefficient: $\alpha_T = 2 \times 10^{-4}/°C$

Answers. x: $\dfrac{1}{x}\dfrac{dx}{dT}$ (units of 10^{-4})

       k: 0.40

       τ: 3.45

       L^2:   2.27

7.5. Find the temperature coefficients, due to expansion, of fast leakage, thermal leakage, and effective multiplication factor for the reactor of Problem 7.4, using age theory and the constant critical buckling $B^2 = 0.010$, $L^2 = 4.0 \text{ cm}^2$, $\tau = 50 \text{ cm}^2$.

Answer. x: $\dfrac{1}{x}\dfrac{dx}{dT}$ (units of 10^{-4})

       $\mathscr{L}_f$: -1.72

       $\mathscr{L}_t$: -0.09

       k_e: -1.41

7.6. The flux distribution across the diameter of a tubular fuel element is approximately uniform with value ϕ. In this hollow metal cylinder with internal radius r_0 and external radius r_1, identical internal and external coolant temperatures, conductivity k, find the radius r_m

at which the fuel temperature is a maximum, and determine the radial temperature drop.

Answer.

$$r_m = \sqrt{\frac{r_1^2 - r_0^2}{2 \ln r_1/r_0}}$$

$$T = \frac{\phi\Sigma_f}{2kc}\left[r_m^2 \ln\left(\frac{r_m}{r_1}\right) - \frac{(r_m^2 - r_1^2)}{2} \right]$$

7.7. Estimate the power level at which a thermally insulated, homogeneous, water-moderated reactor will start to boil, with a step δk_e of 0.002, starting power level 100 watts, temperature 80°C, effective neutron lifetime 0.0929 sec, mass 15,000 gm, specific heat 4 joules/gm-°C, temperature coefficient -1.3×10^{-4}/°C.

Answer. 9.1 kw.

7.8. In a circulating fuel reactor, some of the delayed neutrons are emitted outside the core. Write an approximate differential equation for C_i, relating fluid volume flow rate v, core volume V, assuming that the time θ that the fluid remains in the external loop is relatively short.

Answer.

$$\frac{dC_i}{dt}\left(1 + \frac{v}{V}\theta\right) = -\lambda_i C_i + \frac{k_e\beta_i n}{l}$$

7.9. Solve the following simultaneous equations of a system with initial step δk_e, negative temperature coefficient α, constant power removal rate P_0, and average neutron lifetime $\bar{l}$:

$$\frac{1}{P}\frac{dP}{dt} = \frac{(\delta k_e)_0 - |\alpha|T}{l}$$

$$\frac{dT}{dt} = \frac{P - P_0}{C}$$

for the power-temperature characteristic. Show that the maximum temperature is $2(\delta k_e)_0/|\alpha|$.

Answer.

$$\frac{P}{P_0} - 1 - \ln\frac{P}{P_0} = \frac{C}{P_0\bar{l}}\left[T(\delta k_e)_0 - |\alpha|T^2/2\right]$$

7.10. Investigate the conditions under which the removal of water from a heterogeneous reactor would result in an increase in reactivity.

7.11. A water-boiler type reactor of core volume 12.7 liters (see § 1.4 and Kasten, References) is operating steadily at power level 25 kw. Radiolytic gases are being developed (due to the dissociation of water by fission products) at a rate of 11.1 liters/minute, and their average residence time in the core is 5 sec.   (a) Find the average void fraction due to gas bubbles.   (b) Assuming that the void coefficient is -0.33, find the reactivity value of the voids.

Answers.   (a) 0.0678, (b) -0.00224.

7.12. The Brookhaven natural-uranium–graphite reactor is cooled by introducing air in a gap at the center of the reactor and allowing it to flow in both directions.   Derive a formula for the temperature distribution along the coolant axis, assuming the flux to be essentially a chopped-sine function in that direction.

7.13. Show that the integral of the volcano kernel for age-diffusion theory is

$$\int_{-H/2}^{H/2} G_v(z,z')\, dz' = \frac{1}{\Sigma_{am}}\left[\frac{1}{k(z)} + \frac{e^{-H/2}\cosh z/L - 1}{\eta} + G(z)\right]$$

where $k(z)$ is given by Equation (7.55) and $G(z) = g_2(\frac{1}{2}H + z) - g_1(\frac{1}{2}H + z) + g_2(\frac{1}{2}H - z) - g_1(\frac{1}{2}H - z)$, where the g functions are used in Equation (3.82).

References

Schultz, M. A., *Control of Nuclear Reactors and Power Plants.*   New York: McGraw-Hill Book Company, Inc. (1955).

Peaceful Uses of Atomic Energy, Volume 5, *Physics of Reactor Design.* New York: Columbia University Press (1956).

   Dietrich, J. R., "Experimental Determinations of the Self-Regulation and Safety of Operating Water Moderated Reactors," Paper P/481.

Goodman, C., Editor, *Science and Engineering of Nuclear Power*, Vol. II, Chap. 8, "Pile Kinetics," by Harry Soodak.   Cambridge, Mass.: Addison Wesley Press, Inc. (1949).

Feshbach, H., G. Goertzel, and H. Yamauchi, "Estimation of Doppler Effect in Fast Reactors," *Nuclear Science and Engineering*, March 1956, p. 4.

Wigner, E. P., and J. E. Wilkins, Jr.   *Effect of the Temperature of the Moderator on the Velocity Distribution of Neutrons with Numerical Calculations for H as a Moderator*, AECD-2275 (1944).

Durham, Franklin P., "Radiolytic-Gas Bubbling Improves Convective Heat Transfer in Supo," *Nucleonics* May 1955, p. 42.

Welton, T. A., *A Stability Criterion for Reactor Systems*, ORNL-1894 (1955).

Schultz, M. A., and J. C. Conner, "Reactor Power Calibration," *Nucleonics*, February 1954, p. 8.

Weinberg, A., "Recent Advances in Reactor Technology," *Nucleonics*, May 1953, p. 18.

Rose, M. E., W. Miranker, P. Leak, G. Rabinowitz, and V. L. Sailor. *A Table of the Integral* $\psi(x,t)$, BNL-257(T-40) (1953).

Fleck, Joseph A., Jr., "Kinetics of Circulating Reactors at Low Power," *Nucleonics*, October 1954, p. 52.

Margulies, R. S., *Combined Effects of Delayed Neutrons and Temperature on Reactor Kinetics*, BNL-280 (T-47) (1954).

Chernick, J., *Dependence of Reactor Kinetics on Temperature*, BNL-173 (T-30) (1951).

Roe, G. M., *The Absorption of Neutrons in Doppler-Broadened Resonances*, KAPL-1241 (1954).

The Reactor Handbook, Volume 1, *Physics*, AECD-3645 (1955), Chapter 1.6.   Volume 2, *Engineering*, AECD-3646 (1955).

Lyon, Richard N., Ed., *Liquid Metals Handbook*, 2nd Ed., Washington: U. S. Government Printing Office (June 1952).

Siegel, R., and H. Hurwitz, Jr.   *The Effect of Temperature Coefficients on Reactor Stability and Reactor Transfer Function*, KAPL-1138 (1955).

Goertzel, G., and William A. Loeb, "Non-Uniform Fuel Distributions in Nuclear Reactors," *Nucleonics*, September 1954, p. 42.

Ergen, W. K., "Kinetics of the Circulating Fuel Nuclear Reactor," *Journ. Appl. Phys.*, **25**, 702 (1954).   (See also ORNL-CF-53-3-231.)

Nuclear Engineering, Part I.   New York: American Institute of Chemical Engineers (1954).

     Kasten, Paul R., "Reactor Dynamics of the Los Alamos Water Boiler."

Banister, Arthur W., *Effects of Uranium Burnout in Thermal Reactors*, Master's Thesis, North Carolina State College, Raleigh, (1956).

Chapter 8

REACTOR CONTROL

The means by which stable and safe operation of a reactor can be guaranteed are described in this chapter. The problem of reactor control includes several aspects: (a) the mechanical systems, such as control elements, that provide the ability to adjust power level and shut down the reactor; (b) the processes and events, such as poison accumulation and fuel burnup, that require positive counteraction; (c) the "built-in" features, such as the burnable poisons, that can give control on a long-time basis.

8.1. *Control rods*

The most widely used mechanical controls for thermal reactors consist of rods or plates containing a neutron-absorbing element such as boron, cadmium, or hafnium. These movable absorbers are usually inserted parallel to the vertical axis of the core, to allow fall on release. Electric, pneumatic, or hydraulic drives provide the necessary motive power for adjustment. Figure 8.1 shows a typical arrangement. The nomenclature is as follows: A *safety* is kept in reserve for emergency shutdown; the *shim* provides adjustment for processes with a long time cycle, such as fuel consumption and general fission product buildup; the *regulating* element is used to adjust the power level of the reactor and to compensate for short-term changes in reactivity. The absorber may displace moderator or fuel upon insertion, or may be guided by a hollow channel.

Insertion of a control element results in the removal of neutrons from the cycle, and a negative δk_e is supplied. The δk_e

value of a set of rods fully inserted can be estimated by a comparison of the critical infinite multiplication factors, without rods k_0 and with rods k_1, according to this logic: The critical equation for the first case is

$$1 = k_0 \mathcal{L}_f \mathcal{L}_t \tag{8.1}$$

If the higher fuel loading concentration implied by k_1 were used in the reactor without any absorber present, the reactor would be super-critical, to an extent that

$$k_e = k_1 \mathcal{L}_f \mathcal{L}_t \tag{8.2}$$

The reactivity $\rho = \delta k_e / k_e$ may be computed from Equation (8.2). The leakage factors for the two cases may be different.   In the

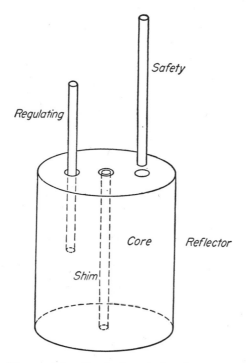

Figure 8.1.   Typical control rod system.

special case of a reactor with strong thermal neutron absorption, the thermal leakage is relatively small, and the fast leakage factor is almost constant.   Thus, approximately, $k_e = k_1/k_0$, $\delta k_e = (k_1 - k_0)/k_0$, and the reactivity is

$$\rho \simeq \frac{k_1 - k_0}{k_1} \qquad (8.3)$$

Modified one-group model. As a simple introduction to the method of analysis, we first derive the critical condition for a bare cylindrical reactor of height H, radius R, with a cylindrical control rod of radius a that is perfectly opaque to thermal neutrons, lying along the central axis. The modified one-group theory (§ 3.5), in which the buckling is set at $B^2 = (k - 1)/M^2$, will be used. The results will be expected to be accurate for a large reactor, fueled with low-enrichment uranium. On the assumption that the flux along a line parallel to the z-axis is everywhere proportional to the function $\cos \pi z/H$, the *radial* flux distribution is governed by the modified Bessel equation:

$$\frac{d^2\phi}{dr^2} + \frac{1}{r}\frac{d\phi}{dr} + B_r^2\phi = 0 \qquad (8.4)$$

where

$$B_r^2 = B^2 - (\pi/H)^2 \qquad (8.5)$$

Without a control rod, the critical condition is simply

$$B_{r0} = 2.4048/R_0$$

A linear combination of the two solutions of Equation (8.4) is

$$\phi(r) = AJ_0(B_r r) + CY_0(B_r r) \qquad (8.6)$$

Two boundary conditions are applied. The first is conventional, that ϕ must vanish at the extrapolated outer boundary of the core. The second is that ϕ must be of such form at the rod radius a that ϕ/ϕ' is equal to an extrapolation distance d as discussed in § 2.3. For a black cylinder, this distance varies with the ratio of rod radius to core transport mean free path, a/λ_t, as shown in Figure 8.2. It will be noted that for large radii, d/λ_t approaches 0.71, as for a plane. From Equation (8.6), at the extrapolated radius R,

$$AJ_0(B_r R) + CY_0(B_r R) = 0$$

Hence the arbitrary coefficients are related by

$$-\frac{C}{A} = \frac{J_0(B_r R)}{Y_0(B_r R)} \equiv \psi(B_r R)$$

where the function $\psi(B_r R)$ is used as an abbreviation. From the boundary condition at the rod surface, the ratio of coefficients is also

$$-\frac{C}{A} = \frac{\dfrac{J_0(B_r a)}{d} + B_r J_1(B_r a)}{\dfrac{Y_0(B_r a)}{d} + B_r Y_1(B_r a)} \equiv \psi(a)$$

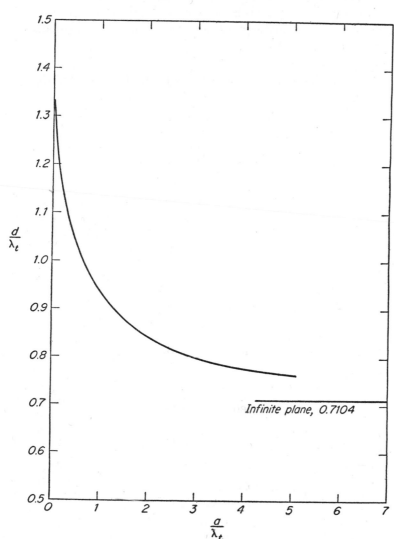

Figure 8.2. Thermal extrapolation distance for black cylinder. (After Davison and Kushneriuk.)

Hence the critical condition is

$$\psi(B_r R) = \psi(a) \qquad (8.7)$$

The new materials buckling may be computed from Equation (8.7). It is found that the function $\psi(a)$ is insensitive to the value of B_r. This suggests that a value of $\psi(a)$ based on the original critical reactor *without* rods be computed, and the new B_r obtained from $\psi(B_r R)$. The latter may be approximated by inspection of the Bessel functions by

$$\frac{\psi(B_r R)}{1.018} \simeq 2.4048 - B_r R = (B_{r0} - B_r)R = -(\Delta B_r)R$$

If the rod effect is small, and leakage changes are slight, differentials may be used to compute reactivity. Since

$$k = 1 + \left[B_r^2 + \left(\frac{\pi}{H} \right)^2 \right] M^2$$

then

$$\rho \simeq \frac{dk}{k} = \frac{2M^2 B_r \, dB_r}{k} \simeq - \frac{2M^2 B_r \psi(a)}{1.018 k R} \qquad (8.8)$$

Numerical Illustration: A bare cylindrical thermal reactor with $\lambda_t = 2.7$ cm is critical with equal extrapolated height and diameter of 300 cm, $M^2 = 600$ cm², $k = 1.220$. Calculate the reactivity value by modified one-group theory of a central control rod of radius 2.5 cm, assuming the leakage to be negligibly changed by the disturbance.

Solution. The radial buckling is $B_r^2 = (2.4048/R)^2 = 2.57 \times 10^{-4}$ or $B_r = 1.603 \times 10^{-2}$. Thus $B_r a = 0.040$, and from tables of Bessel functions, $J_0(B_r a) \simeq 1$, $J_1(B_r a) = 0.020$, $Y_0(B_r a) = -2.12$, and $Y_1(B_r a) = -16.0$. From Figure 8.2, $d = 2.565$ cm. Using these numbers in Equation (8.7), $\psi(a) = -0.3602$. From Equation (8.8)

$$\rho \simeq \frac{-2(600)(1.603 \times 10^{-2})(-0.3602)}{(1.018)(1.220)(150)} = -0.0372$$

By the insertion of a control rod along the core axis, the radial flux distribution is changed from the standard

$$\phi(r) \sim J_0(2.4048r/R)$$

to

$$\phi(r) \sim J_0(B_r r) - \frac{J_0(B_r R)}{Y_0(B_r R)} Y_0(B_r r)$$

Figure 8.3 compares the original and disturbed fluxes. The depression near the rod is displayed.

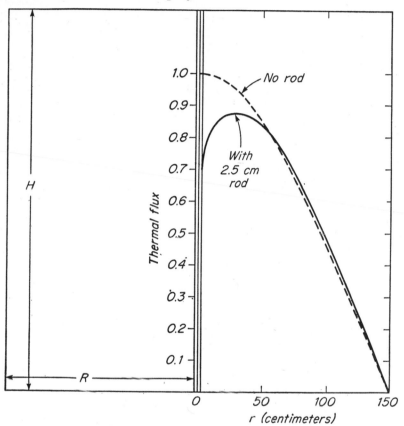

Figure 8.3.   Thermal flux distribution in cylinder with and without control rod.

8.2. *Reactivity values of control rods by the two-group model*

The infinite multiplication factor with a control rod inserted can be calculated more accurately for a thermal reactor by two-group (or modified two-group) theory. The fast and slow diffusion equations (5.9) through (5.12) are applicable to the core and reflector media, along with the various group constants. The presence of a cylindrical rod in the core necessitates the introduction of two new boundary conditions. Extrapolation distances d_1 and d_2 for the fast and thermal fluxes into the absorber are proposed.

$$\frac{\phi_1(a)}{\phi_1'(a)} = d_1 \tag{8.9}$$

$$\frac{\phi_2(a)}{\phi_2'(a)} = d_2 \tag{8.10}$$

where the prime denotes differentiation with respect to r.

The procedure for finding the critical conditions by two-group theory for a bare cylinder of extrapolated radius R will be presented, and the extension to reflected systems and off-center rods and rings of rods merely indicated. The general solutions of Equations (5.9) and (5.10) for a case where now there are no restrictions imposed by finiteness at the origin are

$$\phi_1 = X + Y \tag{8.11}$$
$$\phi_2 = S_1 X + S_2 Y \tag{8.12}$$

where

$$X = A J_0(\bar{\mu} r) + B Y_0(\bar{\mu} r) \tag{8.13}$$
$$Y = C I_0(\bar{\nu} r) + E K_0(\bar{\nu} r) \tag{8.14}$$

Note that the arbitrary coefficients are absorbed in the functions X and Y. The parameters $\bar{\mu}$ and $\bar{\nu}$ are the solutions of the buckling equation (5.15), modified in accordance with Equations (5.32) and (5.33) to account for the finite core height. The boundary conditions on fluxes at R are

$$\phi_1(R) = 0 \tag{8.15}$$
$$\phi_2(R) = 0 \tag{8.16}$$

which can be true only if

$$X(R) = 0 \tag{8.17}$$

and

$$Y(R) = 0 \tag{8.18}$$

Equations (8.9), (8.10), (8.17), and (8.18) constitute a set from which the critical determinant Δ can be found to be

$$\Delta = |a_{ij}| = 0 \tag{8.19}$$

where i and j are the indices of the element in the ith row and jth column as listed below.   The elements are

$$a_{11} = J_0(\bar{\mu}R)$$
$$a_{12} = Y_0(\bar{\mu}R)$$
$$a_{13} = a_{14} = a_{21} = a_{22} = 0$$
$$a_{23} = I_0(\bar{\nu}R)$$
$$a_{24} = K_0(\bar{\nu}R)$$
$$a_{31} = J_0(\bar{\mu}a)/d_1 + \bar{\mu}J_1(\bar{\mu}a) \qquad\qquad (8.20)$$
$$a_{32} = Y_0(\bar{\mu}a)/d_1 + \bar{\mu}Y_1(\bar{\mu}a)$$
$$a_{33} \simeq 0, \qquad a_{43} \simeq 0$$
$$a_{34} = K_0(\bar{\nu}a)/d_1 + \bar{\nu}K_1(\bar{\nu}a)$$
$$a_{41} = S_1[J_0(\bar{\mu}a)/d_2 + \bar{\mu}J_1(\bar{\mu}a)]$$
$$a_{42} = S_1[Y_0(\bar{\mu}a)/d_2 + \bar{\mu}Y_1(\bar{\mu}a)]$$
$$a_{44} = S_2[K_0(\bar{\nu}a)/d_2 + \bar{\nu}K_1(\bar{\nu}a)]$$

The critical condition can be reduced to

$$\psi(\bar{\mu}R) = \psi(a) \qquad\qquad (8.21)$$

where

$$\psi(\bar{\mu}R) = a_{11}/a_{12} \qquad\qquad (8.22)$$

and

$$\psi(a) = \frac{a_{31}a_{44} - a_{41}a_{34}}{a_{32}a_{44} - a_{42}a_{34}} \qquad\qquad (8.23)$$

The function $\psi(a)$ is insensitive to core size and fuel concentration.   The analogy to the roles played by α and α' in Equation (5.42) is evident.   The thermal extrapolation distance d_2 may be obtained from Figure 8.2.   The extrapolation length for fast neutrons d_1 depends on the internal composition of the rod and its moderating ability for fast neutrons.   By the use of Equations (5.21) and (5.34), the modified inverse diffusion length for fast neutrons in the rod will be

$$\bar{\kappa}_{1r} = \sqrt{1/\tau_r + (\pi/H)^2} \qquad\qquad (8.24)$$

The solution of the diffusion equation (5.11) for fast neutrons in a non-multiplying cylinder is $\phi_{1r} \sim I_0(\bar{\kappa}_{1r}r)$.   Application of continuity of fast flux and current across the core-rod boundary yields the result

$$\frac{\phi_1(a)}{\phi_1'(a)} = d_1 = \frac{D_1 I_0(\bar{\kappa}_{1r}a)}{D_{1r}\bar{\kappa}_{1r}I_1(\bar{\kappa}_{1r}a)} \qquad\qquad (8.25)$$

The thermal and fast flux distributions in the core can be calculated by use of the arbitrary coefficients, which turn out to be

$$A = -M/\psi$$
$$B = M$$
$$C = -a_{24}/a_{23}$$
$$E = 1$$

(8.26)

where

$$M = \frac{a_{34}}{(a_{31}/\psi) - a_{32}}$$

(8.27)

Numerical Illustration: Find the reactivity value of a centrally located 1-in. diameter hollow shell that is black to thermal neutrons, for an aluminum-water-U^{235} core containing 3.5 kg of U as in § 5.4.

Solution. The fast extrapolation distance d_1 into the internal void of the shell, where no moderation of fast neutrons takes place, is *infinite.* From the value of $D_2 = 0.2611$ cm, $\lambda_t = 3D_2 = 0.783$ cm and according to Figure 8.2, the thermal extrapolation distance for a 1.27 cm radius rod is 0.681 cm. The 3.5 kg loading will give a critical bare equivalent core of radius $R = j_0/\bar{\mu} = 29.94$ cm and with an axial buckling $B^2 = (\pi/H)^2 = 0.001650$. A calculation table is formed to calculate the reactivity.

$\bar{\mu}^2$	0.006452	$K_1(\bar{\nu}a)$	1.136
$\bar{\mu}$	0.08032	S_1	0.3110
$\bar{\nu}^2$	0.2720	S_2	−3.195
$\bar{\nu}$	0.5215	$1/d_1$	0
a	1.27	$1/d_2$	1.468
$\bar{\mu}a$	0.1026	a_{31}	0.0041
$\bar{\nu}a$	0.6623	a_{32}	−0.5084
$J_0(\bar{\mu}a)$	0.9974	a_{34}	0.5924
$J_1(\bar{\mu}a)$	0.05123	a_{41}	0.4681
$Y_0(\bar{\mu}a)$	−1.518	a_{42}	−0.8511
$Y_1(\bar{\mu}a)$	−6.330	a_{44}	−5.184
$K_0(\bar{\nu}a)$	0.7017	$\psi(a) = \psi(\bar{\mu}R)$	−0.0951

Application of Equation (8.8) with $\bar{\mu}$ replacing B_r gives $\bar{\mu}R = 2.4982$, and assuming R is fixed at 29.94 cm, the new critical $\bar{\mu}$ for the reactor is 0.08344. Hence $\mu^2 = \bar{\mu}^2 + (\pi/H)^2 = 0.008612$. Extrapolation of a plot of μ^2 vs. k based on the reactor design problem of § 5.4 yields $k_1 = 1.5675$, while k_0 was 1.5367. Thus from Equation (8.3), the reactivity is $0.0308/1.5675$ or 0.0196.

Formulas for other core geometries. The critical condition for a ring of M eccentric rods each at distance d from the central axis in a bare reactor is approximately

$$\psi(\bar{\mu}R) \simeq \frac{MJ_0^2(\bar{\mu}d)\psi(a)}{1 + I\psi(a)} \tag{8.28}$$

The term

$$I = \sum_{m=2}^{M} Y_0(\bar{\mu}r_{1m}) \tag{8.29}$$

involving the distances from the first rod to each of the others, represents the mutual "interaction" of the rods. Equation (8.28) is also applicable to a single eccentric rod with $M = 1$, and I is not used.

For the reflected reactor with a single eccentric rod at distance d from the axis (or central rod, $d = 0$), Price (see References) has shown that

$$\alpha = \alpha' + \frac{J_0^2(\bar{\mu}d)\psi(a)}{\psi(\mu R)} (\epsilon - \alpha') \tag{8.30}$$

where the functions α and α' have been defined in Table 5.3 and by Equation (5.43) for the reflected two-group core, and $\epsilon = -\bar{\mu}Y_1(\bar{\mu}R)/Y_0(\bar{\mu}R)$.

General remarks on control elements. (a) *Shape factors.* The effectiveness of control elements of other shapes besides the cylinder can be estimated. From electrostatic analogy, it can be shown that the thin absorbing strip of width w and the cross-shaped element of width $w/\sqrt{2}$ are approximately equivalent to a circular rod of radius $w/4$. Another useful rule of thumb states that odd-shaped systems are equivalent if the *perimeters* measured by wrapping a string about the elements are the same. This rule is satisfied by the electrostatic prediction of the relation of strip and cross, but differs by a factor $4/\pi$ for the relation of strip and circle.

Partly inserted rods. The problem of a single rod extending only part way into the core is reserved until perturbation theory is discussed in § 8.6. The calculation of reactivity value of partly inserted set of *multiple rods* is beset with serious mathematical difficulties. A trick that may be used to estimate the reactivity is to compute a uniformly distributed poison concentration that is equivalent to the fully inserted set of rods. The partial insertion is then treated by a two-region calculation, the upper part of the reactor containing that concentration of poison, the lower part not.

(c) *Control in fast reactors.* Because of the exceedingly short cycle time of a fast reactor, it is not safe to provide a large potential excess multiplication. Thus the excess is limited to around 1 per cent, just above β, rather than 10 per cent or more as in thermal reactors. No xenon-poison effect is observed in the fast reactor, and temperature effects are small. Methods of control include movable fuel elements and absorbing rods of materials such as boron, which has a cross section of 3.5 barns at the mean fast neutron energy.

8.3. *Reactivity changes with time in a converter reactor*

During the long-term irradiation of fuel in a converter reactor for the production of new fissionable fuel from U^{238} or thorium, slow reactivity changes with time occur. The trend is due to the buildup and burnout of the sequence of isotopes used or produced. Estimates of the rate of production thus come out as by-products of the reactivity calculation.

To illustrate the method of analysis, consider a heterogeneous natural-uranium reactor operating at a constant flux over a period of many months. The isotopic ratio U^{238}/U^{235} at the start is 139. After irradiation, there will be present U isotopes of mass 235, 236 and 238, plutonium isotopes 239, 240, 241 and 242, and fission products. Without reference to details of construction, assume that the initial values of f, p, and η are known, and that the neutron leakage is negligible. The net rate of growth (or decline) of the number of atoms per cubic centimeter of a given isotope is of the form

$$\frac{dN}{dt} = -\lambda N + g(t) \tag{8.31}$$

where λ is $\phi\sigma$, and the terms on the right side of the equation represent burnup and production respectively. If g is zero, the solution is

$$N = N_0 e^{-\lambda t} \qquad (8.32)$$

where N_0 is the initial number. If g is not zero, the solution is of the form

$$N = e^{-\lambda t}\left[N_0 + \int_0^t e^{+\lambda t}g(t)\,dt\right] \qquad (8.33)$$

The simplest case is the burnup of U^{235},

$$\frac{dN_{235}}{dt} = -N_{235}\sigma_{235}\phi \qquad (8.34)$$

where ϕ is the *average* flux in the fuel element. The solution is

$$N_{235}(t) = N_{235}(0)e^{-\lambda_{235}t} \qquad (8.35)$$

The U^{238} is removed by both resonance and thermal capture, to form Pu^{239}, which in turn is burned. The appropriate equations are

$$\frac{dN_{238}}{dt} = -N_{238}\sigma_{238}\phi - R \qquad (8.36)$$

$$\frac{dN_{239}}{dt} = -N_{239}\sigma_{239}\phi + N_{238}\sigma_{238}\phi + R \qquad (8.37)$$

where R denotes the resonance capture rate, derived below.

Consider a typical fast neutron of energy below the fast fission threshold. Its chance of experiencing resonance capture is $1 - p$, and of escaping capture is p. The fractional thermal absorption in U^{238} is $f\Sigma_{238}/\Sigma_F$, where F stands for all fuels. The ratio of resonance to thermal absorption is

$$\frac{1 - p}{pf\Sigma_{238}/\Sigma_F}$$

and

$$R = \frac{\phi(1 - p)\overline{\Sigma}}{p} \qquad (8.38)$$

where

$$\overline{\Sigma} = \Sigma_F + \frac{V_m}{V_F}\frac{\overline{\phi}_m}{\phi}\Sigma_m \qquad (8.39)$$

It is noted that $\Sigma_F = N_{235}\sigma_{235} + N_{238}\sigma_{238} + N_{239}\sigma_{239}$ is variable with time, while it can be presumed that $\overline{\phi}_m/\phi$ and p remain essentially constant. The fraction of U^{238} that is removed is small, over the times of interest, and N^{238} can be considered constant for purposes of integrating Equation (8.37). It becomes

$$\frac{dN_{239}}{dt} = -\lambda'_{239}N_{239} + \lambda'_{235}N_{235} + g_1 \qquad (8.40)$$

where

$$\lambda'_{235} = \left(\frac{1}{p} - 1\right)\phi\sigma_{235}$$

and

$$\lambda'_{239} = \left(2 - \frac{1}{p}\right)\phi\sigma_{239}$$

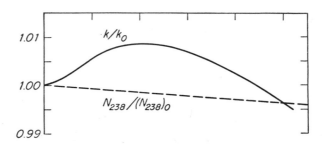

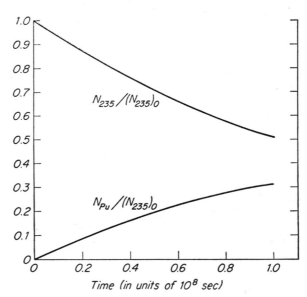

Figure 8.4. Isotopic changes in converter reactor: $\phi = 10^{13}/\text{cm}^2\text{-sec}; f = p = 0.9.$

and the constant

$$g_1 = \frac{\phi \Sigma_{238}}{p} + \frac{1-p}{p} \frac{V_m}{V_F} \bar{\phi}_m \Sigma_m$$

Integration may be performed by the use of Equation (8.33). Figure 8.4 shows a plot of N_{235}, N_{238}, N_{239} and k as a function of time, for operation at a constant flux in the fuel of $10^{13}/\text{cm}^2$-sec in a natural-U reactor for which $p = 0.9$ and $f = 0.9$. Fast fission, leakage, and poisons were ignored to simplify the illustration.

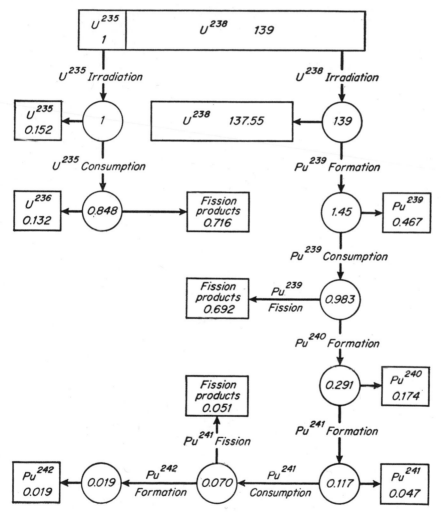

Figure 8.5. Conversion of natural uranium.

The analysis of secondary processes follows the same pattern. The Pu^{239} that is consumed goes into fission products and Pu^{240}; the latter is converted into Pu^{241}, which in turn forms Pu^{242} and fission products. Successive integrations yield the composition of the fuel at any time in the cycle. Figure 8.5 illustrates a case in which about one atom out of 60 in a fuel slug is burned out.

8.4. *Control by burnable poison*

The high rate of consumption of fissionable fuel in a power reactor necessitates frequent replacement of fuel elements with attendant reprocessing cost. One solution is to load the reactor with excess fuel to accommodate burnup, plus a uniformly distributed "burnable poison" to cancel the initial reactivity. As the reactor operates, both fuel and poison will be destroyed, in general at different rates, and the reactivity of the system will vary. A simplified analysis of this response is presented for a reactor operating at constant power. At the outset, time zero, the core will be composed of three classes of materials, each with macroscopic absorption cross section such that the reactor is just critical.

fuel: Σ_{U0}
burnable poison: Σ_{p0}
moderator and other materials: Σ_m

Let the critical thermal utilization at time zero be given by

$$\frac{1}{f_0} = 1 + \frac{\Sigma_m + \Sigma_{p0}}{\Sigma_{U0}} \tag{8.41}$$

The rate of removal of fuel nuclei per cubic centimeter is

$$\frac{dN_U}{dt} = -\phi\Sigma_U \tag{8.42}$$

If the power is assumed to be constant, this burnup rate is independent of time, and for any time t,

$$\phi\Sigma_U = \phi_0\Sigma_{U0} \tag{8.43}$$

where ϕ_0 is the flux at time zero.

Combining Equations (8.42) and (8.43),

$$\Sigma_U(t) = \Sigma_{U0}(1 - \phi_0\sigma_U t) \tag{8.44}$$

and the flux must change with time according to

$$\phi = \frac{\phi_0}{1 - \phi_0 \sigma_U t} \tag{8.45}$$

The rate of burnout of poison nuclei per unit volume is

$$\frac{dN_p}{dt} = -\phi \Sigma_p = -\frac{\phi_0 N_p \sigma_p}{1 - \phi_0 \sigma_U t} \tag{8.46}$$

Integrating Equation (8.46)

$$\Sigma_p = \Sigma_{p0}(1 - \phi_0 \sigma_U t)^{\sigma_p/\sigma_U} = \Sigma_{p0}\left(\frac{\Sigma_U}{\Sigma_{U0}}\right)^{\sigma_p/\sigma_U} \tag{8.47}$$

The reactivity variation may be estimated from Equation (8.3)

$$\rho = \frac{\delta k_e}{k_e} = 1 - \frac{k_0}{k} = 1 - \frac{f_0}{f} \tag{8.48}$$

If Equation (8.41) is introduced, with its counterpart for any time t,

$$\frac{\delta k_e}{k_e} = \frac{\Sigma_m(1 - \Sigma_{U0}/\Sigma_U) + \Sigma_{p0}[1 - (\Sigma_U/\Sigma_{U0})^{(\sigma_p/\sigma_U)-1}]}{\Sigma_m + \Sigma_{p0} + \Sigma_{U0}} \tag{8.49}$$

The general trend of the reactivity is to rise at first, since the burnable poison is removed more rapidly than fuel. Once a large fraction of the poison is gone, the fuel removal will result in a decrease in reactivity.

Numerical Illustration: A thermal reactor core is just critical with $f = 0.8$ without poison or extra fuel. The fuel mass is doubled, and boron is added. Determine the flux and reactivity-fuel characteristic, including the maximum reactivity excursion, and the fraction of the initial fuel that is left by the time the reactor goes sub-critical.

Solution. The absorption cross section of U^{235} is 597.5 barns, and that of B^{10}, the effective poison, is 3555 barns. Thus $\sigma_p/\sigma_U = 5.95$. In order to achieve an $f = 0.8$, Σ_m must be $0.25\Sigma_{Uc}$, where Σ_{Uc} is the *critical* fuel cross section without excess or poison. The amount of poison that must be added as the operation at power starts must be $\Sigma_{p0} = 0.25\Sigma_{Uc}$ also, if the fuel loading is changed to give $\Sigma_{U0} = 2\Sigma_{Uc}$. The working formulas become

$$\Sigma_p/\Sigma_{p0} = x^n, \qquad \phi/\phi_0 = 1/x$$
$$\frac{\delta k_e}{k_e} = 0.1(2 - x^{-1} - x^{n-1})$$

where $x = \Sigma_U/\Sigma_{U0}$ and $n = 5.95$. The results are plotted in
Figures 8.6 and 8.7. The maximum $\delta k_e/k_e$ is approximately
0.043 and the reactor goes sub-critical when 51 per cent of the
fuel remains.

8.5. *Transient fission product poisons*

The absorption of thermal neutrons by fission products that
build up as a reactor operates must be anticipated in the choice of
fuel concentration and control. The amount of poisoning is a
function of flux, operating schedule, cross sections, and the mode
of removal of fission products. One special isotope, Xe^{135}, has a
very high cross section, 2.87×10^6 barns (maxwellian thermal

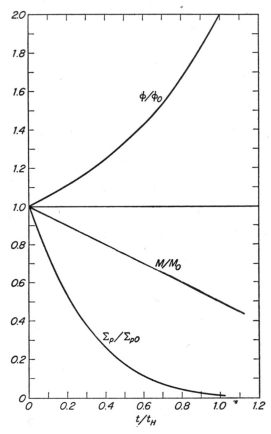

Figure 8.6. Trends in flux, mass, and burnable
poison (t_H = time to consume half the fuel).

value), and a relatively short half-life, which results in a reactivity change with time that demands immediate control.

The fission decay chain in which Xe^{135} arises is

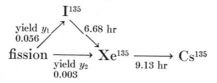

A competition of processes exists—formation, radioactive decay, and burnout.

The rates at which the numbers of nuclei of the isotopes per cm^3 of the fuel volume change with time may be charted:

| | Formation | | Removal | |
	Fission	Decay of parent	Decay	Burnout by flux
Iodine-135.......	$\phi\Sigma_f y_1$	...	$\lambda_I N_I$	...
Xenon-135.......	$\phi\Sigma_f y_2$	$\lambda_I N_I$	$\lambda_{Xe} N_{Xe}$	$N_{Xe}\sigma_{Xe}\phi$

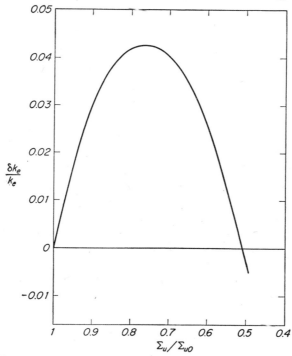

Figure 8.7.   Reactivity excursion with burnable poison.

The λ's are decay constants, the y's atom yields per fission. These rates are applicable at any time during the operation cycle of startup, steady conditions, and during shutdown.

Steady operation. If the reactor has been operating continually for a long time at local flux ϕ, rates of formation and removal are equal. Thus

$$N_{\mathrm{I}} = \frac{y_1 \phi \Sigma_f}{\lambda_{\mathrm{I}}} \tag{8.50}$$

$$N_{\mathrm{Xe}} = \frac{(y_1 + y_2)\phi \Sigma_f}{\lambda_{\mathrm{Xe}} + \phi \sigma_{\mathrm{Xe}}} \tag{8.51}$$

The extent of core poisoning by Xe^{135} can be estimated from the number of atoms. The thermal utilization without poison is given by

$$\frac{1}{f_0} - 1 = \frac{\overline{\phi}_m \Sigma_m V_m}{\overline{\phi}_{\mathrm{U}} \Sigma_{\mathrm{U}} V_{\mathrm{U}}}$$

while that if poison builds up is

$$\frac{1}{f_1} - 1 = \frac{\overline{\phi}_m \Sigma_m V_m}{\overline{\phi}_{\mathrm{U}} \Sigma_{\mathrm{U}} V_{\mathrm{U}}} + \frac{\Sigma_{\mathrm{Xe}}}{\Sigma_{\mathrm{U}}}$$

where the volume occupied by the poison is the uranium volume, and the fluxes are assumed to be unchanged by the poison. Thus the local change in $1/f$ is

$$\Delta \frac{1}{f} = \frac{1}{f_1} - \frac{1}{f_0} = \frac{\Sigma_{\mathrm{Xe}}}{\Sigma_{\mathrm{U}}} \tag{8.52}$$

Combining Equations (8.51) and (8.52),

$$P \equiv \Delta \frac{1}{f} = \frac{(y_1 + y_2)(\sigma_{f\mathrm{U}}/\sigma_{a\mathrm{U}})}{1 + \dfrac{\lambda_{\mathrm{Xe}}/\sigma_{\mathrm{Xe}}}{\phi}} \tag{8.53}$$

which is often called the poisoning. Values of the constants are as follows:

$$\lambda_{\mathrm{I}} = 2.88 \times 10^{-5} \ \mathrm{sec}^{-1}$$
$$\lambda_{\mathrm{Xe}} = 2.11 \times 10^{-5} \ \mathrm{sec}^{-1}$$
$$\sigma_{\mathrm{Xe}} = 2.87 \times 10^{-18} \ \mathrm{cm}^2$$
$$\lambda_{\mathrm{Xe}}/\sigma_{\mathrm{Xe}} = 7.35 \times 10^{12}/\mathrm{cm}^2\text{-sec}$$
$$y_1 = 0.056$$

$$\dot{y}_2 = 0.003$$

$$y = y_1 + y_2 = 0.059$$

$$\sigma_{fU}/\sigma_{aU} = 0.539 \quad \text{(natural U, see § 4.5)}$$

$$\sigma_{fU}/\sigma_{aU} = 0.844 \quad (\text{U}^{235})$$

Thus for pure U^{235}, Equation (8.53) becomes

$$\Delta \frac{1}{f} = \frac{0.0498}{1 + \dfrac{7.35 \times 10^{12}}{\phi}}$$

The maximum change in $1/f$, for very high flux density, i.e., $\phi \gg \lambda_{Xe}/\sigma_{Xe} = 7.35 \times 10^{12}$, is calculated to be 0.0498 for U^{235} and 0.0318 for natural U. For low fluxes, $\phi \ll 7.35 \times 10^{12}$, the poisoning effect is $\phi/(7.35 \times 10^{12})$ times these limiting levels, and is of little importance.

Numerical Illustration: A heterogeneous water-moderated core, 20 per cent U^{235} isotopic content, operating at central thermal flux $2 \times 10^{13}/\text{cm}^2\text{-sec}$, has a clean critical thermal utilization of 0.80. Find the poisoning effect in terms of the change in $1/f$ at the center of the core.

Solution. The ratio σ_{fU}/σ_{aU} for this isotopic concentration in a maxwellian flux at thermal energy is

$$\frac{(0.20)(504.4)}{(0.20)(597.5) + (0.80)(2.44)} = 0.831$$

Thus from Equation (8.53)

$$\Delta \frac{1}{f} = \frac{(0.059)(0.831)}{1 + \dfrac{7.35 \times 10^{12}}{2 \times 10^{13}}} = 0.0359$$

Transient after shutdown. The equilibrium poisoning is no higher than 0.05, because of the continued burnout of Xe^{135} by the thermal flux. If the reactor is shut down after a period of steady operation, the flux goes almost to zero, but the iodine continues to feed xenon into the system by decay. The poison builds up to a maximum, after which the rate of decay of xenon exceeds the supply from iodine. The transient is governed by the equation

$$\frac{dN_{Xe}}{dt} = -\lambda_{Xe}N_{Xe} + \lambda_I(N_I)_0 e^{-\lambda_I t} \qquad (8.54)$$

where $(N_I)_0$ is the accumulation of iodine at shutdown, time zero. Integrating Equation (8.54), with $(N_{Xe})_0$ as the number of xenon atoms present at shutdown,

$$N_{Xe} = (N_{Xe})_0 e^{-\lambda_{Xe} t} + \frac{(N_I)_0 \lambda_I}{\lambda_{Xe} - \lambda_I} (e^{-\lambda_I t} - e^{-\lambda_{Xe} t}) \qquad (8.55)$$

Figure 8.8 shows a plot of $\Delta(1/f)$ vs. time after shutdown for several fluxes in the range of 10^{12} to 3×10^{14}, computed from Equa-

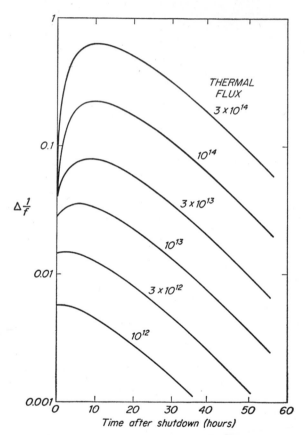

Figure 8.8. Xe^{135} transient after shutdown, for U^{235} fission.

tion (8.55), and assuming equilibrium conditions prior to shutdown. The reactivity excursion is about 20 per cent for high fluxes. This necessitates a very effective control rod system, if it is hoped to override the xenon transient at all times.

8.6. *Calculation of reactivity by perturbation methods*

Several classes of problems involving localized or distributed poisons can be solved by the use of perturbation theory. Some particular applications are cited.

(a) The critical fuel mass of a core with an absorbing metal container in turn surrounded by a spherical reflector can be computed by treating the container as a perturbation of the simpler two-region system.

(b) The determination of reactivity loss due to the fission product Xe^{135}, the distribution of which in a core is flux-dependent, is discussed in § 8.5.

(c) A spatial variation in moderator density in a boiling reactor core results from the usual non-uniform power distribution. An estimate of the reactivity change from a reference critical condition can be made.

(d) The reactivity value of a partially-inserted control rod can be approximated, for use in the establishment of criteria on drive mechanisms.

The simplest perturbation theory is based on the *one-group model* of neutron motion. The critical reactor obeys the equation

$$D \, \nabla^2\phi + (k - 1)\Sigma_a\phi = 0 \qquad (8.56)$$

Now assume that the absorption cross section and k are changed by adding or removing a poison in such a way that the coefficient of ϕ is changed to a new value $(k' - 1)\Sigma_a'$, and that the reactor is super-critical. The diffusion coefficient is taken to be constant. The time-dependent equation is thus

$$D \, \nabla^2\phi' + (k' - 1)\Sigma_a'\phi' = \frac{1}{v} \frac{\partial\phi'}{\partial t} \qquad (8.57)$$

The flux will increase with period T, the reciprocal of which is ν, so that $\partial\phi'/\partial t = \phi'/T$ or $\nu\phi'$, as in Equation (6.36). By analogy with § 6.3, use of the relations $\nabla^2\phi' = -B^2\phi'$, $D/\Sigma_a' = L'^2$, and $k'/(1 + B^2L'^2) = k_e$, allows Equation (8.57) to be written

$$k'\Sigma_a'v \frac{\delta k_e}{k_e} \phi' = \nu\phi' \qquad (8.58)$$

Now multiply Equation (8.58) by the original flux distribution ϕ and integrate over the reactor coordinates. The result is

$$\frac{\delta k_e}{k_e} \int k' \Sigma_a' v \phi \phi' \, dV = v \int \phi \phi' \, dV \qquad (8.59)$$

The inverse period v may be eliminated by multiplying Equations (8.56) and (8.57) by ϕ' and ϕ respectively, again integrating over the reactor, and subtracting equations. This gives

$$\int v \, \delta[(k-1)\Sigma_a] \phi \phi' \, dV = v \int \phi \phi' \, dV \qquad (8.60)$$

where $\delta[(k-1)\Sigma_a]$ is the change in this parameter. Let us consider the special case in which a poison is added, but the fuel cross section is unchanged, so that $k\Sigma_a = p\eta\Sigma_{aU}$ is constant. Thus $\delta[(k-1)\Sigma_a] = -\delta\Sigma_a$. Comparing Equations (8.59) and (8.60), and assuming that the disturbed flux ϕ' and the original flux ϕ are approximately the same, gives the absorption reactivity by perturbation theory,

$$\rho = \frac{\delta k_e}{k_e} = \frac{-\int \delta\Sigma_a \phi^2 \, dV}{\int k\Sigma_a \phi^2 \, dV} \qquad (8.61)$$

One might expect that the reactivity should be proportional to the fractional change in absorption, but the need for a weighting factor of ϕ^2 is surprising. A plausible argument may be advanced to justify it. At a point where the flux is ϕ, the rate of loss of neutrons from the cycle is $\phi\Sigma_a$. This removal competes with the fission process. Now, the probability that a fission neutron will remain in the reactor to maintain the cycle is greatest for those produced near the center, where ϕ is large. Thus an absorption in the region of high flux is more important than one in a low flux, and an additional factor of ϕ must be applied.

A generalization of Equation (8.61) that includes changes in neutron speed, fuel cross section, and diffusion coefficient, as well as absorption, may also be derived. The result, stated without proof, is

$$\rho = \frac{\delta k_e}{k_e} = \frac{\int \{\delta[(k-1)\Sigma_a v]\phi^2 - \delta(Dv) \, |\nabla\phi|^2\} \, dV}{\int k\Sigma_a v \phi^2 \, dV} \qquad (8.62)$$

where $\nabla\phi$ is the gradient of the flux. Several applications of the perturbation equations or the ϕ^2 weighting principle are now analyzed.

Comparison of localized and distributed poisons. Consider the reactivity effect of a poison of volume V_p, cross section

Σ_a. The ratio of effect when located at the center of a bare sphere of volume V_R, to that when distributed throughout the core is derived. The perturbation at the center is proportional to $V_p\Sigma_a\phi_c^2$ where ϕ_c is the central flux. In the distributed case, the amount of poison absorption per unit volume is $V_p\Sigma_a/V_R$ and the poison effect is proportional to

$$\int_0^R \frac{V_p\Sigma_a}{V_R}\,[\phi(r)]^2 4\pi r^2\,dr$$

Inserting $\phi(r) = \phi_c\dfrac{\sin \pi r/R}{\pi r/R}$ and integrating, the latter becomes $\dfrac{3}{2\pi^2}\,V_p\Sigma_a\phi_c^2$. The ratio of reactivities is thus $2\pi^2/3$, or the poison is 6.58 times as effective at the center of the core as when uniformly distributed. Similar large factors relate the effects of poisons in cubes and cylinders.

Reactivity of partially inserted control rod. Let us visualize the control rod first as a weak absorber that does not disturb the flux appreciably. If it has a cross section that is larger than the core by an amount Σ_a, then a rod completely inserted in a bare reactor of height H creates a reactivity effect measured by

$$(\delta k_e)_{\max} \sim \int_0^H \Sigma_a\phi^2\,dz$$

assuming flux is constant radially. The partially inserted rod, with tip a distance z from the top, has a worth

$$\delta k_e \sim \int_0^z \Sigma_a\phi^2\,dz$$

Now letting $\phi = \phi_c \sin \pi z/H$, we find $(\delta k_e)_{\max} \sim H/2$, while

$$\delta k_e \sim \frac{H}{\pi}\left[\frac{1}{2}\frac{\pi z}{H} - \frac{1}{4}\sin\frac{2\pi z}{H}\right]$$

Their ratio is

$$\frac{(\delta k_e)}{(\delta k_e)_{\max}} = \frac{z}{H} - \frac{\sin 2\pi z/H}{2\pi} \tag{8.63}$$

A plot of this ratio appears in Figure 8.9. This was derived under the assumption that the rod was a weak absorber. It turns out however, that the formula is surprisingly accurate for an absorber that is black to thermal neutrons. This function is slowly vary-

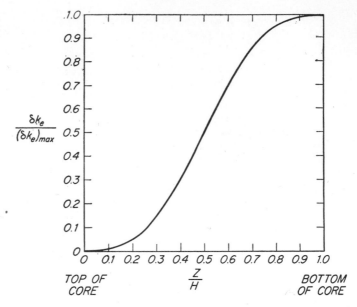

Figure 8.9. Control rod worth as a function of position.

ing near $z = 0$ and $z = H$, with a maximum slope at $z = H/2$ equal to twice the average slope. The rate of increase of multiplication at any position with rod speed v is

$$\frac{d(\delta k_e)}{dt} = \frac{2v}{H}(\delta k_e)_{\max} \sin^2 \pi z/H \qquad (8.64)$$

Numerical Illustration: With a rod withdrawal rate of 1.5 ft/min, find the time required for δk_e to reach $\beta = 0.0073$ in a bare reactor of height 3 ft, total rod value $(\delta k_e)_{\max} = 0.05$. Also find the rate of increase of reactivity at this instant.

Solution. Letting $u = 2\pi vt/H$, we may write Equation (8.63) as $u - \sin u = (2\pi)(0.0073)/0.05 = 0.9173$. Solving by trial and error, $u = 1.872$ and $t = (3)(1.872)/(2\pi)(1.5) = 0.60$ min. From Equation (8.64) the rate of increase of δk_e is $d(\delta k_e)/dt = [(2)(1.5)(0.05)/3] \sin^2 0.936 = 0.0402/$min.

Xenon poison. The local effect of equilibrium Xe^{135} poison on thermal utilization in a reactor was shown in § 8.5 to be given by

$$P = \Delta \frac{1}{f} = \frac{y\sigma_{fU}/\sigma_{aU}}{1 + \dfrac{\lambda_{Xe}/\sigma_{Xe}}{\phi}} \tag{8.65}$$

The proper average value of $\Delta(1/f)$ over a fixed-fuel reactor is the ϕ^2 weighted average

$$\overline{P} = \frac{\int \phi^2 P \, dV}{\int \phi^2 \, dV} = P_m \frac{\int \dfrac{\phi^3 \, dV}{\phi + \phi_1}}{\int \phi^2 \, dV} \tag{8.66}$$

where $P_m = y\sigma_{fU}/\sigma_{aU}$ is the maximum poisoning for very high flux levels and $\phi_1 = \lambda_{Xe}/\sigma_{Xe} = 7.35 \times 10^{12}$. Numerical integration is required in the evaluation of $\overline{P}$. It is convenient to express Equation (8.66) in the same form as Equation (8.65).

$$\overline{P} = \frac{P_m}{1 + \phi_1/\phi_e} \tag{8.67}$$

where ϕ_e is an effective flux. For large flux, $\phi_e \simeq \overline{\phi^2}/\overline{\phi}$, and for small flux, $\phi_e \simeq \overline{\phi^3}/\overline{\phi^2}$, which take on the following values for the two important unreflected geometries.

	Sphere	Finite cylinder
$\phi_1 \gg \phi_c$	$0.500\phi_c$	$0.490\phi_c$
$\phi_1 \ll \phi_c$	$0.618\phi_c$	$0.613\phi_c$

An empirical value of ϕ_e that is accurate near $\phi_1/\phi_c = 1$ is $\phi_e \simeq 0.588\,\phi_c$. It will be noted that the ratio ϕ_e/ϕ_c is not at all sensitive to flux level, and is independent of reactor dimensions.

Distributed coolant. The perturbation method is now applied to find the effect of a coolant distributed according to the flux. This was derived in § 7.4 by differential equations methods. The introduction of an extra poison $\Sigma_p(z)$ will require a uniform reduction in moderator cross section by amount $\Delta\Sigma_m$ to maintain criticality. From Equation (8.61), this implies that

$$\int \delta\Sigma_a \phi^2 \, dV = 0$$

Thus for a slab reactor, $\Sigma_p = \Sigma_{pc} \cos \dfrac{\pi z}{H}$, and

$$\int_{-H/2}^{H/2} \left(\Sigma_{pc} \cos \frac{\pi z}{H} - \Delta\Sigma_m \right) \left(\cos \frac{\pi z}{H} \right)^2 dz = 0$$

Integration yields $\Delta\Sigma_m = (8/3\pi)\Sigma_{pc}$, as found in § 7.4. A similar analysis will give the effect of fuel consumption.

For disturbances of reactors normally calculated by two-group theory, a more advanced approach is recommended: the two-group perturbation theory. References are listed at the end of the chapter on this subject.

Problems

8.1. A bare-equivalent cubical reactor of extrapolated side s has a safety blade consisting of a thin sheet of absorber that cuts the reactor in two. Show that critical equation with blade inserted according to modified one-group theory is approximately $B_x s/2 = \pi$. Are the halves of the reactor really isolated, as would be implied by this result? Show how this defect can be remedied by the use of two-group theory.

8.2. The control rod guide for a bare cylindrical reactor of height H consists of a hollow tube of radius a mounted along the central axis of the core. Assuming that both the fast and thermal fluxes have zero slope at the tube surface, derive a critical condition for the reactor.

Answer.

$$\frac{J_0(\bar\mu R)}{Y_0(\bar\mu R)} = \frac{J_1(\bar\mu a)}{Y_1(\bar\mu a)}$$

8.3. Compute the fast extrapolation distance into a cylindrical control rod of radius 0.5 in. composed of B_4C, density 2 gm/cm³, in a cylindrical reactor of extrapolated height 75 cm, $D_1 = 1.1$ cm. Assume that the age and fast diffusion coefficient of B_4C are the same as for graphite with the *same total atom density*.

Answer. 310 cm.

8.4. Find the equivalent rod radius for (a) an absorbing strip and (b) for a cross, each of 3-in. width. Estimate equivalent rod radii by the string perimeter method, for (c) the elliptical element of semi-axes $a = 2$ in., $b = 1$ in., and (d) the square element of side $s = 3$ in.

Answers. (a) 0.75 in.; (b) 1.06 in.; (c) by elliptic functions, 1.542 in.; by approximate formula, 1.581 in.; (d) 1.910 in.

8.5. Show that the relative reactivity values of small eccentric and central control rods correspond to the prediction by perturbation theory, § 8.6.

8.6. (a) Calculate the new critical radius of the aluminum-water-U^{235} reactor (Numerical Illustration, § 8.2) if the materials constants are not changed. (b) Calculate and plot the radial thermal flux distribution.

Answers. (a) 31.10 cm; (b) $\phi_2 \simeq 4.16 J_0(\bar{\mu}r) + 0.396 Y_0(\bar{\mu}r) - 3.195 K_0(\bar{\nu}r)$.

8.7. Set up and solve differential equations for the fuel consumption and U^{233} production in a homogeneous breeder core containing a solution of U^{235} and Th^{232}, with initial atom ratio $N_{Th-232}/N_{U-235} = 10$, and constant thermal flux of $10^{14}/cm^2$-sec. Note the following maxwellian thermal cross sections and neutrons per absorption.

	U^{235}	Th^{232}	U^{233}
$\bar{\sigma}_f$	504.4	. . .	472.5
$\bar{\sigma}_a$	597.5	6.2	518.6
η	2.08	. . .	2.31

Answers. Where t is in units of 10^8 sec,

$$\frac{N_{235}}{(N_{235})_0} = e^{-5.975t}, \qquad \frac{N_{233}}{(N_{235})_0} = 0.121(e^{-0.062t} - e^{-5.186t})$$

8.8. Investigate the error incurred in Problem 8.7 by ignoring the intermediate breeding stage Pa^{233}, half-life 27.4 days, absorption cross section 140 barns.

8.9. Calculate an effective value for η (neutrons per absorption in total fuel) by the time the reactor of Problem 8.7 has operated for 1 yr.
Answer. 2.16.

8.10. (a) Show that if the flux is assumed to be uniform through the cells of a natural or slightly enriched heterogeneous converter reactor, the rate of change with time of k is given by

$$\frac{1}{k}\frac{dk}{dt} = \frac{1}{S}\frac{dS}{dt} - \frac{f}{\Sigma_F}\frac{d\Sigma_F}{dt}$$

where S is the sum of $N\sigma_f\nu$ for all fuels, and Σ_F is the sum of $N\sigma_a$ for all fuels.

(b) Evaluate the initial $\frac{1}{k}\frac{dk}{dt}$ for the following reactor: average thermal flux $10^{13}/cm^2$-sec, U enriched to 1.4 per cent U^{235}, $V_1/V_0 = 200$, $f = 0.9$, $p = 0.9$, $\epsilon = 1.04$.
Answer. $-9.0 \times 10^{10}/$sec.

8.11. Estimate the rate at which a control rod of reactivity value 0.0001 per in. of travel must move to accomodate the buildup of Xe poison in a 200-liter homogeneous highly enriched U^{235} reactor with $\Sigma_{aU} = 0.08$, $\Sigma_{am} = 0.02$, that has been running at power 20 megawatts, and is suddenly cut back to low power but remains critical.
Answer. 3.4 in./min.

8.12. Investigate the reactivity trend with the element lithium as a burnout poison (σ_a for Li^6 at 2200 meters/sec is 945 barns) instead of boron in the illustrative example of § 8.4. What poison cross section is needed to achieve an initial reactivity rise?

Answer. $\sigma_p > 2\sigma_U$.

References

Glasstone, Samuel, and Milton C. Edlund, *The Elements of Nuclear Reactor Theory.* New York: D. Van Nostrand Co. (1952).

Murray, Raymond L., and John W. Niestlie, "Reactor Control Rod Theories," *Nucleonics*, February 1955, p. 18.

Davison, B., and S. Kushneriuk, *Linear Extrapolation Length for a Black Sphere and a Black Cylinder*, MT-214. Ottawa: National Research Council of Canada (1946).

Garabedian, H. L., *Control Rod Theory for a Cylindrical Reactor*, AECD-3666 (1950, declassified 1955).

Garabedian, H. L., *Theory of Homogeneous Control of a Cylindrical Reactor*, AECD-3667 (1950, declassified 1954).

Bogaardt, M., and N. Bustraan, "Producing Plutonium in U-D$_2$O Reactors," *Nucleonics*, December 1954, p. 32.

Harrer, J. M., and J. A. Deshong, Jr., "Discontinuous Servo for Control of Power Reactors." *Nucleonics*, January 1954. p. 44.

Lundby, A., and N. Holt, "Kinetic Behavior of a Thermal Heavy-Water Reactor," *Nucleonics*, January 1954, p. 22.

Taraba, F. R., "Nomograms for Uranium Burnup," *Nucleonics*, August 1954, p. 51.

Gold, Louis, "Production of Nuclear Fuels by Induced Radioactive Chains," *Nucleonics*, April 1953, p. 40.

Weinberg, A. M., *Perturbation Theory*, Chapter 20, "Reactor Physics Notes." (Unpublished)

McMurray, H. L., *Perturbation Theory and Applications*, AECD-3656 (1952).

Peaceful Uses of Atomic Energy, Volume 5, *Physics of Reactor Design.* New York: Columbia University Press (1956).

Spinrad, B. I., J. C. Carter, and C. Eggler, "Reactivity Changes and Reactivity Lifetimes of Fixed Fuel Elements in Thermal Reactors," Paper P/835.

Bernstein, Seymour, and E. C. Smith, "The Cross Section of the Fission Product Poison Xe^{135} as a Function of Energy," Paper P/591.

Price, William T., *Theory of the Reflected Reactor with Eccentric Control Rod*, Master's Thesis, North Carolina State College, Raleigh (1955).

Chapter 9

TRANSPORT THEORY

‖‖

The diffusion theory of neutron motion in a reactor is adequate for a large portion of reactor design problems.   Certain modifications such as the arbitrary introduction of the transport mean free path and the extrapolation distance tend to correct some of the defects of diffusion theory.   Whenever the reactor problem involves strong absorption, a special neutron source, or a need for accurate flux data at a boundary, it is necessary to turn to the better physical approximation provided by *transport theory*, which takes explicit account of the *directions* of motion of neutrons in addition to the number density.   In this chapter, the terminology, fundamental formulas, and uses of transport theory for neutrons of one speed are presented, along with a demonstration of the transition to diffusion theory.

9.1. *Distribution of flux in direction*

The flux as defined in § 2.2 was associated with neutrons having a common speed* and without regard to the *directions of motion*.   Should one attach velocity vectors to the n neutrons instantaneously found in a unit volume of an infinite medium, the pattern would be as shown in Figure 9.1(a).   An equal number of vectors would pass through every element of area on a sphere of unit radius constructed about the origin.   This uniform distribution is designated as an *isotropic* flux, for which the diffusion

---

* In the case of thermal neutrons, it was recognized that the neutrons had a variety of speeds, but it was found possible to replace the maxwellian distribution with a *group* having common speed.

method is exact. Consider instead the situation as shown in Figure 9.1(b) that exists very near the surface of a bare reactor. Since practically no neutrons return from the right, there can be very few neutrons with vectors pointing toward the left. The flux is *anisotropic*, with a variation in the distribution of vectors piercing the sphere. In order to describe the flux properly, a further breakdown besides position and energy is needed. An angle or angles must be introduced. Consider again the slab system employed in the analysis of current, § 2.3. Neutrons with

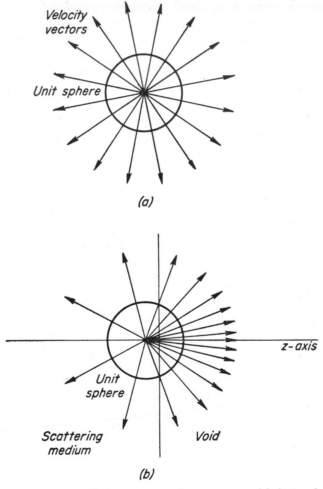

Figure 9.1. Velocity vectors of n neutrons: (a) isotropic flux, (b) anisotropic flux near boundary of medium.

different directions of motion may be distinguished by the use of two angles: θ between the velocity vector and the z-axis, and φ, an azimuthal angle, as shown in Figure 9.2. Now let us restrict

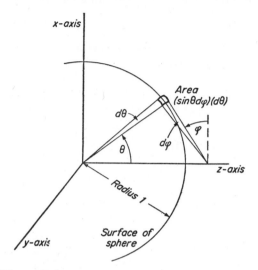

Figure 9.2.　Angle-dependent neutron density.

attention to the differential number of neutrons that are aimed in a range $d\theta$ at θ and $d\varphi$ at φ. The corresponding area on the sphere of unit radius drawn to surround the origin of all neutron velocity vectors is $(1 \cdot d\theta)(1 \cdot \sin \theta \cdot d\varphi)$ or $\sin \theta \, d\theta \, d\varphi$, which we designate $d\Omega$, the element of solid angle. If $N(z,\theta,\varphi)$ denotes the number of neutrons per *unit* solid angle, then $N(z,\theta,\varphi) \, d\Omega$ is the number of neutrons with vectors through the differential area. They constitute a flux of magnitude $N(z,\theta,\varphi)v \, d\Omega$ or $\Phi(z,\Omega) \, d\Omega$, where Ω is an abbreviation for the coordinates θ,φ and where

$$\Phi(z,\Omega) = N(z,\Omega)v \qquad (9.1)$$

is the flux per unit solid angle. This new function is dependent on both position and angle. Hence it is more general than the flux as usually defined, which is the total or *scalar* flux,

$$\phi(z) = \int \Phi(z,\Omega) \, d\Omega \qquad (9.2)$$

The integral is taken over all direction angles θ and φ. To show that this scalar flux has the same meaning as the flux ordinarily used in diffusion theory, consider an isotropic distribution, for which $N = n/4\pi$, $\Phi = nv/4\pi$. Then Equation (9.2) becomes

$$\phi(z) = \int_{\theta=0}^{\theta=\pi} \int_{\varphi=0}^{\varphi=2\pi} \frac{nv}{4\pi} \sin \theta \, d\theta \, d\varphi = nv$$

9.2. Derivation of the Boltzmann or transport equation

A new neutron balance equation analogous to Equation (3.8) of diffusion theory is established, considering, as before, the flows in and out of a volume element in space. An accounting is also kept of gains and losses from a selected range of angles.

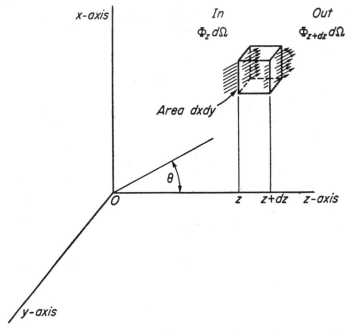

Figure 9.3.   Geometry for deriving flow term in transport equation.

Suppose the neutrons of interest are directed at an angle θ with respect to the z-axis, as shown in Figure 9.3. The number crossing the area $dx \, dy$ per second from below is

$$(\Phi)_z \, d\Omega \, dx \, dy \cos \theta$$

where the factor cos θ accounts for the oblique crossing and the subscript denotes the point of measurement. The number leaving is

$$(\Phi)_{z+dz} \, d\Omega \, dx \, dy \, \cos \theta$$

and the *net* number leaving is

$$\frac{\partial \Phi}{\partial z} \, d\Omega \, dx \, dy \, dz \, \cos \theta$$

The partial derivative is used because the flux depends on z, φ and θ. The *leakage* per unit volume is therefore

$$L = \frac{\partial \Phi}{\partial z} \, d\Omega \, \cos \theta \tag{9.3}$$

The *absorption* rate per unit volume is clearly

$$A = \Phi \, d\Omega \, \Sigma_a \tag{9.4}$$

Any neutron that is scattered at all within the element is deflected in direction and thus removed from our attention. The rate of loss due to *scattering-out* per unit volume is thus

$$S_o = \Phi \, d\Omega \, \Sigma_s \tag{9.5}$$

Neutrons may appear in the volume element because of artificial sources or slowing into the range. Let the rate of *supply* per unit volume be

$$Q = S \, d\Omega \tag{9.6}$$

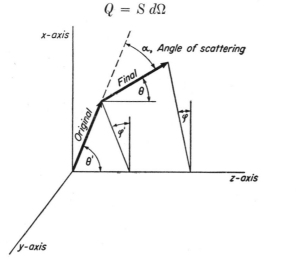

Figure 9.4. Transfer of neutrons from direction Ω' to direction Ω by scattering.

where S is the source per unit solid angle, a function of z. For most purposes, S is taken to be isotropic, of magnitude $S_T/4\pi$, where S_T is the total number of neutrons emitted per second per unit volume.

The final term in the balance, having to do with scattering-in, provides considerably more complication than did the previous terms. Neutrons from other directions of motion θ' and φ' may be scattered while in the volume element, and enter the ranges of angles of interest at θ and φ. Figure 9.4 shows how the angles are related. Now the flux in the range $d\Omega'$ from which neutrons come is

$$\Phi(z,\Omega')\,d\Omega'$$

and the scattering rate per unit volume is

$$\Phi(z,\Omega')\,d\Omega'\,\Sigma_s$$

Let the chance that a neutron will scatter through an angle α and enter $d\Omega$ be denoted by $f(\mu_0)\,d\Omega$ where $\mu_0 = \cos\alpha$. The contribution to $d\Omega$ from $d\Omega'$ is thus

$$\Phi(z,\Omega')\,d\Omega'\,\Sigma_s f(\mu_0)\,d\Omega$$

That due to all initial directions is the integral over θ' and φ', or

$$\mathcal{S}_i = \int_{\Omega'} \Phi(z,\Omega')\,d\Omega'\,\Sigma_s f(\mu_0)\,d\Omega \tag{9.7}$$

which represents the *scattering-in* term.

The neutron balance equation for steady-state is abbreviated

$$L + A + \mathcal{S}_o = Q + \mathcal{S}_i$$

Using Equations (9.3) to (9.7) and cancelling out a common factor $d\Omega$,

$$\cos\theta\,\frac{\partial\Phi(z,\Omega)}{\partial z} + \Phi(z,\Omega)\Sigma = S + \int_{\Omega'} \Phi(z,\Omega')\Sigma_s f(\mu_0)\,d\Omega' \tag{9.8}$$

The terms representing absorption and scattering have been grouped by use of $\Sigma = \Sigma_s + \Sigma_a$. The equation may be rewritten in a standard notation, as follows. (a) Let $\cos\theta = \mu$, whence $\sin\theta\,d\theta = -d(\cos\theta) = -d\mu$. The range of μ is from 1 to -1 as θ goes from 0 to π. (b) Let the *differential* microscopic cross section for scattering $\sigma_s(\mu_0)$ be the probability per nucleus of scattering through an angle α, whose cosine is μ_0, into a *unit solid angle*. (If the scattering were equally probable in all directions, $\sigma_s(\mu_0)$

would be $1/4\pi$ times the usual scattering cross section.)   Thus $\Sigma_s f(\mu_0) = \mathfrak{N}\sigma_s(\mu_0)$, where $\mathfrak{N}$ is now the number of nuclei per cm³. The *Boltzmann transport equation* (one dimension, monoenergetic neutrons) is then

$$\mu \frac{\partial \Phi}{\partial z} + \Phi\Sigma = S + \int_{-1}^{1} \int_{0}^{2\pi} \Phi'\mathfrak{N}\sigma_s(\mu_0) \, d\mu' \, d\varphi' \qquad (9.9)$$

Since the equation contains the flux, its derivative, and its integral, it must be solved for Φ as a function of position and angle by special methods.   In the one-dimensional problem, it will eventually be possible for Φ to be written functionally as $\Phi(z,\mu)$ since it does not depend explicitly on the angle φ.

9.3. *Rigorous solution for heavy element*

As discussed in § 2.5, the scattering of neutrons in the laboratory system by a heavy element such as uranium is very close to being symmetric.   Even though scattering would be strictly symmetric only with an infinitely heavy target, little error is incurred in setting $\sigma_s(\mu_0) = \sigma_s/4\pi$.   Equation (9.9) simplifies to

$$\mu \frac{\partial \Phi(z,\mu)}{\partial z} + \Phi(z,\mu)\Sigma = S(z) + \frac{\phi(z)\Sigma_s}{4\pi} \qquad (9.10)$$

where use was made of Equation (9.2).   The functional dependence is brought back for emphasis of the fact that Φ is still a function of two variables.

Consider a plane source of unit strength per unit area, located at the origin in an infinite medium.   By use of the Fourier transform, the angular dependence can be eliminated, to obtain $\phi(z)$. The result according to Marshak, Hurwitz, and Brooks (see References) has two parts:

$$\phi(z) = \phi_1(z) + \phi_2(z) \qquad (9.11)$$
$$\phi_1(z) = Ae^{-\kappa z} \qquad (9.12)$$

where κ is the solution of a transcendental equation

$$\kappa/\Sigma = \tanh \kappa/\Sigma_s \qquad (9.13)$$

and

$$A = \frac{(\kappa/\Sigma_s)[1 - (\kappa/\Sigma)^2]}{(\kappa/\Sigma)^2 - \Sigma_a/\Sigma} \qquad (9.14)$$

$$\phi_2(z) = \frac{1}{2} \int_1^\infty \frac{e^{-\eta \Sigma z} \, d\eta/\eta}{\left[1 - \frac{\Sigma_s}{\eta \Sigma} \tanh^{-1}\left(\frac{1}{\eta}\right)\right]^2 + \left(\frac{\pi \Sigma_s}{2\eta \Sigma}\right)^2} \quad (9.15)$$

with η as a variable of integration.   Figure 9.5 shows the separate terms in Equation (9.11) and their sum.   Two important features

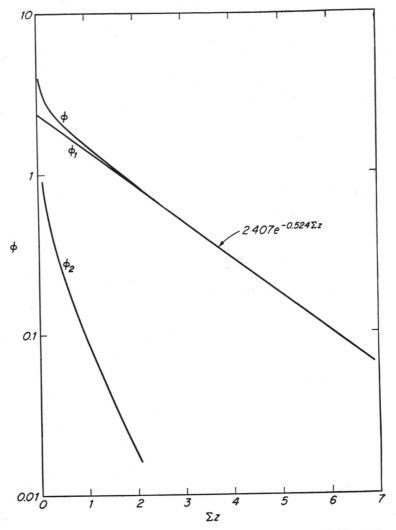

Figure 9.5.   Flux distribution from unit plane source, $\Sigma_a/\Sigma = 0.1$, isotropic scattering.

of this result should be noted.   (a) The term ϕ_2 is small except near the source.   If one is interested in fluxes far from the source, i.e., several mean free paths away, ϕ_1 is the main term.   (b) The flux as given by ϕ_1 is exponential in character, as is predicted by diffusion theory, where the flux due to a unit plane source is

$$\phi(z) = \frac{Le^{-z/L}}{2D} \quad \begin{array}{l} \text{diffusion theory flux} \\ \text{from plane source} \end{array} \quad (9.16)$$

In place of $1/L$ in the exponent, Equation (9.12) has κ.   In order to bring the results into conformity, merely let Σ_a in Equation (9.13) be assumed very small compared with Σ_s.   The result is readily shown to be

$$\kappa \simeq \sqrt{3\Sigma_a\Sigma_s}$$

If we recall that for a heavy element, $\Sigma_s \simeq \Sigma_t$,

$$\kappa \simeq 1/L$$

We thus deduce that diffusion theory is applicable if two conditions are met—the point of observation is far from the source, and the absorption is small.   It is suggested, however, that even fairly strong absorbers can be treated with diffusion theory if we borrow κ as calculated from Equation (9.13) to use whenever $1/L$ would appear.   An adjustment in the amplitude of the diffusion theory flux, Equation (9.16) by a factor $2AD/L$ will further bring the diffusion result into line.

9.4. *Spherical harmonics solution*

The solution of the transport equation just completed had two defects: (a) Information regarding *angular* distribution was lost in the process of obtaining a better approximation for $\phi(z)$; (b) The scattering in the laboratory system had to be assumed isotropic.   The spherical harmonics approach now described can yield $\Phi(z,\Omega)$ for *any* scattering element.   First it is proposed that $\Phi(z,\mu)$ or the corresponding $N(z,\mu)$ can be written as an infinite power series in the variable μ, with coefficients that depend on z. Actually it is preferable to use a set of functions of μ, the Legendre polynomials $P_l(\mu)$, for the expansion.   These are

l	$P_l(\mu)$
0	1
1	μ
2	$\frac{1}{2}(3\mu^2 - 1)$
3	$\frac{1}{2}(5\mu^3 - 3\mu)$
.	.
.	.

The angular neutron density is expressed as

$$N(z,\mu) = \frac{1}{4\pi}\left[N_0(z)P_0(\mu) + 3N_1(z)P_1(\mu) + 5N_2(z)P_2(\mu) + \cdots\right]$$

or more compactly,

$$N(z,\mu) = \sum_{l=0}^{\infty} \frac{2l+1}{4\pi} N_l(z)P_l(\mu) \tag{9.17}$$

The analogy to the Fourier series expansion of a function of one dimension is evident.

The various coefficients $N_l(z)$ are determined by use of the property of Legendre polynomials that

$$\int_{-1}^{1} P_l(\mu)P_m(\mu)\,d\mu = \begin{cases} 0 & \text{if } m \neq l \\ \dfrac{2}{2l+1} & \text{if } m = l \end{cases} \tag{9.18}$$

If both sides of Equation (9.17) are multiplied by $P_m(\mu)\,d\mu$ and integration from -1 to 1 performed, all terms on the right drop out except the one with $m = l$ and

$$N_l(z) = 2\pi \int_{-1}^{1} N(z,\mu)P_l(\mu)\,d\mu \tag{9.19}$$

By use of Equation (9.19) a physical meaning may be attached to the first two coefficients $N_l(z)$. Let $l = 0$. Then

$$N_0(z) = 2\pi \int_{-1}^{1} N(z,\mu)\,d\mu$$

which is also the *total neutron density* by comparison with Equation (9.2). Now let $l = 1$, and multiply both sides of (9.19) by v:

$$N_1(z)v = 2\pi \int_{-1}^{1} N(z,\mu)v \cos\theta\, d(\cos\theta)$$

The integral on the right is the net number of neutrons crossing a square centimeter perpendicular to the z-axis (see § 9.2), i.e., the *net current density, j*. Thus $N_1 = j/v$.

The next step is to expand the differential scattering cross section $\sigma_s(\mu_0)$ in another Legendre series in the scattering angle μ_0.

$$\sigma_s(\mu_0) = \sum_{l=0}^{\infty} \frac{2l+1}{4\pi} \sigma_{sl} P_l(\mu_0) \qquad (9.20)$$

The coefficients σ_{sl} are constants; the first of these is

$$\sigma_{s0} = 2\pi \int_{-1}^{1} \sigma_s(\mu_0) \, d\mu_0 = \sigma_s \qquad (9.21)$$

which is the *total* scattering cross section, as usually defined. The second is

$$\sigma_{s1} = 2\pi \int_{-1}^{1} \sigma_s(\mu_0)\mu_0 \, d\mu_0 = \bar{\mu}_0 \sigma_{s0} \qquad (9.22)$$

where $\bar{\mu}_0 = 2/(3A)$ is the average cosine of the scattering angle. Higher order coefficients σ_{s2}, σ_{s3}, etc., are seldom needed, but it may be noted that they are negligible (see Problem 9.3).

Diffusion equation. The first use of the spherical harmonics method will be to derive a differential equation that describes the flux $\phi(z)$, whereby further implications regarding the diffusion theory will be revealed. The source S will be omitted for simplicity.

First assume that the neutron density and flux have the minimum possible variation with angle, short of being isotropic, i.e.,

$$N(z,\mu) = \frac{N_0}{4\pi} + \frac{3N_1\mu}{4\pi} \qquad (9.23)$$

where the higher coefficients N_2, N_3, etc. are neglected. Insert Equation (9.23) in Equation (9.9) and multiply through by $P_0(\mu) \, d\mu \, d\varphi = d\mu \, d\varphi$. Integration from -1 to 1 on μ and 0 to 2π on φ, with $P_l(\mu)$ and Equation (9.18), reduces the left side of Equation (9.9) to the form

$$\frac{dN_1}{dz} + N_0 \Sigma$$

A special theorem of Legendre functions (Marshak, et al.) is now introduced.

$$\int_{\Omega} P_l(\mu) \, d\Omega \int_{\Omega'} N(z,\mu')\sigma_s(\mu_0) \, d\Omega' = \sigma_{sl} N_l(z) \qquad (9.24)$$

Using this, the right side of Equation (9.9) becomes $\Re\sigma_s N_0$. Thus

$$\frac{dN_1}{dz} + \Re(\sigma - \sigma_s)N_0 = 0 \qquad (9.25)$$

If, instead, Equation (9.23) is inserted in Equation (9.9), multiplied by $P_1(\mu)\, d\mu\, d\varphi = \mu\, d\mu\, d\varphi$, and integrated again, one obtains

$$\frac{1}{3}\frac{dN_0}{dz} + \Re(\sigma - \sigma_{s1})N_1 = 0 \qquad (9.26)$$

Eliminating N_1 by differentiation of Equation (9.26) and combining with Equation (9.25) gives

$$\frac{1}{3}\frac{d^2N_0}{dz^2} - \Re(\sigma - \sigma_{s1})\Re\sigma_a N_0 = 0 \qquad (9.27)$$

Now if σ_a is much less than σ_s, as was found in § 9.3 to be a requirement for diffusion theory to hold, then with the aid of Equations (9.20) and (9.21), $\sigma - \sigma_{s1} \simeq \sigma_s(1 - \bar\mu_0)$. This is also the transport cross section σ_t. The final form of Equation (9.27) is thus the same as the diffusion equation (3.8),

$$\frac{\lambda_t}{3}\frac{d^2N_0}{dz^2} - N_0\Sigma_a = 0$$

This natural appearance of λ_t justifies its previous arbitrary use in place of λ_s. We see now that the conventional diffusion equation is actually a simple form of the transport equation.

9.5. *Spherical harmonics treatment of heterogeneous reactors*

Modification of diffusion theory to include κ instead of $1/L$, λ_t instead of λ_s, and adjustment of flux amplitudes are of benefit in approaching correct solutions for some problems, particularly if absorption is not too great in comparison with scattering. The heterogeneous reactor, with natural or enriched fuel separate from the moderator, is not sufficiently well described by diffusion theory even as modified in certain cases. In natural-U, the absorption and scattering cross sections are approximately equal. Enrichment in U^{235} makes the ratio Σ_a/Σ_s even less favorable to diffusion theory. An outline of the spherical harmonics solution of such a problem is presented. Consider a unit cell of a reactor consisting of flat fuel plates, with adjacent moderator, as sketched in Figure 4.2, resembling the geometry of the MTR (see § 1.4).

This two-region problem is solved by first converting the one-dimensional transport equation into a set of coupled ordinary differential equations. The series expansions of $N(z,\mu)$ and $\sigma_s(\mu_0)$ in the Legendre polynomials are employed. For greater generality, the scattering in the laboratory system is allowed to be non-isotropic. For each of the two media, fuel and moderator, there is a set of these differential equations that are solved subject to certain boundary conditions. The series for $N(z,\mu)$ given in Equation (9.17) is inserted in the *left* side of Equation (9.9) and a theorem of Legendre polynomials is invoked.

$$\mu P_l(\mu) = \frac{(l+1)P_{l+1}(\mu) + lP_{l-1}(\mu)}{2l+1} \tag{9.28}$$

The left side becomes

$$\frac{v}{4\pi} \sum_{l=0}^{\infty} [(l+1)P_{l+1}(\mu) + lP_{l-1}(\mu)] \frac{dN_l}{dz} + (2l+1)\Sigma N_l P_l(\mu)$$

The series in $N(z,\mu)$ and that in $\sigma_s(\mu_0)$, Equation (9.20) are inserted in the integral on the *right* side of Equation (9.9). The result, as proved by Weinberg, using the properties of Legendre functions, is

$$\Re v \sum_{l=0}^{\infty} \frac{(2l+1)}{4\pi} \sigma_{sl} N_l P_l(\mu)$$

Equating the two sides of the transformed Equation (9.9), an equation of the form

$$aP_0(\mu) + bP_1(\mu) + cP_2(\mu) + \cdots = 0$$

is obtained, where $a, b, c, \cdots$ are functions of z but not of μ. If it is to be true for all angles θ, cosines μ, the coefficient of each Legendre polynomial $a, b, c, \cdots$ must vanish identically, which gives the set of equations

$$\frac{d}{dz}[lN_{l-1} + (l+1)N_{l+1}] + (2l+1)(\Sigma - \Sigma_{sl})N_l = \frac{S_T}{v}\delta_{l,0}$$

Let Σ_T stand for $\Sigma - \Sigma_{s1} = \Sigma_a + \Sigma_t$, where Σ_t is the transport cross section, and $\delta_{l,0}$ is 1 if $l = 0$, zero if $l \neq 0$. The first four of the set are displayed, with only one approximation made, namely, to let σ_{s2} be zero.

$$\frac{dN_1}{dz} + \Sigma_a N_0 = \frac{S_T}{v}$$

$$2\frac{dN_2}{dz} + \frac{dN_0}{dz} + 3\Sigma_T N_1 = 0$$

$$3\frac{dN_3}{dz} + 2\frac{dN_1}{dz} + 5\Sigma N_2 = 0 \qquad (9.29)$$

$$4\frac{dN_4}{dz} + 3\frac{dN_2}{dz} + 7\Sigma N_3 = 0$$

. . . .

The partial integro-differential equation has been replaced by an infinite set of coupled ordinary linear differential equations. It is easy to see how additional equations could be developed as needed. There will be a set of these equations for the fuel, and another for the moderator, where the cross sections are different. Looking forward to the end result, if the coefficients $N_1(z)$, $N_2(z)$, etc. can be found for both the fuel and moderator, the complete density distribution $N(z,\mu)$ can be formed by using the series, Equation (9.17). Assuming the series to be convergent, we may obtain any accuracy of flux distribution in angle that is desired, by computing only a definite number of the N_l, assuming the rest of them to be negligible for our purpose. Such approximations are designated by the term "P_n approximation," where n is the largest subscript of the N_l that is retained, and $n + 1$ equations must be solved to find the set of N_l. Thus the P_1 approximation, which resembles diffusion theory, keeps N_0 and N_1, and makes use of two equations only. The P_3 approximation keeps N_0 through N_3, and uses 4 equations.

For illustration, we now develop the P_3 solution of the coupled Equations (9.29) for the thermal neutron density in the fuel, in which it is assumed that the thermal source S is zero. Omitting N_4, the solution of the first four equations is achieved by operator methods, or the equivalent, trial substitution in Equation (9.29) of

$$N_i(z) = N_{ij}e^{k_j z} \qquad (9.30)$$

where N_{ij} are arbitrary constants and the k_j are to be found.

$$\Sigma_a N_{0j} + k_j N_{1j} = 0$$
$$k_j N_{0j} + 3\Sigma_T N_{1j} + 2k_j N_{2j} = 0 \qquad (9.31)$$
$$2k_j N_{1j} + 5\Sigma N_{2j} + 3k_j N_{3j} = 0$$
$$3k_j N_{2j} + 7\Sigma N_{3j} = 0$$

If non-zero solutions for the N_{ij} are to be obtained, the determinant formed by their coefficients must equal zero.

$$
\begin{vmatrix}
\Sigma_a & k_j & 0 & 0 \\
k_j & 3\Sigma_T & 2k_j & 0 \\
0 & 2k_j & 5\Sigma & 3k_j \\
0 & 0 & 3k_j & 7\Sigma
\end{vmatrix} = 0 \tag{9.32}
$$

The resulting equation is

$$
(k_j^2 - 3\Sigma_a\Sigma_T)(9k_j^2 - 35\Sigma^2) = 28k_j^2\Sigma_a\Sigma
$$

or

$$
ax^2 + bx + c = 0 \tag{9.33}
$$

where
$$
x = k_j^2, \quad a = 9
$$
$$
b = -[(27\Sigma_T + 28\Sigma)\Sigma_a + 35\Sigma^2]
$$
$$
c = 105\Sigma_a\Sigma_T\Sigma^2
$$

When materials constants are assigned, quadratic equation (9.33) may be solved. Approximations that may be used as a check on the solution of Equation (9.33) if the absorption is weak, as in the moderator, are

$$
k_j \simeq \pm\sqrt{3\Sigma_a\Sigma_t}, \quad \pm\sqrt{\frac{35}{3}}\,\Sigma
$$

The four roots $k_1 = -k_2$ and $k_3 = -k_4$ correspond to four solutions e^{k_1z}, e^{k_2z}, e^{k_3z} and e^{k_4z}, and the general solution is a linear combination,

$$
N_i(z) = \sum_{j=1}^{4} N_{ij}e^{k_jz}
$$

The solution for the moderator is of the same form except that a particular integral, $S_T/(v\Sigma_a)$ is added to N_0, and of course k_j values are different.

The arbitrary constants N_{ij} are related, as can be proved by solving Equations (9.31) for the following coupling coefficients.

$$
r_{1j} = \frac{N_{1j}}{N_{0j}} = \frac{-\Sigma_a}{k_j}
$$

$$
r_{2j} = \frac{N_{2j}}{N_{0j}} = \frac{1}{2}\left(\frac{3\Sigma_a\Sigma_T}{k_j^2} - 1\right) = \frac{14\Sigma_a\Sigma}{35\Sigma^2 - 9k_j^2} \tag{9.34}
$$

$$
r_{3j} = \frac{N_{3j}}{N_{0j}} = \frac{1}{3k_j}(2\Sigma_a - 5\Sigma r_{2j}) = -\frac{6\Sigma_a k_j}{35\Sigma^2 - 9k_j^2}
$$

Alternate forms are given for r_{2j} and r_{3j}; it will be found that one form will give much greater accuracy than the other, depending on the sizes of numbers combined.

Boundary conditions. We must distinguish the solutions and associated constants for the moderator from those of the fuel. The following notation is adopted.

$$\text{fuel}\quad N_i = \sum_{j=1}^{4} N_{ij}e^{k_i z} \qquad (9.35)$$

$$\text{moderator}\quad \overline{N}_i = \sum_{j=1}^{4} \overline{N}_{ij}e^{\overline{k}_i z} + \frac{S_T}{v\Sigma_a}\delta_{i0} \qquad (9.36)$$

where the term involving S_T appears only for $i = 0$. The arbitrary coefficients N_{ij} and $\overline{N}_{ij}$ can be found by applying boundary conditions at three planes: $z = 0$, $z = w$, and $z = W$. First consider the situation at the plane $z = 0$, the mid-plane of the fuel region. If all cells in the lattice are the same, the neutron density $N(0,\mu)$ must be the same for angles θ as for angles $\pi - \theta$, i.e., the angular distribution is symmetric about the angle $\theta = \pi/2$. This means that $N(0,\mu) = N(0,-\mu)$, which according to Equation (9.17) can be true only if $N_1(0) = 0$ and $N_3(0) = 0$. Substitute the condition $N_3(0) = 0$ in the fourth of Equations (9.29), remembering that N_4 has been ignored. The result is $dN_2(0)/dz = 0$. Now insert this in the second of Equations (9.29), along with $N_1(0) = 0$. We find that $dN_0(0)/dz = 0$. In summary, we may say that at the boundary, about which the density $N(z,\mu)$ is symmetric, the odd harmonics N_1 and N_3 are zero and the *slopes* of the even harmonics N_0 and N_2 are zero. The same argument may be applied to the cell boundary, $z = W$, which gives four more boundary conditions,

$$d\overline{N}_0(W)/dz = 0, \quad \overline{N}_1(W) = 0, \quad d\overline{N}_2(W)/dz = 0, \quad \overline{N}_3(W) = 0$$

Recalling that N_0 and N_1 really are total neutron density and $1/v$ times the net current, we see that the conditions $dN_0/dz = 0$ and $N_1 = 0$ are identical to the familiar boundary conditions of diffusion theory. Physical meaning cannot be attached to the remaining boundary conditions.

It is evident that the flux distribution in angle and position must be the same at $z = w$ whether the plane is approached from the moderator side or the fuel side. Thus $N(w,\mu) = \overline{N}(w,\mu)$ and if this is true for all angles corresponding to μ, the harmonics must all satisfy the relation $N_i(w) = \overline{N}_i(w)$. Thus the final set of boundary conditions needed is:

$$N_0(w) = \overline{N}_0(w), \; N_1(w) = \overline{N}_1(w), \; N_2(w) = \overline{N}_2(w), \; N_3(w) = \overline{N}_3(w)$$

The boundary conditions involving symmetry can best be introduced by the use of hyperbolic functions. A rearrangement of Equation (9.30) for $i = 0$ will illustrate. Now, if in

$$N_0(z) = N_{01}e^{k_1z} + N_{02}e^{k_2z} + N_{03}e^{k_3z} + N_{04}e^{k_4z}$$

we let

$$N_{01} = \frac{M_{01} + M_{02}}{2}, \qquad N_{02} = \frac{M_{01} - M_{02}}{2},$$

$$N_{03} = \frac{M_{03} + M_{04}}{2}, \qquad N_{04} = \frac{M_{03} - M_{04}}{2}$$

and use $k_2 = -k_1$, $k_4 = -k_3$, we find

$$N_0(z) = M_{01} \cosh k_1z + M_{02} \sinh k_1z + M_{03} \cosh k_3z + M_{04} \sinh k_4z$$

The coefficients of sinh terms must vanish if $dN_0(0)/dz$ is to be 0. Thus

$$N_0(z) = M_{01} \cosh k_1z + M_{03} \cosh k_3z$$

The conversion is repeated for N_1, N_2 and N_3, with note that $r_{11} = -r_{12}$, $r_{21} = r_{22}$, $r_{31} = -r_{32}$, $r_{13} = -r_{14}$, $r_{23} = r_{24}$, and $r_{33} = -r_{34}$. The moderator is treated similarly, but with use of solutions of the form $\sinh \overline{k}(z - W)$ and $\cosh \overline{k}(z - W)$. The boundary condition at $z = w$ is then applied to the set, giving four equations from which the four unknown arbitrary coefficients may be found. The complete solution in a form that is most convenient for calculations is:

$$N_0(z) = \Delta_1 \cosh k_1z + \Delta_3 \cosh k_3z$$
$$N_1(z) = r_{11}\Delta_1 \sinh k_1z + r_{13}\Delta_3 \sinh k_3z$$
$$N_2(z) = r_{21}\Delta_1 \cosh k_1z + r_{23}\Delta_3 \cosh k_3z$$
$$N_3(z) = r_{31}\Delta_1 \sinh k_1z + r_{33}\Delta_3 \sinh k_3z$$
$$\overline{N}_0(z) = \overline{\Delta}_1 \cosh \overline{k}_1(z - W) + \overline{\Delta}_3 \cosh \overline{k}_3(z - W) + \Delta$$
$$\overline{N}_1(z) = \overline{r}_{11}\overline{\Delta}_1 \sinh \overline{k}_1(z - W) + \overline{r}_{13}\overline{\Delta}_3 \sinh \overline{k}_3(z - W)$$
$$\overline{N}_2(z) = \overline{r}_{21}\overline{\Delta}_1 \cosh \overline{k}_1(z - W) + \overline{r}_{23}\overline{\Delta}_3 \cosh \overline{k}_3(z - W)$$
$$\overline{N}_3(z) = \overline{r}_{31}\overline{\Delta}_1 \sinh \overline{k}_1(z - W) + \overline{r}_{33}\overline{\Delta}_3 \sinh \overline{k}_3(z - W)$$

where

$$\Delta_1 = \begin{vmatrix} R_{13} & \bar{R}_{11} & \bar{R}_{13} \\ R_{23} & \bar{R}_{21} & \bar{R}_{23} \\ R_{33} & \bar{R}_{31} & \bar{R}_{33} \end{vmatrix} \qquad \bar{\Delta}_1 = -\begin{vmatrix} R_{11} & R_{13} & \bar{R}_{13} \\ R_{21} & R_{23} & \bar{R}_{23} \\ R_{31} & R_{33} & \bar{R}_{33} \end{vmatrix}$$

$$\Delta_3 = -\begin{vmatrix} R_{11} & \bar{R}_{11} & \bar{R}_{13} \\ R_{21} & \bar{R}_{21} & \bar{R}_{23} \\ R_{31} & \bar{R}_{31} & \bar{R}_{33} \end{vmatrix} \qquad \bar{\Delta}_3 = \begin{vmatrix} R_{11} & R_{13} & \bar{R}_{11} \\ R_{21} & R_{23} & \bar{R}_{21} \\ R_{31} & R_{33} & \bar{R}_{31} \end{vmatrix}$$

$$\Delta = \Delta_1 \cosh k_1 w + \Delta_3 \cosh k_3 w$$
$$- \bar{\Delta}_1 \cosh \bar{k}_1(w - W) - \bar{\Delta}_3 \cosh \bar{k}_3(w - W)$$

and

$$\begin{aligned} R_{1j} &= r_{1j} \sinh k_j w & \bar{R}_{1j} &= \bar{r}_{1j} \sinh \bar{k}_j(w - W) \\ R_{2j} &= r_{2j} \cosh k_j w & \bar{R}_{2j} &= \bar{r}_{2j} \cosh \bar{k}_j(w - W) \\ R_{3j} &= r_{3j} \sinh k_j w & \bar{R}_{3j} &= \bar{r}_{3j} \sinh \bar{k}_j(w - W) \end{aligned}$$

Numerical Illustration: Find the flux distribution and the angular distribution by the P_3 approximation for an infinite heterogeneous array of 0.5-in. wide natural-U plates separated by a graphite moderator with a center-line spacing of 12 in. (Compare numerical illustration § 4.1.)

Solution. The basic constants assumed will be the same as for the previous numerical illustration.

	N	σ_s	σ_a	Σ_s	Σ_t	Σ_a	Σ
graphite	0.0827	4.8	0.0040	0.3970	0.3748	3.31×10^{-4}	0.3973
natural U	0.0480	8.3	6.74	0.398	0.398	0.324	0.722

Calculations are given in the following table:

	Fuel		*Moderator*
k_1	0.69103	$\bar{k}_1$	0.019287
k_3	1.7260	$\bar{k}_3$	0.78370
w	0.635	$W - w$	14.605
$k_1 w$	0.43880	$\bar{k}_1(w - W)$	-0.28169
$k_3 w$	1.0960	$\bar{k}_3(w - W)$	-11.446
r_{11}	-0.46887	$\bar{r}_{11}$	-0.017162
r_{13}	-0.18772	$\bar{r}_{13}$	-4.2236×10^{-4}
r_{21}	0.23482	$\bar{r}_{21}$	3.3345×10^{-4}
r_{23}	-0.38222	$\bar{r}_{23}$	-0.49970
r_{31}	-0.09633	$\bar{r}_{31}$	-6.9375×10^{-6}
r_{33}	0.39162	$\bar{r}_{33}$	0.42249
R_{11}	-0.21241	$\bar{R}_{11}$	4.8985×10^{-3}
R_{13}	-0.24948	$\bar{R}_{13}$	19.750

	Fuel		*Moderator*
R_{21}	0.25779	$\overline{R}_{21}$	3.4677×10^{-4}
R_{23}	−0.63570	$\overline{R}_{23}$	-2.3367×10^{4}
R_{31}	−0.04364	$\overline{R}_{31}$	1.9802×10^{-6}
R_{33}	0.52046	$\overline{R}_{33}$	-1.9756×10^{4}
Δ_1	−119.400	$\overline{\Delta}_1$	6773.8
Δ_3	−31.388	$\overline{\Delta}_3$	5.6385×10^{-4}
		Δ	−7254.0

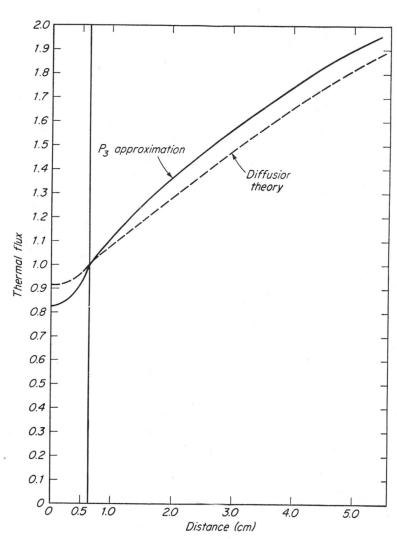

Figure 9.6.   Comparison of P_3 approximation and diffusion theory.

The flux solutions, with sign reversed throughout, are

Fuel: $(k_1 = 0.69103, k_3 = 1.7260)$

$N_0(z) = 119.400 \cosh k_1 z + 31.388 \cosh k_3 z$

$N_1(z) = -55.98 \sinh k_1 z - 5.892 \sinh k_3 z$

$N_2(z) = 28.04 \cosh k_1 z - 12.00 \cosh k_3 z$

$N_3(z) = -11.50 \sinh k_1 z + 12.29 \sinh k_3 z$

Moderator: $(\bar{k}_1 = 0.019287, \bar{k}_3 = 0.78370)$

$\bar{N}_0(z) = -6773.8 \cosh \bar{k}_1(z - W) - 5.6385 \times 10^{-4}$
$\qquad \cosh \bar{k}_3(z - W) + 7254.0$

$\bar{N}_1(z) = 116.25 \sinh \bar{k}_1(z - W) + 2.381 \times 10^{-7}$
$\qquad \sinh \bar{k}_3(z - W)$

$\bar{N}_2(z) = -2.259 \cosh \bar{k}_1(z - W) + 2.818 \times 10^{-4}$
$\qquad \cosh \bar{k}_3(z - W)$

$\bar{N}_3(z) = 4.699 \times 10^{-2} \sinh \bar{k}_1(z - W) - 2.382 \times 10^{-4}$
$\qquad \sinh \bar{k}_3(z - W)$

The total neutron density $N_0(z)$ as a function of position, in the vicinity of the fuel plate, is plotted in Figure 9.6 normal-

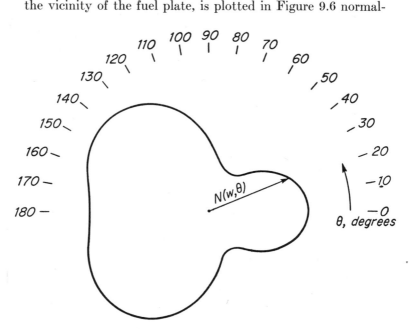

Figure 9.7.   Angular distribution of neutron density at boundary of fuel, P_3 approximation.

ized to unity at $z = w$. It will be noted that there is a more pronounced depression of the flux than for diffusion theory. This is reflected in the thermal utilization values: For P_3, $f = 0.941$; for diffusion theory, $f = 0.951$. Experimental measurements are found to confirm this trend.

The angular distribution of neutrons $N(z,\mu)$ may be evaluated from Equation (9.17):

$$N(z,\mu) \simeq$$

$$\frac{1}{4\pi} [N_0(z) + 3N_1(z)P_1(\mu) + 5N_2(z)P_2(\mu) + 7N_3(z)P_3(\mu)]$$

At the fuel-moderator interface, $z = w = 0.635$ cm, the spatial coefficients are

$$N_0(w) = 183.28$$
$$N_1(w) = -33.192$$
$$N_2(w) = 10.826$$
$$N_3(w) = 11.124$$

Inserting the Legendre polynomials $P_1 = \mu$, $P_2 = \frac{1}{2}(3\mu^2 - 1)$, $P_3 = \frac{1}{2}(5\mu^3 - 3\mu)$, the polar graph of $N(w,\theta)$ shown in Figure 9.7 is obtained. There are fewer neutrons directed at the angles near zero (emerging from the fuel) than near π (entering the fuel) because of the difficulty neutrons have in traversing the metal without absorption.

9.6. *Integral form of transport equation*

The total flux of neutrons of one speed at a point in a homogeneous medium can be represented by a simple integral expression. It can be proved to be equivalent to the Boltzmann equation for isotropic scattering, but may also be derived from a simple physical logic. Assume that the flux at a point r' is $\phi(r')$. The number of scattering events per unit volume is $\phi(r')\Sigma_s$, which can be visualized as a point source S. The uncollided flux due to this source at the surface of a spherical shell, of radius $|r - r'|$ from the point, is clearly

$$\frac{Se^{-\Sigma|r-r'|}}{4\pi|r - r'|^2}$$

Multiplying this by the Σ_s gives the collision rate per unit volume; the total collision rate at a point r due to all such scattering sources is the integral over all space:

$$\phi(r)\Sigma_s = \int_{r'} \Sigma_s S(r') \frac{e^{-\Sigma|r-r'|} \, dr'}{4\pi|r - r'|^2}$$

where dr' is the volume element at r'. Inserting $S(r') = \phi(r')\Sigma_s$ and cancelling Σ_s yield

$$\phi(r) = \int_{r'} \phi(r')\Sigma_s \frac{e^{-\Sigma|r-r'|} \, dr'}{4\pi|r - r'|^2} \tag{9.37}$$

This may be generalized to include slowing-down or artificial sources of strength $q(r')$ by substituting for $\phi(r')\Sigma_s$ in Equation (9.37) the complete source,

$$Q(r') = q(r') + \phi(r')\Sigma_s \tag{9.38}$$

Finally, by defining the *point transport kernel*,

$$K_{pt}(r,r') = \frac{e^{-\Sigma|r-r'|}}{4\pi|r - r'|^2} \tag{9.39}$$

Equation (9.37) becomes

$$\phi(r) = \int_{r'} Q(r')K_{pt}(r,r') \, dr' \tag{9.40}$$

This may be compared with similar integral forms for diffusion theory in § 3.5. The kernel is recalled to be simply the flux at a point r due to a unit source at point r'. To each coordinate system, there pertains a kernel of different form. The *plane transport kernel* may be derived, by analogy with Equation (3.78), to be

$$K_{pl}(z,0) = 2\pi \int_z^\infty r \, dr \, K_{pt}(r,0) \tag{9.41}$$

An inverse relation is obtained by differentiating both sides with respect to z:

$$K_{pt}(r,0) = \left[-\frac{1}{2\pi z} \frac{dK_{pl}(z,0)}{dz} \right]_r \tag{9.42}$$

Now letting $K_{pt}(r,0) = e^{-\Sigma r}/4\pi r^2$, Equation (9.41) becomes

$$K_{pl}(z,0) = \frac{1}{2} \int_z^\infty \frac{e^{-\Sigma r} \, dr}{r} = \frac{1}{2} \int_x^\infty \frac{e^{-y} \, dy}{y}$$

where $y = \Sigma r$ and $x = \Sigma z$. This is one half the tabulated function $E_1(x)$, which is closely related to the exponential integral. It belongs to a set of functions defined by the recursion relations

$$E_n(x) = \int_x^\infty E_{n-1}(x)\, dx = x^{n-1} \int_x^\infty e^{-y}\, dy/y^n \qquad (9.43)$$

$$E_n(x) = \frac{1}{n-1}\left[e^{-x} - xE_{n-1}(x)\right] \qquad n > 1$$

$$E_0(x) = \frac{e^{-x}}{x}$$

Graphs of $E_1(x)$, $E_2(x)$, and $E_3(x)$ are shown in Figure 9.8. The

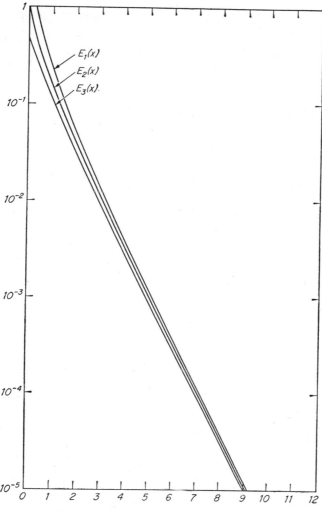

Figure 9.8. $E_n(x)$ for $n = 1, 2,$ and 3.

plane transport kernel for two points separated by a distance $z - z'$ is thus

$$K_{pl}(z,z') = \frac{E_1(\Sigma|z - z'|)}{2} \tag{9.44}$$

It is of interest to note that *any* transport kernel can be derived from its corresponding diffusion kernel by the transformation

$$K(x,x') = D \int_\Sigma^\infty G(\kappa,x,x') \, d\kappa \tag{9.45}$$

where κ is the inverse diffusion length and D is the diffusion coefficient.

It may also be noted that the point and plane transport kernels are applicable to the attenuation of gamma rays, except that Σ is replaced by μ, the absorption coefficient.

9.7. *Applications to neutron absorption problems*

Two examples of the use of the integral form of transport theory are given: (a) the activation of a metal foil inserted in a reactor to measure flux; (b) the depression of flux in a fuel-moderator lattice.

Foil activation. First, let us find the flux in an infinite moderator of absorption cross section Σ_a, with a uniform slowing down source of strength q. It is clear that ϕ does not depend on position, so that evaluation at $r = 0$ is sufficient. According to Equations (9.39) and (9.40),

$$\phi(0) = [q + \phi(0)\Sigma_s] \int_0^\infty \frac{e^{-\Sigma r'}}{4\pi(r')^2} 4\pi(r')^2 \, dr'$$

Integrating,

$$\phi = \frac{q + \phi\Sigma_s}{\Sigma}$$

or rearranging, with $\Sigma = \Sigma_s + \Sigma_a$,

$$\phi = \frac{q}{\Sigma_a} \tag{9.46}$$

This result coincides with our knowledge that the rate of absorption $\phi\Sigma_a$ is equal to the rate of slowing down q, in an infinite medium in steady state.

Now suppose a small sphere of radius R, absorption cross section Σ_f, is placed at the origin. In and near the sphere, the flux will be depressed. The neutrons that are removed constitute a net *negative source*, of magnitude $\phi(\Sigma_f - \Sigma_a)$ per unit volume. The general source *inside* the sphere now becomes

$$Q(r') = q + \phi(r')\Sigma_s - \phi(r')(\Sigma_f - \Sigma_a)$$

while that *outside* is

$$Q(r') = q + \phi(r')\Sigma_s$$

We evaluate the flux at $r = 0$, the center of the sphere, by inserting these sources in Equation (9.40) and simplifying.

$$\phi(0) = \frac{q}{\Sigma_a} - (\Sigma_f - \Sigma_a) \int_0^R \phi(r') K_{\mathrm{pt}}(0,r') 4\pi (r')^2\, dr$$

As a first approximation, let $\phi(r')$ be q/Σ_a, the undisturbed value. The resulting fractional change in flux is

$$\frac{\Delta\phi}{\phi} = \frac{\Sigma_a - \Sigma_f}{\Sigma} (1 - e^{-\Sigma R}) \tag{9.47}$$

It will be noted that this formula predicts no flux disturbance if $\Sigma_f = \Sigma_a$, or if the sphere radius is zero, which serves as a partial check of the method.

Numerical Illustration: Estimate the flux at the center of a cobalt sphere of 1-millimeter radius, placed in a large graphite reactor with undisturbed thermal flux $10^{12}/\mathrm{cm}^2$-sec.

Solution. The microscopic cross section of cobalt is 32.8 barns, $N = 0.091$, from which $\Sigma_f = 2.98$ cm. The macroscopic absorption cross section of graphite, Σ_a, is negligible in comparison, but Σ_s is 0.397 cm^{-1}. Inserting numbers in Equation (9.47), $\Delta\phi/\phi = -(2.98/0.397)(1 - e^{-0.0397}) = -0.29$ and $\phi = 7.1 \times 10^{11}/\mathrm{cm}^2$-sec. Even with this small sphere the flux depression is serious. It should be pointed out that a better approximation than Equation (9.47) is needed for larger dimensions or absorption cross sections.

Self-shielding in fuel-moderator lattice. The average thermal flux in a fuel plate is lower than in surrounding moderator, because of self-shielding by the metal. The foregoing analysis may be modified to give the flux distribution. Consider an infinite array of fuel plates with moderator between them, with plate separation d, width $2w$. The fuel is assumed to provide a negative source of strength $\phi(\Sigma_f - \Sigma_a)$, where Σ_a is the moderator absorption cross section. The flux at any point z is given by

$$\phi(z) = \int_{\substack{\text{all}\\ \text{space}}} [q + \phi(z')\Sigma_s]K_{p1}(z,z')\,dz'$$
$$- \int_{\substack{\text{fuel}\\ \text{only}}} \phi(z')(\Sigma_f - \Sigma_a)K_{p1}(z,z')\,dz' \quad (9.48)$$

The first integral is the undisturbed flux $\phi_0 = q/\Sigma_a$; if this value is inserted in the second integral and Equation (9.44) applied, the term is reduced to

$$\phi_0(\Sigma_f - \Sigma_a) \int_{\substack{\text{fuel}\\ \text{only}}} \frac{E_1(\Sigma|z - z'|)\,dz'}{2} \quad (9.49)$$

This may be integrated by use of the functions listed in Equations (9.43). For the center of the fuel plate, the amount of this depression is the infinite series

$$\frac{\phi_0(\Sigma_f - \Sigma_a)}{\Sigma} \Big\{ E_2(0) - E_2(\Sigma w) + E_2[\Sigma(d + w)]$$
$$- E_2[\Sigma(d + 3w)] + \cdots \Big\} \quad (9.50)$$

Numerical Illustration: Estimate the thermal flux at the center of natural uranium fuel plates of width $2w = 0.15$ in., with D_2O-gap, $d = 0.39$ in., similar to those proposed for a boiling heavy-water reactor (International Conference, Volume 3, Paper P/695).

Solution. The necessary cross sections are $(\Sigma_s)_{D_2O} = 0.488$ cm$^{-1} \simeq \Sigma$, $(\Sigma_a)_U = 0.324 = \Sigma_f$, while $(\Sigma_a)_{D_2O} = \Sigma_a$ is negligible. The dimensions are $w = 0.1905$ cm, $d = 0.9906$ cm. A table of calculations is formed.

z'		$\Sigma z'$	E_2	ΔE_2
	0	0	1.000 ⎱	
				0.265
$0w$	0.1905	0.0930	0.735 ⎰	
$d + w$	1.1811	0.5764	0.287 ⎱	
				0.074
$d + 3w$	1.5621	0.7623	0.213 ⎰	
$2d + 3w$	2.5527	1.2457	0.104 ⎱	
				0.023
$2d + 5w$	2.9337	1.4316	0.081 ⎰	
$3d + 5w$	3.9243	1.9151	0.042 ⎱	
				0.009
$3d + 7w$	4.3053	2.1010	0.033 ⎰	
			Integral	0.371

The fractional change in flux from Equation (9.50) is thus

$$\frac{(0.324)(0.371)}{0.488} = 0.246$$

In order to obtain a more correct measure of the *relative* depression, the same quantity should be evaluated for a number of points in the system, including the moderator.

Problems

9.1. Find the solution of the one-dimensional transport equation for a purely absorbing semi-infinite medium with no internal source, but an isotropic plane source of S neutrons/cm²-sec at the surface $z = 0$.
Answer.

$$N(z,\mu) = \frac{S}{4\pi} e^{-\Sigma_a z/\mu}$$

9.2. Show that for $\Sigma_a \ll \Sigma$ the transcendental equation (9.13) may be approximated by $\kappa \simeq \sqrt{3\Sigma_a\Sigma} \left(1 - \frac{2}{5}\frac{\Sigma_a}{\Sigma}\right)$.

9.3. Making use of the fact that the cosines of the angle of scattering in the laboratory μ and center of mass μ_c are related by $\mu = \frac{(1 + A\mu_c)}{\sqrt{1 + 2A\mu_c + A^2}}$, show that the scattering function σ_{s2} is given by $(\sigma_s/8)[5 - 3A^2 - 3(A^2 - 1)^2(\ln \alpha)/(4A)] \simeq 5\sigma_s/A^2$ and that $\sigma_{s3} = 0$.

9.4. Check the fact that $P_3(\mu) = \frac{1}{2}(5\mu^3 - 3\mu)$ is a solution of the Legendre equation

$$\frac{d}{d\mu}\left[(1 - \mu^2)\frac{dy}{d\mu}\right] + l(l + 1)y = 0.$$

9.5. Compare the calculated values of thermal utilization f according to three levels of approximation: (a) homogeneous, (b) P_1, and (c) P_3, for a U²³⁵ water–stainless-steel system. Assume the fuel element geometry to be similar to the MTR, with eighteen 0.060-in. by 2.75-in. by 24-in. plates, each containing 15 gm of U²³⁵ and the remainder stainless steel, of density 8.0 gm/cm³. Let the water gap between adjacent plates be 0.117 in. and the side plates be 0.125 in. by 3.17 in. by 24 in.

9.6. Using the point diffusion kernel, Equation (9.47), derive a formula analogous to Equation (9.47) for the fractional change in flux in the center of a spherical absorber.

Answer.

$$\frac{\Sigma_a - \Sigma_f}{\Sigma} [1 - (1 + R/L)e^{-R/L}]$$

9.7. Using the diffusion kernel, Problem 9.6, find the value of the flux at the center of a 1-mm cobalt sphere.

9.8. The diffusion kernel for a spherical shell source, i.e., the flux due to a shell of radius r' emitting one neutron per second, is

$$\frac{1}{8\pi rr'\kappa D} \left[e^{-\kappa(r-r')} - e^{-\kappa(r+r')}\right]$$

where r is the distance from the center of the shell. Derive, by the use of Equation (9.42), the corresponding transport kernel.

Answer.

$$\frac{1}{8\pi rr'} \left\{E_1[\kappa(r - r')] - E_1[\kappa(r + r')]\right\}$$

9.9. Compute κ by Equation (9.13), by its approximation (Problem 9.2), and by $\sqrt{3\Sigma_a\Sigma}$ for thermal neutrons in the following materials:

	ρ (gm/cm³)	$\bar{\sigma}_a$	$\bar{\sigma}_s$
Natural U	19.0	6.74	8.3
Liquid Na	0.90	0.448	4.0
Liquid Bi	10.0	0.028	9.0

Answer.

	Equation (9.13)	Approximation	$\sqrt{3\Sigma_a\Sigma}$
U	0.675	0.687	0.838
Na	0.0554	0.0555	0.578
Bi	0.0251	0.0251	0.0251

References

Marshak, R. E., H. Brooks, and H. Hurwitz, Jr., "Introduction to the Theory of Diffusion and Slowing Down of Neutrons," *Nucleonics*, May 1949, p. 10, June 1949, p. 43, July 1949, p. 53, August 1949, p. 59.

MacRobert, T. M., *Spherical Harmonics*, 2nd Ed. New York: Dover Publications, Inc. (1947).

Wigner, E. P., *Solution of Boltzmann's Equation for Monoenergetic Neutrons in an Infinite Homogeneous Medium*, CP-1120 (1943).

Mark, J. Carson, *The Spherical Harmonic Method*, Part I, CRT-340 or NRC No. 1588 (1944), Part II, CRT-338 or NRC No. 1589 (1945). Ottawa: National Research Council of Canada.

Carlson, Bengt, *Neutron Diffusion-Spherical Harmonics Theory*, MDDC-236 (1946).

Weinberg, Alvin M., and L. C. Noderer. *Theory of Neutron Chain Reactions*, AECD-3471 (1951). (See also AECD-3405, 3410, and 3411.)

Case, K. M., F. De Hoffmann, G. Placzek. *Introduction to the Theory of Neutron Diffusion*, Volume I. Washington: U. S. Government Printing Office (1953).

Feurzig, Wallace, and B. I. Spinrad, *Numerical Solution of Transport Theory Problems for Spheres and Cylinders*, ANL-5049 (1953).

Wilson, A. H., *The General Properties of the Transport Equation and its Use in Determining the Multiplication in Bodies Having Spherical Symmetry*, AERE MS 105A (1950).

The Reactor Handbook, Volume I, *Physics*, AECD-3645 (1955), Chapter 1.3.

Peaceful Uses of Atomic Energy, Volume 5, *Physics of Reactor Design*. New York: Columbia University Press (1956).

Tait, J. H., "The Calculation of the Fine Structure of the Thermal Neutron Flux in a Pile, by the Spherical Harmonics Method," Paper P/433.

Chapter 10

NEUTRON SLOWING AND
MULTIGROUP METHODS

Most theories of neutron distributions and reactor criticality have as a fundamental basis the *energy-dependent transport equation*, which is an extension of the one-velocity case treated in Chapter 9. Because of mathematical difficulty, many approximate versions have been developed for special situations, in particular for heavy elements and for hydrogenous mixtures. An attempt will be made to correlate these simplified methods.

As an indication of the way analytic formulas are adapted for high-speed computing machines, one version of the *multigroup* method is presented. Also, the *electrical analogue* of a two dimensional reactor will be discussed.

10.1. *The energy-dependent transport equation*

One more variable, lethargy, is added to the flux function $\Phi(z,\Omega)$ described in § 9.1, which was a function only of the spatial coordinate and the direction variables. We now generalize to define $\Phi(z,u,\Omega)$ as the flux per unit lethargy range, per unit solid angle of directions, at the point z, lethargy u, direction Ω. The balance equation in steady state that is exactly analogous to Equation (9.8) or (9.9), except that lethargy dependence is included, is

$$\mu \frac{\partial \Phi}{\partial z}(z,u,\Omega) + \Phi(z,u,\Omega)\Sigma(u) =$$

$$S + \int_0^u du' \int_{\Omega'} \Phi(z,u',\Omega')\Sigma_s(u')f(u',u,\Omega',\Omega)\,d\Omega' \quad (10.1)$$

The first term on the left represents the net spatial flow out of a

268

unit volume; the second term is the rate of removal of the selected neutrons by absorption and scattering. The source term is self-evident. The integral expression is the most complicated, as in the one-velocity case.

Neutrons are gained by scattering from other lethargy values u' and directions Ω', into the range about u and Ω. The number of scattering events per second at u' and Ω' is proportional to $\Phi(z,u',\Omega')\Sigma_s(u')$. Integration over all u' from initial lethargy taken as 0 to that of interest u, and over Ω' accounts for the total scattering-in source. The scattering probability function f is dependent on both of the energies and both of the directions.

At this point certain physical assumptions are made. (a) The scattering is strictly elastic, governed by the classical formulas of energy and momentum conservation. (b) The scattering is isotropic in the center-of-mass system. Both of these are accurate for the relatively low energy neutrons involved in reactor problems. (c) Effectively, the scattering targets are individual atoms, rather than molecules which exhibit chemical binding effects. Under these conditions the dependence of the scattering probability f on variables u', u, Ω', Ω reduces to a dependence on the cosine of the angle α between initial and final neutron directions, labeled μ_0, and on the difference in lethargies $u - u' \equiv \Delta u$. Thus $f(u,u',\Omega,\Omega') = f(\mu_0,\Delta u)$. Further, there is a direct relation between direction change and energy change if energy and momentum are conserved. With a particular Δu, there can be only *one* possible μ_0,[*] the value of which can be obtained by combining Equations (2.27), (2.28), and (2.38). It is

$$\mu_{01} = \left(\frac{A+1}{2}\right)e^{-\Delta u/2} - \left(\frac{A-1}{2}\right)e^{\Delta u/2} \qquad (10.2)$$

Integration over angle combinations other than those which satisfy this connection is not allowed or gives zero contribution to the selected neutron group. This may be expressed mathematically by making f proportional to the delta function,[*] $\delta(\mu_0 - \mu_{01})$. As may be verified by use of Equation (2.33),

---

[*] The properties of the delta-function are: $\int \delta(x)\,dx = 1$, where $\delta(x) = 0$ except when $x = 0$. $\delta(x)$ may be viewed geometrically as a rectangle of zero width, infinite height, area unity. Also $\int f(x)\delta(x)\,dx = f(0)$, and $\int f(x)\delta(x-a)\,dx = f(a)$. Multiplication of the delta-function by $f(x)$ scales it up by $f(x)$ everywhere, but only the value at the origin means anything.

$$f(\mu_0, \Delta u) = \frac{(A + 1)^2}{8\pi A} e^{-\Delta u} \delta(\mu_0 - \mu_{01}) \qquad (10.3)$$

The first step in solving Equation (10.1) is to propose that $\Phi(z,u,\Omega)$ and $f(\mu_0,\Delta u)$ may be expanded into a pair of Legendre series.

$$\Phi(z,u,\Omega) = \sum_{l=0}^{\infty} \frac{2l + 1}{4\pi} \phi_l(z,u) P_l(\mu) \qquad (10.4)$$

$$f(\mu_0, \Delta u) = \sum_{l=0}^{\infty} \frac{2l + 1}{4\pi} f_l(\Delta u) P_l(\mu_0) \qquad (10.5)$$

The function $\phi_0(z,u)$ is the total neutron flux over all directions of motion per unit lethargy at point z, lethargy u. A special neutron source is now proposed. Assume that 1 neutron/cm²-sec is released at lethargy zero at the plane $z = 0$, with random initial directions. This may be expressed by

$$S = \delta(z)\, \delta(u)/4\pi \qquad (10.6)$$

These expressions are inserted in the transport equation. The result is multiplied by $d\mu$ and integrated over the range -1 to 1, and separately multiplied by $\mu\, d\mu\, d\varphi = P_l(\mu)\, d\mu\, d\varphi$ and integrated, in analogy with the procedure used to reduce Equation (9.9). The theorems of Equations (9.18) and (9.24) are invoked to evaluate the integrals. It is now assumed that only the terms $\phi_0(z,u)$ and $\phi_1(z,u)$ in the Legendre series are to be retained, implying only a slightly anisotropic flux distribution in angle, i.e., far from sources. Let $\psi_0(z,u) \equiv \phi_0(z,u)\Sigma_s(u)$ be the collision density and $\psi_1(z,u) \equiv \phi_1(z,u)\Sigma_s(u)$. The equations simplify to

$$\frac{1}{\Sigma_s(u)} \frac{\partial \psi_1(z,u)}{\partial z} + \psi_0(z,u) \frac{\Sigma(u)}{\Sigma_s(u)} = \delta(z)\delta(u) +$$
$$\int_0^u du'\, \psi_0(z,u') f_0(\Delta u) \qquad (10.7)$$

$$\frac{1}{3\Sigma_s(u)} \frac{\partial \psi_0(z,u)}{\partial z} + \psi_1(z,u) \frac{\Sigma(u)}{\Sigma_s(u)} = \int_0^u du'\, \psi_1(z,u') f_1(\Delta u) \qquad (10.8)$$

The functions f_0 and f_1 are closely related to σ_{s0} and σ_{s1} as used previously. The similarity to the first two of Equations (9.29) in the one-velocity case is evident. By ignoring $\phi_2(z,u)$ and higher coefficients, we have reduced the problem to the diffusion approximation. At this point, we may go in two directions. The first is to find the total flux distribution as a function of position and lethargy, $\phi_0(z,u)$. By the introduction of certain approximations, the results of age theory are developed. The second is to derive an expression for the average value of z^2 at which neutrons cross the lethargy u, in the special case of a hydrogen–heavy-element mixture.

10.2. *Age theory*

We assume that the collision density does not vary rapidly with lethargy, which will be true if the *scattering cross section is a relatively smooth function*. A linear variation in the collision density obtained from the first two terms of a Taylor's expansion is taken to be adequate for small Δu.

$$\psi_0(z,u') = \psi_0(z,u) - \Delta u \frac{\partial \psi_0(z,u)}{\partial u} \tag{10.9}$$

Also, $\psi_1(z,u')$ is set equal to $\psi_1(z,u)$, on the assumption that fewer terms in the series expansion of ψ_1 are needed than in ψ_0. This may be shown to be approximately correct if the *distance from the source is not excessive*. Inserting these approximations to the components in Equations (10.7) and (10.8),

$$\frac{1}{\Sigma_s} \frac{\partial \psi_1}{\partial z} + \psi_0 \frac{\Sigma}{\Sigma_s} = \delta(z) \, \delta(u) + \psi_0 \int_{u_1}^{u} du' f_0(\Delta u) - $$
$$\frac{\partial \psi_0}{\partial u} \int_{u_1}^{u} du' \, \Delta u \, f_0(\Delta u) \tag{10.10}$$

$$\frac{1}{3\Sigma_s} \frac{\partial \psi_0}{\partial z} + \psi_1 \frac{\Sigma}{\Sigma_s} = \psi_1 \int_{u_1}^{u} du' f_1(\Delta u) \tag{10.11}$$

The range of integration should be scrutinized. Since neutrons colliding with a nucleus with certain A value can lose only an energy down to $E = E_0[(A - 1)/(A + 1)]^2$, the maximum lethargy change is $(\Delta u)_{max} = -\ln [(A - 1)/(A + 1)]^2$. Thus the lower limit of integration should be taken as $u - (\Delta u)_{max} \equiv u_1$. Each of the integrals has a simple interpretation. That multiplying ψ_0 is simply 1, the total probability of scattering; the coefficient of $\partial \psi_0/\partial u$ is the average Δu or average change in logarithm of the energy, i.e., ξ; the third is the average cosine of the scattering angle $\bar{\mu}_0$ (compare Equation 9.22). Thus

$$\frac{1}{\Sigma_s}\frac{\partial \psi_1}{\partial z} + \psi_0 \frac{\Sigma}{\Sigma_s} = \delta(z)\delta(u) + \psi_0 - \xi \frac{\partial \psi_0}{\partial u} \qquad (10.12)$$

$$\frac{1}{3\Sigma_s}\frac{\partial \psi_0}{\partial z} + \psi_1 \frac{\Sigma}{\Sigma_s} = \psi_1\bar{\mu}_0 \qquad (10.13)$$

Combining Equations (10.12) and (10.13), defining

$$\Sigma_t = \Sigma - \Sigma_s\bar{\mu}_0$$

a slightly modified transport cross section including absorption, and letting $\psi_0 = \phi_0\Sigma_s$, we obtain the lethargy–position-dependent flux

$$D \frac{\partial^2 \phi_0}{\partial z^2} - \phi\Sigma_a + \delta(z)\delta(u) = \frac{\partial q}{\partial u} \qquad (10.14)$$

In terms of $q = \xi\Sigma_s\phi$ and $d\tau = du/(3\xi\Sigma_s\Sigma_t)$, this becomes

$$\frac{\partial^2 q}{\partial z^2} - \frac{q\Sigma_a}{D} + \delta(z)\delta(\tau) = \frac{\partial q}{\partial \tau} \qquad (10.15)$$

which is the Fermi *age equation* for a plane monoenergetic source with absorption (compare Equation 3.41).

Age theory is capable of predicting rather accurately the spatial distribution of neutrons in moderators with nuclei as light as carbon, and gives reasonably good answers with D_2O. The accuracy obtained for the latter is surprising in view of the simplifying assumption that the slowing process is continuous. For moderators containing hydrogen, age theory is far from correct, and it is necessary to return to the more general Equations (10.7) and (10.8).

10.3. *Solution for hydrogenous mixture*

A "rigorous" solution of the diffusion approximation of transport equations (10.7) and (10.8) can be made for an infinite-sized mixture of hydrogen and an infinitely heavy element. For real elements such as oxygen in the case of water, the result will be a fair approximation. We seek the value of $\bar{z^2}/2$, or one half of the average square of the coordinate of the slowing-down distribution of neutrons, $q(z,u)$, due to a monoenergetic source of neutrons at $u = 0$. In analogy with the slowing from a *point source* as described in Chapter 3, $\bar{z^2}/2 = \tau$ in the case of age theory. Although the word "age" is widely used to identify this quantity, it is preferable to let $\overline{z^2}/2 = L_s^2$, where L_s is called the "slowing-down length."   By definition,

$$\overline{z^2} = \frac{\int_{-\infty}^{\infty} z^2 q(z,u)\,dz}{\int_{-\infty}^{\infty} q(z,u)\,dz}$$

but since $q(z,u)$ is proportional to the total flux $\phi_0(z,u)$ and the scattering cross section $\Sigma_s(u)$,

$$2L_s^2 = \overline{z^2} = \frac{\int z^2 \psi_0(z,u)\,dz}{\int \psi_0(z,u)\,dz} \tag{10.16}$$

The method of obtaining $\psi_0(z,u)$ is outlined.

The scattering probability f for a mixture is a composite function:

$$f(\mu_0,\Delta u) = \frac{\Sigma_{sH} f_H}{\Sigma_s} + \frac{\Sigma_{sE} f_E}{\Sigma_s} = cf_H + (1 - c)f_E \tag{10.17}$$

where the weighting factors are the fractional scattering cross sections for each element.   From Equation (10.2) with $A = 1$,

$$\mu_{01} = e^{-\Delta u/2} \tag{10.18}$$

and from Equation (10.3),

$$f_H = \frac{e^{-\Delta u}}{2\pi} \delta(\mu_0 - \mu_{01}) \tag{10.19}$$

Now assume that a neutron changes direction upon scattering with the heavy element, but no energy loss is experienced.   This condition is described mathematically by setting

$$f_E = \frac{\delta(u - u')}{4\pi} \tag{10.20}$$

which states that unless $u' = u$, the probability of scattering is zero, but that the direction of motion after collision is random over the 4π solid angle about the point of impact.   Thus combining Equations (10.17), (10.19) and (10.20),

$$f(\mu_0,\Delta u) = c\frac{e^{-\Delta u}}{2\pi} \delta(\mu_0 - \mu_{01}) + (1 - c) \frac{\delta(u - u')}{4\pi} \tag{10.21}$$

The Fourier transform is taken of both sides of Equations (10.7) and (10.8), with absorption disregarded, reducing them to

$$\frac{-iy}{\Sigma_s(u)}\,\bar{\psi}_1(y,u) + \bar{\psi}_0(y,u) = \delta(u) + \int_0^u du'\,\bar{\psi}_0(y,u')f_0(\Delta u) \quad (10.22)$$

$$-\frac{iy}{3\Sigma_s(u)}\,\bar{\psi}_0(y,u) + \bar{\psi}_1(y,u) = \int_0^u du'\,\bar{\psi}_1(y,u')f_1(\Delta u) \quad (10.23)$$

The functions f_0 and f_1 are obtained from Equations (9.21), (9.22), (10.21) and the properties of the δ-function.

$$f_0(\Delta u) = 2\pi \int_{-1}^1 d\mu_0\, f(\mu_0,\Delta u) = ce^{-\Delta u} + (1-c)\delta(\Delta u) \quad (10.24)$$

$$f_1(\Delta u) = 2\pi \int_{-1}^1 d\mu_0\mu_0 f(\mu_0,\Delta u) = ce^{-3\Delta u/2} \quad (10.25)$$

The solution of Equations (10.22) and (10.23) is laborious, and the reader is referred to the paper by Marshak (see References) for further details. The final result for the square of the slowing-down length is a sum of seven terms,

$$3L_s^2 = \frac{\lambda^2(0)}{c(0)} + \frac{\lambda^2(u)}{c(u)} + \int_0^u \frac{\lambda^2(u')\,du'}{c(u')} + \lambda(0)\lambda(u)F(0,u)$$

$$+ \lambda(u)\int_0^u \lambda(u')F(u',u)\,du' + \lambda(0)\int_0^u \lambda(u')F(0,u')\,du'$$

$$+ \int_0^u \lambda(u')\int_0^{u'} \lambda(u'')F(u'',u')\,du''\,du' \quad (10.26)$$

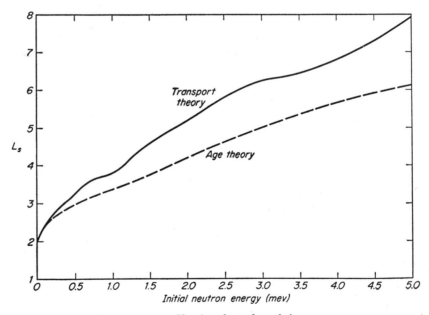

Figure 10.1. Slowing-down length in water.

where

$$F(x,y) = e^{-[3/2(y-x)+\int_x^y c(t)dt]}$$
$$\lambda(u) = 1/\Sigma_s(u)$$
$$c(u) = \Sigma_{sH}(u)/\Sigma_s(u)$$

Figure 10.1 shows a plot of the slowing-down length for neutrons of various initial energies in water, obtained by this formula. Note should be made of the large error incurred by the use of age theory.

If the slowing-down length of neutrons as a function of energy E_0 is known, the value of L_s^2 for a fission spectrum may be obtained by integration of

$$L_s^2(E) = \int_E^\infty L_s^2(E_0)S(E_0)\,dE_0$$

where $S(E_0) \simeq 0.484e^{-E_0} \sinh \sqrt{2E_0}$.

10.4. *Improvements in age theory for hydrogenous mixtures*

The slowing of neutrons in hydrogenous materials is poorly represented by age theory, because of the large possible energy loss per collision. Various methods based on approximations of the general transport equation have been devised to correct this difficulty. Hurwitz and Zweifel have extended the spherical harmonics method to a "B_3 approximation" that is more accurate than the P_3 counterpart. The Greuling-Goertzel method improves on age-diffusion theory in cases where absorption and leakage are large. The Goertzel-Selengut method, which takes specific account of the energy loss in hydrogen for an absorbing, multiplying medium, will now be outlined, followed by a discussion of the Flügge-Tittle semi-empirical method.

Goertzel-Selengut method. We return to the Equations (10.7) and (10.8) in $\psi_0(z,u)$ and $\psi_1(z,u)$. We may dispense immediately with the second equation, by assuming that it can be converted into the form of Equation (10.13) by the age theory treatment, giving

$$\psi_1 = \frac{-1}{3\Sigma_t}\frac{\partial\psi_0}{\partial z} \tag{10.27}$$

which is noted to be Fick's law of diffusion. Here Σ_t is $\Sigma - \Sigma_s \bar{\mu}_0$, where $\bar{\mu}_0$ is the cross section weighted sum of average cosines of scattering angles of all elements in the system. The improvement over age theory lies in the manner of treating the scattering integral in Equation (10.7). Suppose that the medium in which neutrons are slowing consists of hydrogen (H) plus one heavier element (E); then

$$\int_0^u du'\, \psi_0(z,u') f_0(\Delta u) = I_{\mathrm{H}} + I_{\mathrm{E}} \tag{10.28}$$

where

$$I_{\mathrm{H}} = \int_0^u du'\, \phi_0(z,u') \Sigma_{s\mathrm{H}}(u') f_{0\mathrm{H}}(\Delta u) \tag{10.29}$$

and

$$I_{\mathrm{E}} = \int_{u_1}^u du'\, \phi_0(z,u') \Sigma_{s\mathrm{E}}(u') f_{0\mathrm{E}}(\Delta u) \tag{10.30}$$

The integral I_{H} will be left intact, with no approximations, thus guaranteeing the proper description of energy loss due to collisions with hydrogen. Now apply the lethargy expansion of age theory equation (10.9) to the function $\phi_0(z,u') \Sigma_{s\mathrm{E}}(u')$, which will be labeled $\psi_{0\mathrm{E}}(z,u')$.

$$\psi_{0\mathrm{E}}(z,u') = \psi_{0\mathrm{E}}(z,u) - \Delta u \frac{\partial \psi_{0\mathrm{E}}(z,u)}{\partial u}$$

Insert this in I_{E}, Equation (10.30), and integrate to obtain

$$I_{\mathrm{E}} = \psi_{0\mathrm{E}}(z,u) - \xi_{\mathrm{E}} \frac{\partial \psi_{0\mathrm{E}}(z,u)}{\partial u}$$

Equation (10.7) now becomes

$$\frac{1}{\Sigma_s} \frac{\partial \psi_1}{\partial z} + \psi_1 \frac{\Sigma}{\Sigma_s} = I_{\mathrm{H}} + \psi_{0\mathrm{E}} - \xi_{\mathrm{E}} \frac{\partial \psi_{0\mathrm{E}}}{\partial u} + \delta(z)\delta(u)$$

Combining with Equation (10.27) and simplifying by returning to flux notation,

$$D \frac{\partial^2 \phi_0}{\partial z^2} - \phi_0(\Sigma_a + \Sigma_{s\mathrm{H}}) + I_{\mathrm{H}} + \delta(z)\delta(u) = \xi_{\mathrm{E}} \frac{(\phi_0 \Sigma_{s\mathrm{E}})}{\partial u} \tag{10.31}$$

It is recommended that use of the sum $\Sigma_{s\mathrm{E}} + \Sigma_a$ should be made in place of $\Sigma_{s\mathrm{E}}$ in the right side, for greater accuracy. Further, defining

$$q(z,u) = \xi_{\mathrm{E}} \phi_0(z,u) [\Sigma_{s\mathrm{E}}(u) + \Sigma_a(u)]$$

and recalling from Equation (10.24) that $f_{0H}(\Delta u) = e^{-\Delta u}$, we arrive at the general Goertzel-Selengut formula for a plane source of monoenergetic neutrons:

$$D(u) \frac{\partial^2}{\partial z^2} \phi_0(z,u) - \phi_0(z,u)[\Sigma_a(u) + \Sigma_{sH}(u)]$$

$$\text{(a)} \hspace{5cm} \text{(b)}$$

$$+ \int_0^u \phi_0(z,u')\Sigma_{sH}(u')e^{-(u-u')} du' + \delta(z)\delta(u) = \frac{\partial q(z,u)}{\partial u} \quad (10.32)$$

$$\text{(c)} \hspace{4cm} \text{(d)} \hspace{2cm} \text{(e)}$$

It will be well to identify the various terms in sequence: (a) gain from spatial flow, (b) removal by absorption and hydrogen scattering, (c) total supply from smaller lethargies because of scattering with hydrogen, (d) source, and finally, (e) net loss by scattering with the heavy element. Comparison of Equation (10.32) with Equation (10.14) for age theory and the formula used to derive Equation (2.42) for a pure hydrogen moderator is instructive.

The Goertzel-Selengut method may readily be extended from this case of a plane source, with unique initial lethargy, to a reactor, with fission occurring throughout the neutron energy spectrum. Let the fission rate per unit volume and unit lethargy range be $\phi_0(z,u)\Sigma_f(z,u)$. The total fission rate per unit volume is the integral over all lethargy:

$$\int \phi_0(z,u')\Sigma_f(z,u') \, du'$$

It is conventional to separate this into the epithermal and thermal fission components, i.e., into

$$\int_0^{u_t} \phi_0(z,u')\Sigma_f(z,u') \, du' + \phi_t(\Sigma_f)_t$$

This, when multiplied by the fission neutron energy spectrum $S(u)$, normalized to one neutron, and multiplied by ν, the number of neutrons per fission, gives the source term for Equation (10.32). Finally, it should be emphasized that the treatment is not restricted to a plane geometry problem. Replacement of z by a general coordinate r and $\partial^2/\partial z^2$ by ∇^2 in that coordinate system is all that is necessary. The solution of the equation for either q or ϕ_0 is best achieved by use of a computing machine, although the special case of a finite bare reactor with only hydrogen as moderator can be handled analytically.

Flügge-Tittle method.   A semi-empirical recipe for estimating ages of mixtures of heavy elements with hydrogen has been developed by Tittle, based on concepts proposed by Christy and Flügge and making use of results from Equation (10.26). The method involves a separate description of the motion of fast neutrons in their first few collisions, where the hydrogen scattering cross section varies rapidly with energy, and the motion below 100 kev, where age theory is rather accurate (compare Figure 10.1).

Consider a point source S of neutrons of energy E_1 located at the origin. The flux of those that have not yet collided at a distance r is

$$\phi = \frac{Se^{-r/\lambda_1}}{4\pi r^2}$$

where λ_1 is the mean free path for these neutrons. The collision rate per unit volume at r is $\phi\Sigma_s$. The mean square displacement for first collisions is readily shown to be

$$\overline{r_1^2} = \frac{\int \phi\Sigma_s r^2\, dV}{\int \phi\Sigma_s\, dV} = 2\lambda_1^2$$

The collided neutrons now form a virtual source at r of strength $\phi\Sigma_s$ per second per unit volume, and have an average energy of $E_2 = E_1/e$ after collision with hydrogen. By extension, the total $\overline{r^2}$ for the several collisions that are required to bring neutrons down to 100 kev is the sum

$$\overline{r^2}(E_1 - 100 \text{ kev}) = 2\lambda_1^2 + 2\lambda_2^2 + 2\lambda_3^2 + \cdots$$

where the λ's are appropriate to E_1, $E_2 = E_1/e$, $E_3 = E_2/e$, $\cdots$. The corresponding slowing-down length is given by

$$l_s^2 = \overline{r^2}/6 = \frac{\lambda_1^2 + \lambda_2^2 + \lambda_3^2 + \cdots}{3} \tag{10.33}$$

The results of calculations by Equation (10.26) for water were analyzed to obtain a formula for λ_i, where $i = 1, 2, 3, \cdots$. It was found that it could be expressed as a function of the actual mean free path in water (λ), and the mean free paths in hydrogen

(λ_H) and oxygen (λ_O), as if each element were separately present. The result was the linear formula

$$\frac{\lambda_i}{\lambda} = 2.155 - 0.119 \frac{\lambda_O}{\lambda_H} \qquad (10.34)$$

The calculation procedure for a given mixture consists of the following steps.

(a) Find the mean free paths in hydrogen, in other materials, and the mixture as a whole, for a series of energies E_1, E_2, and E_3, etc., down to around 100 kev.

(b) Form, from Equation (10.34), the values of λ_i for each energy, i.e., λ_1, λ_2, λ_3, etc., replacing λ_O by λ_{other}.

(c) Compute the square of the slowing-down length to 100 kev from Equation (10.33).

(d) Add to this the age as normally computed from 100 kev to E, the final level of interest, $\tau(100 \text{ kev} - E)$.

The final slowing-down length is thus

$$L_s^2 = l_s^2 + \tau(100 \text{ kev} - E) \qquad (10.35)$$

Numerical Illustration: Calculate the age for 2-mev neutrons to 1.45 ev in an iron-water mixture with metal/water volume ratio 0.29.

Solution. The energies (in mev) are $E_1 = 2$, $E_2 = 0.736$, $E_3 = 0.271$. The microscopic cross section in iron in this range varies rapidly, but is around 3 barns. The following calculation table is made, using $N_H = 2N_O = 0.0518$, $N_{Fe} = 0.0191$.

i	σ_H	σ_O	σ_{Fe}	Σ_H	Σ_O	Σ_{Fe}	Σ
1	2.89	1.6	3	0.150	0.041	0.057	0.248
2	5.05	3.0	3	0.262	0.078	0.057	0.397
3	8.25	3.75	3	0.427	0.097	0.057	0.581

λ_H	λ_{other}	λ	λ_i	$\lambda_i^2/3$
6.67	10.2	4.03	7.96	21.1
3.82	7.4	2.52	4.85	7.8
2.34	6.5	1.72	3.14	3.3

$$l_s^2 = 32.2 \text{ cm}^2$$

The age from 100 kev to 1.45 ev is obtained by numerical integration of

$$\tau = \int_{1.45 \text{ ev}}^{100 \text{ kev}} \frac{du}{3\overline{\xi\Sigma_s}\,\overline{T\Sigma_s}}$$

where
$$\overline{\xi \Sigma}_s = \xi_H (\Sigma_s)_H + \xi_O (\Sigma_s)_O + \xi_{Fe} (\Sigma_s)_{Fe}$$
and
$$\overline{T \Sigma}_s = T_H (\Sigma_s)_H + T_O (\Sigma_s)_O + T_{Fe} (\Sigma_s)_{Fe}$$

with $T = 1 - \overline{\cos \theta} = 1 - (2/3A)$. Cross sections from BNL-325 are used, with the result $\tau(100 \text{ kev} - 1.45 \text{ ev}) = 6.1 \text{ cm}^2$. The final estimate is $L_s^2 = 32.2 + 6.1 = 38.3 \text{ cm}^2$.

10.5. *Multigroup methods for intermediate reactors*

The determination of critical dimensions and flux distributions of reactors in which appreciable fission occurs at a variety of neutron energies or which are of non-uniform composition is almost impossible without resort to electronic computers. The fundamental ideas of the multigroup-multiregion method are presented, with an indication of the way machines are used.

In the two-group approach, described in Chapter 5, the proc-

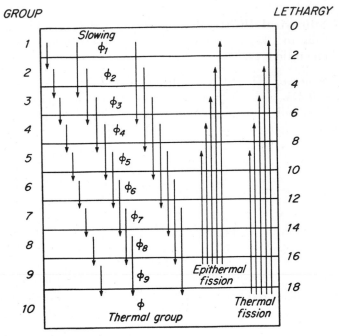

Figure 10.2.   Neutron transfers in multigroup model.

esses experienced by two classes of neutrons, fast and thermal, were represented by differential diffusion equations. The multigroup method is an extension to many classes, but the intent is the same—to solve for flux in the system subject to restrictions on size, shape and materials that constitute the critical condition. A block diagram (Figure 10.2), using lethargy coordinates, refers to a 10-group analysis for a one-region reactor. The case of a multiregion system is readily visualized.

The width in lethargy of the various groups need not be the same; the choice of method of division depends on the detail needed in different regions. As sketched, neutrons are shown slowing from a group to as far as the third one away. A hydrogen moderator can slow neutrons from a group to any below it, while a heavy moderator can change the energy by no more than a factor $\alpha = (A - 1)^2/(A + 1)^2$. The method described below is due to Ehrlich and Hurwitz (see References).

Age-multigroup theory. The age theory approximation implies a continuous slowing, which restricts transfers to adjacent groups. The age-theory equations (3.32) or (10.14), including absorption and a fission source, are used to describe the neutron process in every group:

$$D \nabla^2 \phi - \phi \Sigma_a + S = \frac{\partial q}{\partial u} \tag{10.36}$$

where all quantities except D are functions both of lethargy u and position r. Diffusion in the thermal group is represented by

$$D_0 \nabla^2 \phi_0 - \phi_0 \Sigma_{a0} + q_0 = 0 \tag{10.37}$$

where the zero denotes thermal quantities. This set of equations is to be solved simultaneously. Either the flux ϕ or the slowing-down density q may be eliminated from Equation (10.36) by the substitution of

$$\phi = \frac{q}{\xi \Sigma_s} \tag{10.38}$$

Eliminating ϕ, Equation (10.36) becomes

$$\frac{D}{\xi \Sigma_s} \nabla^2 q - \frac{\Sigma_a q}{\xi \Sigma_s} + S = \frac{\partial q}{\partial u} \tag{10.39}$$

Let us restrict our attention to a particular group of definite lethargy width U, and integrate both sides of the equation over that lethargy range. The source term, for example, becomes $\int S(u)\, du$, which is the same as $\bar{S}U$, from the definition of average $\bar{S} = \int S(u)\, du/U$. The other terms on the left are treated similarly. The right side is changed to

$$\int \frac{\partial q}{\partial u}\, du = q_{\text{out}} - q_{\text{in}}$$

where the subscripts mean neutron flow to and from other groups. Equation (10.39) becomes

$$U\left[\left(\frac{\overline{D}}{\xi\Sigma_s}\right)\nabla^2 \bar{q} - \left(\frac{\overline{\Sigma_a}}{\xi\Sigma_s}\right)\bar{q} + \bar{S}\right] = q_{\text{out}} - q_{\text{in}} \qquad (10.40)$$

If the lethargy width of the group is small, no distinction needs to be made between the average of a product and the product of averages. Of the quantities appearing in Equation (10.40), we may assume that q_{in} is known, from the solution of a higher group equation, but $\bar{q}$ and q_{out} are not. An independent relation between the various q's must be provided. It is clear that they are all rather close to each other in magnitude if there are many closely spaced lethargy groups. One obvious choice is

$$\bar{q} = \frac{q_{\text{in}} + q_{\text{out}}}{2} \qquad (10.41)$$

Other possibilities have been tested by KAPL and ORNL (see References) with certain improvements in accuracy.

By combining Equations (10.40) and (10.41) and letting $U\left(\dfrac{\overline{D}}{\xi\Sigma_s}\right)$ be abbreviated by A, and $U\left(\dfrac{\overline{\Sigma_a}}{\xi\Sigma_s}\right)$ by $B - 2$,

$$A\,\nabla^2 \bar{q} - B\bar{q} + U\bar{S} = -2q_{\text{in}} \qquad (10.42)$$

It is to be noted that q_{in} is the q_{out} for the group above, which is the only coupling between the groups during the slowing process. We may now proceed to the space integration for a spherical system. The only problems that can be handled easily are one-dimensional, semi-infinite slabs, spheres, or infinite cylinders. The Laplacian in spherical coordinates (Equation 3.6) is inserted and a change of variables made as in § 3.2:

$$Q = r\bar{q} \qquad (10.43)$$

to translate Equation (10.42) into the form

$$A \frac{d^2Q}{dr^2} - BQ = -(rU\bar{S} + 2Q_{\text{in}}) \qquad (10.44)$$

Difference equation formulation. The differential equation (10.44) in Q is now converted into a difference equation in the space sketched in Figure 10.3. The sphere is divided into N

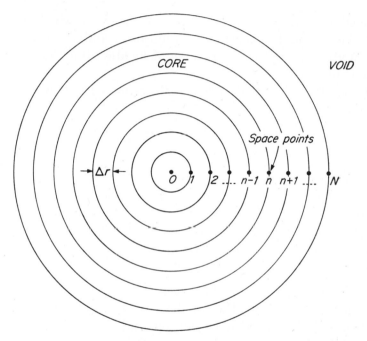

Figure 10.3. Space lattice for solution of difference equations in bare sphere.

shells of radii r_n, thickness Δr. We let the value of Q at r_n be labeled Q_n and ignore points *inside* the zone, but realize, by making Δr small enough, that the slowing-down density at all points will be described.

According to the theory of difference equations (see References) the derivative of a function $Q(r)$ with respect to r can be approximated by a forward first difference quotient,

$$\left[\frac{dQ(r)}{dr}\right]_f \sim \frac{Q(r_n + \Delta r) - Q(r)}{\Delta r} = \frac{Q_{n+1} - Q_n}{\Delta r}$$

or equally well by a backward first difference quotient,

$$\left[\frac{dQ(r)}{dr}\right]_b \simeq \frac{Q(r_n) - Q(r_n - \Delta r)}{\Delta r} = \frac{Q_n - Q_{n-1}}{\Delta r}$$

The second derivative is approximated by

$$\frac{d^2Q(r)}{dr^2} \simeq \frac{\left[\dfrac{dQ(r)}{dr}\right]_f - \left[\dfrac{dQ(r)}{dr}\right]_b}{\Delta r} = \frac{Q_{n+1} - 2Q_n + Q_{n-1}}{(\Delta r)^2} \quad (10.45)$$

In the limit of $\Delta r = 0$, the formulas become exact, which indicates that there should appear in the solution of difference equations the counterparts of the familiar complementary functions and particular integrals.

Using this second derivative, Equation (10.44) for a space point n becomes

$$A\left[\frac{Q_{n+1} - 2Q_n + Q_{n-1}}{(\Delta r)^2}\right] - BQ_n = -[r_n U\bar{S}_n + 2(Q_n)_{\text{in}}] \quad (10.46)$$

Rearranging, a recursion relation is developed,

$$Q_{n+1} = kQ_n - Q_{n-1} - I_n \quad (10.47)$$

where

$$k = 2 + (\Delta r)^2 B/A \quad (10.48)$$

$$I_n = \frac{(\Delta r)^2}{A}[r_n U\bar{S}_n + 2(Q_n)_{\text{in}}] \quad (10.49)$$

The complete solution of difference equation (10.47) consists of two parts, H_n, the solution of the homogeneous equation, with $I_n = 0$, and P_n, a particular solution, and is

$$Q_n = xH_n + P_n \quad (10.50)$$

where x, an arbitrary coefficient, is chosen to make $Q_n = 0$ at the extrapolated radius of the system. The value of Q_0 must also be zero to keep the flux finite at the origin.

Substitution of Equation (10.50) back into Equation (10.47) and use of the homogeneous recursion relation yields:

$$\begin{aligned} H_{n+1} &= kH_n - H_{n-1} \\ P_{n+1} &= kP_n - P_{n-1} - I_n \end{aligned} \quad (10.51)$$

Direct application of the formulas above is found to result in the generation of successively larger numbers, with an attendant loss of accuracy. An alternate set of recursion formulas that is based on the *ratios* of solutions at adjacent space points has been devised to avoid this difficulty. In this form, one works only with Q_n and H_n, without evaluating the particular integral P_n explicitly. By multiplying Equation (10.47) by H_n and Equation (10.51) by Q_n and subtracting, we obtain

$$H_{n+1}Q_n - H_nQ_{n+1} = H_nQ_{n-1} - H_{n-1}Q_n + H_nI_n$$

Repeated use of this equation leads to the identity

$$H_{n+1}Q_n - H_nQ_{n+1} = H_1Q_0 - H_0Q_1 + \sum_{j=1}^{n} H_jI_j$$

Letting $Q_0 = 0$ and $H_0 = 0$,

$$Q_n = \frac{H_n}{H_{n+1}} \left(Q_{n+1} + \sum_{j=1}^{n} \frac{H_jI_j}{H_n} \right) \tag{10.52}$$

Two new variables are defined. The first is

$$\alpha_n = \frac{H_n}{H_{n-1}} \tag{10.53}$$

governed by the recursion relation (10.51), which now becomes

$$\alpha_{n+1} = k - \frac{1}{\alpha_n} \tag{10.54}$$

The second is the summation in Equation (10.52),

$$\beta_n = \frac{H_1I_1}{H_n} + \frac{H_2I_2}{H_n} + \cdots + \frac{H_{n-1}I_{n-1}}{H_n} + I_n$$

By factoring out H_{n-1}/H_n from this sum and using Equation (10.53) it is seen that

$$\beta_n = \frac{\beta_{n-1}}{\alpha_n} + I_n \tag{10.55}$$

Combining equations, the final solution is

$$Q_n = \frac{Q_{n+1} + \beta_n}{\alpha_{n+1}} \tag{10.56}$$

Equations (10.54), (10.55), and (10.56) serve as the working formulas. Since Q_0 must be zero, α_1 is infinite, and the starting value for α_n is $\alpha_2 = k$. The first value of β_n is $\beta_1 = I_1$. The procedure consists of finding α's and β's by working *out* to larger n, and then solving for the Q's by working *in* to smaller n, starting with $Q_N = 0$.

The full benefit of the difference equation formulation of the multigroup theory cannot be realized without use of a computing machine, but the procedure can be illustrated by an idealized example.

Numerical Illustration: Find the flux distribution and effective multiplication factor for a 70-cm radius bare spherical U^{235}-fueled reactor with moderator that resembles graphite, except that the epithermal neutron scattering cross section is constant and zero high energy absorption occurs. Assume epithermal constants

$$\xi = 0.159$$
$$D = 0.889 \text{ cm}$$
$$\Sigma_s = 0.397 \text{ cm}^{-1}$$
$$\xi\Sigma_s = 0.0631 \text{ cm}^{-1}$$

Solution. The lethargy range of epithermal neutrons from $u = 0$ (10 mev) to $u = 18.28$ is divided into four groups of width $U = 4.57$ each. Fission is assumed to supply neutrons at *unique lethargy* $u = 2.285$, which is at the middle of the highest energy group. From age theory, the age of neutrons entering the fifth or thermal group is

$$\tau = \int_{2.28}^{18.28} \frac{D}{\xi\Sigma_s} \, du = \frac{16D}{\xi\Sigma_s} = \frac{(16)(0.889)}{0.0631} = 225 \text{ cm}^2$$

where the total lethargy change is 16. The thermal constants, including U^{235} fuel, are taken to be $k = 1.977$, $D_0 = 0.662$ cm, and $\Sigma_{a0} = 5.243 \times 10^{-3}$ cm^{-1}. Divide the sphere into six equal-width concentric zones of equal thickness $70/6 = 11\frac{2}{3}$ cm, as in Figure 10.3, with seven space points, labeled $n = 0, 1, 2, \cdots, 6 = N$, starting at the origin, $r = 0$. Now for all epithermal lethargy groups,

$$A = \frac{UD}{\xi\Sigma_s} = \frac{(4.57)(0.889)}{0.0631} = 64.4$$
$$B = 2 \quad \text{(no absorption)}$$
$$\frac{(\Delta r)^2}{A} = 2.113$$
$$k = 2 + \frac{2(11\frac{2}{3})^2}{64.4} = 6.226$$

Consider first the highest energy group, which we call group I. In forming the function I_n for its space points, we note that there is no slowing-in source $(Q_n)_{\text{in}}$, but only the fission source $r_n \overline{S}_n U = r_n S_n$. In anticipation of a thermal flux distribution resembling $(\sin \pi r/R)/(\pi r/R)$, the trial spatial fission source S_n is made *equal* to this function.   Calculations of I_n for this group are shown below:

n	r	$\dfrac{\sin(\pi r/R)}{\pi r/R} = S_n$	$(I_n)_\mathrm{I} = \dfrac{(\Delta r)^2}{A}r_n S_n$
0	0	1	0
1	$11\frac{2}{3}$	0.9549	23.54
2	$23\frac{1}{3}$	0.8270	40.77
3	35	0.6366	47.08
4	$46\frac{2}{3}$	0.4135	40.77
5	$58\frac{1}{3}$	0.1910	23.54
6	70	0	0

The tabular application of Equations (10.54), (10.55), and (10.56) for group I is then developed, with starting points for the recursion designated by boxes.

Group I.

n	I_n	α_n	$1/\alpha_n$	α_{n+1}	β_n	$\dfrac{\beta_{n-1}}{\alpha_n}$	Q_{n+1}	$Q_{n+1}+\beta_n$
0	0						5.18	
1	23.54			6.226	$\boxed{I_1=23.54}$		9.08	32.62
2	40.77	$\boxed{k=6.226}$	0.161	6.065	44.56	3.79	10.48	55.04
3	47.08	6.065	0.165	6.061	54.43	7.35	9.07	63.50
4	40.77	6.061	0.165	6.061	49.75	8.98	5.24	54.99
5	23.54	6.061	0.165	6.061	31.75	8.21	$\boxed{Q_6=0}$	31.75
6	0	6.061	0.165		5.24	5.24		

The slowing-in sources for the lattice points in the next lethargy group are now formed.   Noting that q_in for group I is zero, Equation (10.41) gives $q_\mathrm{out} = 2\bar{q}$.   Thus in Equation (10.49), the term $(Q_n)_\mathrm{in}$ for group II is equal to $2Q_n$ for group I.   No fission source being present,

$$[I_n]_\mathrm{II} = \frac{2(\Delta r)^2}{A}\,2[Q_n]_\mathrm{I} = (4.226)2[Q_n]_\mathrm{I}$$

Again, the recursion relations are applied.

Group II.

n	$2[Q_n]_\mathrm{I}$	I_n	β_n	$\dfrac{\beta_{n-1}}{\alpha_n}$	Q_{n+1}	$Q_{n+1}+\beta_n$
0	0	0			9.80	
1	10.36	43.78	$I_1=43.78$		17.08	60.86
2	18.16	76.74	83.79	7.05	19.71	103.80
3	20.96	88.58	102.41	13.83	17.06	119.47
4	18.14	76.66	93.56	16.90	9.86	103.42
5	10.48	44.29	59.73	15.44	0	59.73
6	0	0	9.86	9.86		

Q values for Groups III and IV are calculated similarly, except that

$$[(Q_n)_{in}]_{III} = 2[Q_n]_{II} - [(Q_n)_{in}]_{II}$$

and

$$[(Q_n)_{in}]_{IV} = 2[Q_n]_{III} - [(Q_n)_{in}]_{III}$$

The results are:

Group III.

n	$2[Q_n]_{II}-[(Q_n)_{in}]_{II}$	I_n	β_n	$\dfrac{\beta_{n-1}}{\alpha_n}$	Q_{n+1}	$Q_{n+1}+\beta_n$
0	0	0			8.71	54.11
1	9.24	39.05	39.05		15.06	91.27
2	16.00	67.62	73.91	6.29	17.36	105.24
3	18.46	78.01	90.21	12.20	15.03	91.10
4	15.98	67.53	82.41	14.88	8.69	52.65
5	9.24	39.05	52.65	13.60	0	
6	0	0	8.69	8.69		

Group IV.

n	$2[Q_n]_{III}-[(Q_n)_{in}]_{III}$	I_n	β_n	$\dfrac{\beta_{n-1}}{\alpha_n}$	Q_{n+1}	$Q_{n+1}+\beta_n$
0	0	0			7.71	
1	8.18	34.57	34.57		13.30	47.87
2	14.12	59.67	65.24	5.57	15.30	80.54
3	16.26	68.71	79.47	10.76	13.24	92.71
4	14.08	59.50	72.61	13.11	7.65	80.26
5	8.14	34.40	46.38	11.98	0	46.38
6	0	0	7.65	7.65		

The calculation of thermal flux is similar to that for epithermal groups, with $r\phi_n = \Phi_n$ replacing Q_n. Now $A = D_0 = 0.662$ cm, $B = \Sigma_{a0} = 5.243 \times 10^{-3}$ cm^{-1}, $k = 2 + (\Delta r)^2 B/A = 3.078$. $I_n = [(\Delta r)^2/A](Q_n)_{in} = 205.6(Q_n)_{in}$, where $(Q_n)_{in} = 2[(Q_n)]_{IV} - [(Q_n)_{in}]_{IV}$. Application of recursion formulas (10.54), (10.55), and (10.56) follows:

Thermal Group.

n	$2[(Q_n)]_{IV}-[(Q_n)_{in}]_{IV}$	I_n	α_n	$1/\alpha_n$	α_{n+1}
0	0	0			
1	7.24	1489			
2	12.48	2566	3.078	0.325	2.753
3	14.34	2949	2.573	0.363	2.715
4	12.40	2550	2.715	0.368	2.710
5	7.16	1472	2.710	0.369	2.709
6	0	0	2.709	0.369	2.709

n	β_n	$\dfrac{\beta_{n+1}}{\alpha_n}$	Φ_{n+1}	$\Phi_{n+1}+\beta_n$
0			1102	
1	1489		1904	3393
2	3050	484	2193	5243
3	4057	1108	1896	5953
4	4044	1494	1094	5138
5	2964	1492	0	2964
6	1094	1094		

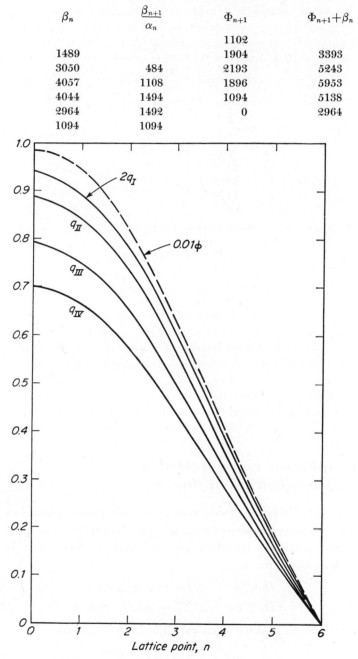

Figure 10.4.   Slowing-down density and thermal flux in sphere by multigroup method.

A test of criticality is made by comparing the initial source $r_n S_n$ and that obtained by the product $\Phi_n \Sigma_a k$, which is the fission neutron yield from thermal absorption. With $\Sigma_a k = (5.243 \times 10^{-3})(1.977) = 0.01036$, we find

n	Calculated $r_n S_n$	Assumed $r_n S_n$	$\dfrac{Calculated}{Assumed}$
0	0	0	1
1	11.42	11.14	1.025
2	19.73	19.30	1.022
3	22.73	22.28	1.020
4	19.65	19.30	1.018
5	11.34	11.14	1.018
6	0	0	1

Another check is the total reactor fast neutron source, which is

$$S_T = \int_0^R 4\pi r^2 \, dr \, S$$

With seven lattice points, S_T is proportional to $\sum_{n=0}^{6} r_n^2 S_n$. From the far-right column of the table above, we find that S_T (calculated)$/S_T$ (assumed) $\simeq 1.02$, which implies an excess multiplication of 0.02 instead of criticality. A slight adjustment of fuel concentration may be made and the calculation repeated to bring k_e to exactly 1.

Figure 10.4 shows the spatial variation of the slowing-down density q and thermal flux ϕ_0 for the five groups. The diminution of q with increasing lethargy is of course due to leakage.

10.6. *Analogue computation of space-dependent flux*

The age-diffusion, two-group, or multigroup equations may also be solved by the use of an analogue computer, which simulates fluxes and currents by electrical quantities. Consider the two-group formulation,

$$D_1 \nabla^2 \phi_1 - \phi_1 D_1/\tau + \eta f \Sigma_2 \phi_2 = 0 \qquad (10.57)$$

$$D_2 \nabla^2 \phi_2 - \phi_2 \Sigma_2 + p \phi_1 D_1/\tau = 0 \qquad (10.58)$$

in a cylindrical system with coordinates r,z, where

$$\nabla^2 = \frac{1}{r} \frac{\partial}{\partial r} \left(\frac{r\partial}{\partial r} \right) + \frac{\partial^2}{\partial z^2}$$

The derivatives are first replaced by their equivalent difference-equation expressions as in § 10.5. A lattice of points in one "quadrant" of the reactor is visualized, as shown in Figure 10.5.

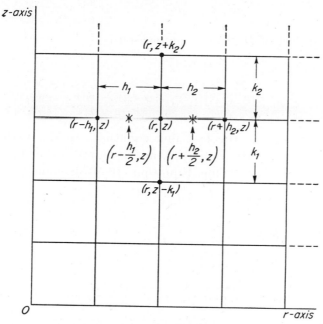

Figure 10.5. Space lattice for analogue computation.

The spacing of points is not necessarily uniform; thus h_1 and h_2 will be used to designate distances to adjacent points; similarly, k_1 and k_2.

Let us designate the product $-Dr\dfrac{\partial\phi}{\partial r}$ (r,z) as a modified radial current $J(r,z)$. Its derivative with respect to r will be defined in difference notation as

$$\frac{\partial J(r,z)}{\partial r} = \frac{J(r + \frac{1}{2}h_2,z) - J(r - \frac{1}{2}h_1,z)}{\frac{1}{2}h_1 + \frac{1}{2}h_2}$$

Each J in turn may be written

$$J(r + \tfrac{1}{2}h_2,z) = (r + \tfrac{1}{2}h_2)\frac{[\phi(r + h_2,z) - \phi(r,z)]}{h_2}$$

$$J(r - \tfrac{1}{2}h_1,z) = (r - \tfrac{1}{2}h_1)\frac{[\phi(r,z) - \phi(r - h_1,z)]}{h_1}$$

Combining, the radial part of each $D \nabla^2 \phi$ is

$$\frac{2D}{h_1 + h_2} \left\{ (r + \tfrac{1}{2}h_2) \frac{[\phi(r + h_2,z) - \phi(r,z)]}{h_2} \right.$$
$$\left. - (r - \tfrac{1}{2}h_1) \frac{[\phi(r,z) - \phi(r - h_1,z)]}{h_1} \right\} \quad (10.59)$$

The axial part of $D \nabla^2 \phi$ by comparison is

$$\frac{2D}{k_1 + k_2} \left\{ \frac{[\phi(r,z + k_2) - \phi(r,z)]}{k_2} \right.$$
$$\left. - \frac{[\phi(r,z) - \phi(r,z - k_1)]}{k_1} \right\} \quad (10.60)$$

Now apply this to the fast flux equation (10.57), with flux ϕ_1 labeled V, an electric potential, and group all other factors into various resistances. Thus Equation (10.59) becomes

$$\frac{[V(r + h_2,z) - V(r,z)]}{R_{h_2}} - \frac{[V(r,z) - V(r - h_1,z)]}{R_{h_1}}$$

while (10.60) becomes

$$\frac{[V(r,z + k_2) - V(r,z)]}{R_{k_2}} - \frac{[V(r,z) - V(r,z - k_1)]}{R_{k_1}}$$

The rest of the fast equation (10.57) is written as

$$\frac{E(r,z) - V(r,z)}{R_a}$$

where $E(r,z)$, proportional to the thermal flux $\phi_2(r,z)$, represents the fast source. The complete fast flux equation becomes

$$\frac{V(r + h_2,z) - V(r,z)}{R_{h_2}} - \frac{V(r,z) - V(r - h_1,z)}{R_{h_1}}$$
$$+ \frac{V(r,z + k_2) - V(r,z)}{R_{k_2}} - \frac{V(r,z) - V(r,z - k_1)}{R_{k_1}}$$
$$+ \frac{E(r,z) - V(r,z)}{R_a} = 0 \quad (10.61)$$

Each of these terms represents a current through a resistance, and the sum is a statement of Kirchhoff's law that the sum of currents to (or away from) a point on a circuit is zero. One unit of the circuit is shown in Figure 10.6, on which the arrows indicate directions of current. The potential $E(r,z)$ is supplied by the network that represents the thermal flux.

A two-group, 800 lattice point circuit in 20-by-20 arrays has been constructed by Pratt and Whitney, as described by Honeck

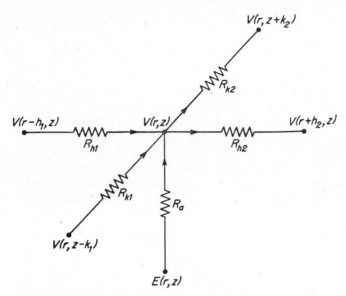

Figure 10.6.   Circuit element simulating difference equation
of space simulator.

and Ott (see References).   An iterative procedure is used to compute the critical condition and flux distribution.   A fuel loading is assumed, and a trial thermal flux put in by choice of potentials $E(r,z)$.   The resulting fast flux potentials are then applied back to the thermal network, and so on.   The condition on criticality is that the total fission rate shall be constant, i.e., the sum of all the thermal potentials weighted by the volume of fuel associated with each is unchanged by an iteration.

Problems

10.1. (a) By comparison of the function $\psi_1(z,\mu)$ appearing in Equations (10.7) and (10.8) with its counterpart $N_1(z)$ in one-velocity transport theory, Chapter 9, explain why ψ_1 would be expected to be small far from the neutron source.   (b) Under what conditions for a pure-hydrogen scatterer will the integral in Equation (10.8) be approximately $2\psi_1(z,u)/3$?   (c) Making use of the results of (b), derive the diffusion theory approximation for lethargy-dependent flux in hydrogen. In what way does it differ from the expression leading to Equation (2.42)?

Answers. (a) Net current small, far from source;

(b) $\psi_1(z,u')$ varying slowly with lethargy;

(c)

$$D(u) \frac{\partial^2 \phi_0(z,u)}{\partial z^2} + \phi_0(z,u)\Sigma_s(u) = \delta(z)\delta(u) + \int_0^u du' \phi(z,u')\Sigma_s(u')e^{-(u-u')}$$

10.2. Using the graph of L_s in water as a function of initial neutron energy, Figure 10.1, and the fission spectrum $S(E)$, calculated the age of fission neutrons to indium resonance 1.45 ev.

Answer. $\simeq 30$ cm^2.

10.3. From the ratio of neutron energy after collision to that before, Equation (2.27), and the differential scattering fraction, Equation (2.29), show that the scattering probability function, Equation (10.3), is correct.

10.4. Verify that $\mu_{01} = \dfrac{(A+1)}{2} e^{-\Delta u/2} - \dfrac{(A-1)}{2} e^{\Delta u/2}$, making use of Equations (2.27), (2.28), and (2.38).

10.5. Show that the solution of the homogeneous form of the difference equation (10.47) and the particular integral are related by

$$\frac{H_{n+1}}{H_n} = \frac{P_{n+1}}{P_n} + \frac{I_n}{P_n}$$

10.6. A bare, spherical, U^{235}-fueled, beryllium-moderated reactor of radius 30 cm has been operated to a point where the fuel has been burned out to give a spatial distribution $\left(1 - 0.2 \dfrac{\sin \pi r/R}{\pi r/R}\right)$. By a two-group, 11 lattice point, difference-equation approach, find the central fuel cross section and the critical thermal fission distribution.

10.7. Apply the Goertzel-Selengut method to obtain the flux as a function of lethargy for a bare, water-moderated, spherical reactor for which these assumptions are made: $\Sigma_a(u)$ is negligible; the source is proportional to the thermal flux and the fission spectrum; $\phi_0(r,u) = R(r)\phi(u)$ and $\nabla^2\phi_0(r,u) = -B^2(u)\phi_0(r,u)$.

10.8. Calculate the neutron age in water from 2 mev to 1.45 ev by use of the Flügge-Tittle method. The graph of L_s in Figure 10.1 may be employed for the region 100 kev down.

References

Ehrlich, R., and H. Hurwitz, Jr., "Multigroup Methods for Neutron Diffusion Problems," *Nucleonics*, February 1954, p. 23. (See also AECD-3595.)

Spooner, R. B., "Using a Reactor Simulator for Design Analysis," *Nucleonics*, April 1954, p. 36.

Greuling, E., F. Clark, and G. Goertzel, *A Multigroup Approximation to the Boltzmann Equation for Critical Reactors*, NDA 10-96.

Noderer, L., *Some Methods for Solving Multigroup Pile Equations*, ORNL-291 (1949).

Thompson, A. S., "Numerical Computation of Neutron Distribution and Critical Size," *Journ. Appl. Phys.*, **22**, 1223 (1951). (See also NAA-SR-48.)

Mandl, M. E., *Multigroup Theory with an Application to Inelastic Scattering in Uranium*, AERE T/R 1500.

Roe, G. M., *Adaptation of Multigroup Methods to Cylindrical Geometries*, KAPL-950 (1954).

Honeck, H. C., and D. J. Ott, "Application of Analog Computing Techniques to the Solution of Neutron Flux Distribution Problems," *Nuclear Engineering*, Part II, Chemical Engineering Progress Symposium Series No. 12, Volume 50. New York: American Institute of Chemical Engineers (1954).

Marshak, R. E., "Theory of the Slowing Down of Neutrons by Elastic Collision with Atomic Nuclei," *Rev. Mod. Phys.*, **19**, 185 (1947).

Tittle, C. W., *Nuclear Shielding Studies I*, "The Slowing Down and Diffusion of Neutrons in Hydrogenous Media," NP-1418. Oak Ridge: Technical Information Division AEC (1949).

Marshak, R. E., H. Brooks, and H. Hurwitz, Jr., "Introduction to the Theory of Diffusion and Slowing Down of Neutrons," *Nucleonics*, May, p. 10, June, p. 43, July, p. 53, August, p. 59 (1949).

Chu, J. C., *Design of a Computer-ORACLE*, ANL-5368 (1954).

Fleck, J. A., *The Energy-Dependent Boltzmann Equation Applied to Criticality Calculations for Bare Graphite-Moderated Reactors*, BNL-298 (1954).

Habetler, G. J., *General One-Space-Dimensional Multigroup*, KAPL-1182 (1954).

Certaine, J., *A Solution of the Neutron Transport Equation*, Introduction and Part I, NYO-3081 (1954).

Hurwitz, H., Jr., and P. F. Zweifel. *Slowing Down of Neutrons in Hydrogenous Moderators*, KAPL-1269 (1955).

Peaceful Uses of Atomic Energy, Volume 5, *Physics of Reactor Design*. New York: Columbia University Press (1956).

Hurwitz, H., Jr., and R. Ehrlich, "Comparison of Theory and Experiment for Intermediate Assemblies," Paper P/608.

Wilkins, J. Ernest, Jr., Robert L. Hellens, and Paul F. Zweifel. "Status of Experimental and Theoretical Information on Neutron Slowing Down Distributions in Hydrogenous Media," Paper P/597.

Scarborough, James B., *Numerical Mathematical Analysis*, 2nd Ed. Baltimore: Johns Hopkins Press (1950).

APPENDICES

Appendix A

BESSEL FUNCTIONS

The Bessel functions are solutions of a differential equation of the form

$$\nabla^2 \phi + B^2 \phi = 0 \qquad (A.1)$$

where cylindrical coordinates are used. Their origin and properties are summarized.

Bessel's *ordinary* differential equation is

$$x^2 \frac{d^2 y}{dx^2} + x \frac{dy}{dx} + (x^2 - \nu^2) y = 0 \qquad (A.2)$$

where the constant ν is the *order* of the equation.

The two solutions, obtained by series methods, are

$$J_\nu(x) \qquad \text{first kind}$$
$$Y_\nu(x) \qquad \text{second kind}$$

The most frequently encountered orders are the zero ($\nu = 0$) and first ($\nu = 1$). Figure A.1 shows $J_0(x)$ and $J_1(x)$; Figure A.2 shows $Y_0(x)$ and $Y_1(x)$. The following relations hold:

$$J_1(x) = -\frac{dJ_0(x)}{dx} \qquad (A.3)$$

$$Y_1(x) = -\frac{dY_0(x)}{dx} \qquad (A.4)$$

The generation of the Bessel equation in a reactor problem is demonstrated. First, the net leakage of neutrons from a unit length of a cylindrical shell of thickness dr and radius r (as in Figure 7.3) is

$$j_{r+dr}[2\pi(r + dr)] - j_r 2\pi r \qquad (A.5)$$

by analogy with Equation (3.1).   However, since

$$j_{r+dr} = j_r + (dj/dr)\, dr$$

this is also

$$2\pi j_r\, dr + 2\pi \frac{dj}{dr}\, dr + 2\pi \frac{dj}{dr}\, (dr)^2$$

Now let $j_r = -D\,(d\phi/dr)$, drop the term in $(dr)^2$ as a second order

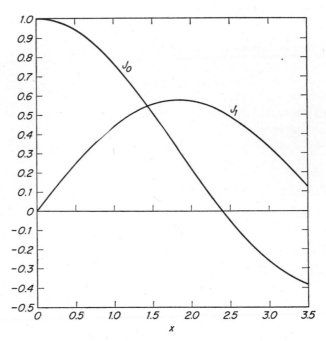

Figure A.1.   Bessel functions $J_0(x)$ and $J_1(x)$.

infinitesimal, and divide by $2\pi r\, dr$, the volume of the shell, to get
the leakage per unit volume,

$$L = -D\!\left(\frac{d^2\phi}{dr^2} + \frac{1}{r}\frac{d\phi}{dr}\right) = -D\,\nabla^2\phi \tag{A.6}$$

The wave equation (3.17) in cylindrical coordinates is thus

$$\frac{d^2\phi}{dr^2} + \frac{1}{r}\frac{d\phi}{dr} + B^2\phi = 0 \tag{A.7}$$

Now change to the variables $y = \phi$ and $x = Br$ and substitute, noting that $d/dr = B(d/dx)$. The result is

$$\frac{d^2y}{dx^2} + \frac{1}{x}\frac{dy}{dx} + y = 0 \qquad \text{(A.8)}$$

which is the same as (A.2) except that $\nu = 0$. The solutions of the original flux equation (A.7) are thus the ordinary, zero-order

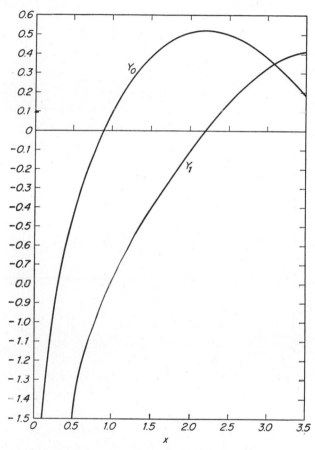

Figure A.2. Bessel functions $Y_0(x)$ and $Y_1(x)$.

Bessel function of the first kind, $J_0(Br)$, and the ordinary, zero-order Bessel function of the second kind, $Y_0(Br)$. The most general solution is the linear combination with arbitrary coefficients,

$$\phi = AJ_0(Br) + CY_0(Br)$$

Bessel's *modified* differential equation is

$$x^2 \frac{d^2y}{dx^2} + x \frac{dy}{dx} - (x^2 + \nu^2)y = 0 \qquad (A.9)$$

which differs from Equation (A.2) only in one sign. Its solution can be found by a change in variables. If $x = iz$ is substituted in Equation (A.9), the equation becomes identical to (A.2). One

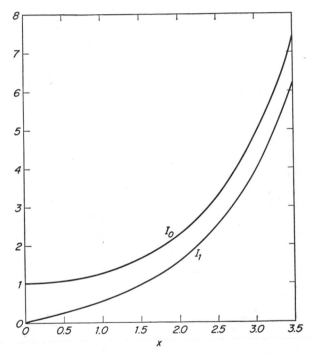

Figure A.3. Bessel functions $I_0(x)$ and $I_1(x)$.

solution is thus $J_\nu(z)$ or rather $J_\nu(ix)$. The first solution of the modified Bessel equation is thus the ordinary Bessel function of *imaginary argument*. It is distinguished by a special symbol $I_\nu(x)$. For integral ν,

$$I_\nu(x) = \frac{1}{i^\nu} J_\nu(ix)$$

The second solution is $K_\nu(x)$.

Plots of these functions for zero and first order are shown in Figures A.3 and A.4. Note that

$$I_1(x) = \frac{d}{dx} I_0(x) \qquad\qquad (A.10)$$

$$K_1(x) = -\frac{d}{dx} K_0(x) \qquad\qquad (A.11)$$

A simple illustration of a reactor situation in which these appear is

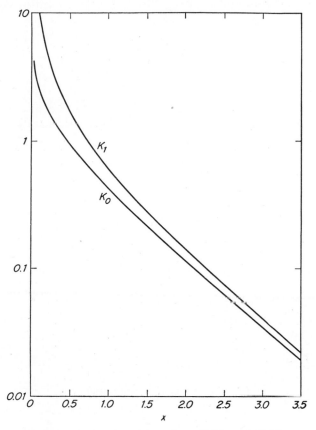

Figure A.4.   Bessel functions $K_0(x)$ and $K_1(x)$.

the reflector of an infinite cylinder. As seen in Equation (3.49) the reflector diffusion equation is

$$D_r \nabla^2 \phi_r - \phi_r \Sigma_r = 0$$

or in cylindrical coordinates,

$$\frac{d^2\phi_r}{dr^2} + \frac{1}{r}\frac{d\phi_r}{dr} - \kappa_r^2\phi_r = 0 \qquad\qquad (A.12)$$

where $\kappa_r^2 = \Sigma_r/D_r$. If we let $y = \phi$ and $z = \kappa_r r$, this immediately becomes Equation (A.9) with $\nu = 0$. The reflector flux solutions are thus $I_0(\kappa_r r)$ and $K_0(\kappa_r r)$. The most general solution is the linear combination with arbitrary coefficients:

$$\phi_r = FI_0(\kappa_r r) + GK_0(\kappa_r r)$$

A study of the graphs of the Bessel functions will reveal which are appropriate to use and which are not. In a medium that contains the origin, the arbitrary coefficients of Y_0 and K_0 must be zero, since these functions go to $-\infty$ and ∞ respectively as the argument goes to zero. On the other hand, the coefficient of I_0 must vanish in the case of a cylinder with infinite reflector, since I_0 increases indefinitely with argument. The region of utility of the J_0 function is usually from the origin to the first root, at $j_0 = 2.40483$, where $J_1 = 0.519147$.

Table A.1

Series Expansions of Bessel Functions

Small Argument, $x \ll 1$

$$J_0(x) = 1 - \frac{1}{(1!)^2}\left(\frac{x}{2}\right)^2 + \frac{1}{(2!)^2}\left(\frac{x}{2}\right)^4 - \frac{1}{(3!)^2}\left(\frac{x}{2}\right)^6 + \cdots$$

$$J_1(x) = \frac{x}{2} - \frac{1}{1!2!}\left(\frac{x}{2}\right)^3 + \frac{1}{2!3!}\left(\frac{x}{2}\right)^5 - \frac{1}{3!4!}\left(\frac{x}{2}\right)^7 + \cdots$$

$$I_0(x) = 1 + \frac{1}{(1!)^2}\left(\frac{x}{2}\right)^2 + \frac{1}{(2!)^2}\left(\frac{x}{2}\right)^4 + \frac{1}{(3!)^2}\left(\frac{x}{2}\right)^6 + \cdots$$

$$I_1(x) = \frac{x}{2} + \frac{1}{1!2!}\left(\frac{x}{2}\right)^3 + \frac{1}{2!3!}\left(\frac{x}{2}\right)^5 + \frac{1}{3!4!}\left(\frac{x}{2}\right)^7 + \cdots$$

Large Argument, $x \gg 1$

$$I_0(x) = \frac{e^x}{\sqrt{2\pi x}}\left(1 + \frac{1^2}{1!8x} + \frac{1^2 \cdot 3^2}{2!(8x)^2} + \frac{1^2 \cdot 3^2 \cdot 5^2}{3!(8x)^3} + \cdots\right)$$

$$I_1(x) = \frac{e^x}{\sqrt{2\pi x}}\left(1 - \frac{1 \cdot 3}{1!8x} - \frac{1^2 \cdot 3 \cdot 5}{2!(8x)^2} - \frac{1^2 \cdot 3^2 \cdot 5 \cdot 7}{3!(8x)^3} - \cdots\right)$$

$$K_0(x) = \sqrt{\frac{\pi}{2x}}\, e^{-x}\left(1 - \frac{1^2}{1!8x} + \frac{1^2 \cdot 3^2}{2!(8x)^2} - \frac{1^2 \cdot 3^2 \cdot 5^2}{3!(8x)^3} + \cdots\right)$$

$$K_1(x) = \sqrt{\frac{\pi}{2x}}\, e^{-x}\left(1 + \frac{1 \cdot 3}{1!8x} - \frac{1^2 \cdot 3 \cdot 5}{2!(8x)^2} + \frac{1^2 \cdot 3^2 \cdot 5 \cdot 7}{3!(8x)^3} - \cdots\right)$$

Series expansions. In certain analyses involving very small or very large values of the coordinate r, series approximations are useful. Table A.1 collects those most likely to be needed.

It is of interest to note that the I_0 function closely resembles an increasing exponential for large x, while K_0 resembles the decreasing exponential.

Integrals of Bessel Functions. The determination of an average flux over a cylindrical region leads to an integral of the form $\int x Z_0(x)\, dx$. Note the following identities:

$$\int x J_0(x)\, dx = x J_1(x) = -x J_0'(x)$$
$$\int x Y_0(x)\, dx = x Y_1(x) = -x Y_0'(x)$$
$$\int x I_0(x)\, dx = x I_1(x) = x I_0'(x) \qquad \text{(A.13)}$$
$$\int x K_0(x)\, dx = -x K_1(x) = x K_0'(x)$$
$$\int x^2 J_0(x)\, dx = \frac{x^2}{2}\left[J_0^2(x) + J_1^2(x) \right]$$

Recursion relations. Higher and lower order Bessel functions and their derivatives may be developed by the use of these general relations:

$$
\begin{array}{cccc}
J & Y & I & K \\
\end{array}
$$

$$\pm Z_{\nu-1} = \frac{\nu}{x} Z_\nu + Z_\nu' \qquad + \quad + \quad + \quad -$$

$$\pm Z_{\nu+1} = \frac{\nu}{x} Z_\nu - Z_\nu' \qquad + \quad + \quad - \quad +$$

where the signs to be used are indicated. Addition, subtraction or differentiation yields additional recursion relations for higher derivatives and negative orders.

Combinations. The need for looking up certain functions with large arguments is sometimes obviated by calculation of a ratio based on the asymptotic series expansions. For large x,

$$\frac{I_1(x)}{I_0(x)} \simeq 1 - \frac{1}{2x} - \frac{1}{8x^2} \qquad \text{(A.14)}$$

$$\frac{K_1(x)}{K_0(x)} \simeq 1 + \frac{1}{2x} - \frac{1}{8x^2} \qquad \text{(A.15)}$$

The Wronskian relations are also listed:

$$J_0(x) Y_1(x) - J_1(x) Y_0(x) = -\frac{2}{\pi x} \qquad \text{(A.16)}$$

$$I_0(x) K_1(x) + I_1(x) K_0(x) = \frac{1}{x} \qquad \text{(A.17)}$$

Tables of functions and references.   The most accessible references that contain tabulated values of the Bessel functions are listed, with a few interpretative comments.

Jahnke, E., and F. Emde, *Tables of Functions.*   New York: Dover Publications (1945).

The eight most important Bessel functions are given for the range $x = 0$ to 10 or 15 in steps of 0.01.   The tables must be used with discretion because of interpolation inaccuracy.   Note the following relations of notation:

Conventional	Jahnke and Emde	Page
$Y_0(x)$	$N_0(x)$	190
$Y_1(x)$	$N_1(x)$	191
$I_0(x)$	$J_0(ix)$	226
$I_1(x)$	$-iJ_1(ix)$	227
$\frac{2}{\pi}K_0(x)$	$iH_1^{(1)}(ix)$	236
$\frac{2}{\pi}K_1(x)$	$-H_1^{(1)}(ix)$	237

Tables of the Bessel Functions $Y_0(x)$, $Y_1(x)$, $K_0(x)$, $K_1(x)$ $0 \leq x \leq 1$, Department of Commerce, National Bureau of Standards, Applied Mathematics Series 1.   Washington: Superintendent of Documents, U. S. Government Printing Office (1948).

These 6- or 7-decimal entries are spaced every 0.001 unit or smaller, and are the best available for small x.

Bessel Functions, Part I, Functions of Orders Zero and Unity, British Association for the Advancement of Science Mathematical Tables, Volume VI.   Cambridge, England: University Press (1937).

The tables of J_0 and J_1 are especially good, with 10 decimals, in 0.001 steps of the argument from $x = 0$ to 25.   The Y_0 and Y_1 go to 25, in 0.01 steps, and the I_0 and I_1 functions go to $x = 5$, in steps of 0.001.   The K_0 and K_1 tables from $x = 0$ to $x = 1$ are inferior to the Department of Commerce tables, but supplement them from $x = 1$ to $x = 5$.

Watson, G. N., *A Treatise on the Theory of Bessel Functions.*
New York: The Macmillan Co. (1944).

The most complete work on the subject.

Gray, Andrew, G. B. Mathews, and T. M. MacRobert, Jr.,
*A Treatise on Bessel Functions and Their Applications to
Physics.* New York: The Macmillan Co. (1931).

Contains many useful integrals and interrelations of functions.

The Reactor Handbook, Volume I, *Physics*, AECD-3645.
Washington: U. S. Government Printing Office (1955).

Figure 1.6.44 gives various integrals of the J_0 function.

Appendix B

PHYSICAL CONSTANTS

(Partly from Cohen, et al., *Reviews of Modern Physics*, Oct. 1955, p. 363.)

	Constant	Value
N_a	Avogadro's number	6.02322×10^{23} (chemical scale*)
e	electronic charge	4.80286×10^{-10} esu
		1.60206×10^{-2} emu
c	velocity of light	2.99793×10^{10} cm/sec
m	electron rest mass	9.1083×10^{-28} gm
m_n	neutron rest mass	1.67470×10^{-24} gm
h	Planck's constant	6.62517×10^{-27} erg-sec
k	Boltzmann's constant	1.38044×10^{-16} erg/deg
E_{2200}	energy of 2200 m/sec neutron	0.0252973 ev
$v_{0.025}$	velocity of 0.025 ev neutron	2187.036 m/sec
$m_{\text{U-235}}$	mass of U^{235} atom	235.11704 (physical scale)

Conversion Factors.

1 ev $= 1.60206 \times 10^{-12}$ erg $= 1.60206 \times 10^{-19}$ watt-sec
1 atomic mass unit $= 931.141$ mev $= 1.65979 \times 10^{-24}$ gm
1 electron mass $= 0.510976$ mev
1 gm $= 5.6100 \times 10^{26}$ mev
$0°C = -273.15°K$
1 calorie $= 4.186$ watt-sec
1 BTU $= 1054.8$ watt-sec

---

* Relation of atomic weights on chemical and physical scales: $M_p = M_c/1.000272$.

Appendix C

LAPLACE TRANSFORMS

The solution of linear differential equations with constant co-efficients is greatly expedited by the use of the Laplace transform. Let $f(t)$ be a function of the independent variable t. Its transform is denoted by

$$\mathcal{L}[f(t)] = \int_0^\infty e^{-st}f(t) \, dt = \bar{f}(s)$$

a function of the transformed variable s. The inverse transform $\mathcal{L}^{-1}$ is defined by

$$\mathcal{L}^{-1}[\bar{f}(s)] = \frac{1}{2\pi i} \int_0^\infty e^{ts}\bar{f}(s) \, ds = f(t)$$

The value of these operations lies in the fact that the Laplace transform of a differential equation with independent variable t becomes an algebraic equation of a function of variable s, to which the inverse transform is applied to obtain the dependent variable of interest. Further, tables of transforms are available to work either backward or forward. A few of those most frequently needed are:

Function, $f(t)$	Transform $\bar{f}(s)$
1^*	$1/s$
$\dfrac{df(t)}{dt}$	$s\bar{f}(s) - \bar{f}(0)$
t	$1/s^2$
e^{at}	$1/(s-a)$
$\sin wt$	$w/(s^2 + w^2)$
$\cos wt$	$s/(s^2 + w^2)$
$\delta(t-a)^{**}$	e^{-as}
$e^{at}f(t)$	$\bar{f}(s-a)$

Function, $f(t)$	*Transform* $\bar{f}(s)$
$\displaystyle\int_0^t f(\tau)d\tau$	$\dfrac{1}{s}\bar{f}(s)$
$\displaystyle\int_0^t f_1(t-\tau)f_2(\tau)\,d\tau$	$\bar{f}_1(s)\bar{f}_2(s)$
$\dfrac{A(s)}{B(s)}$	$\displaystyle\sum_n \dfrac{A(\lambda_n)}{B'(\lambda_n)}\,e^{\lambda_n t}$ †

* Step function, $f(t) = 0$ for $t < 0$, $f(t) = 1$ for $t > 0$.

** Delta function or unit impulse $\delta(t - a) = 0$ for $t \neq a$, $\displaystyle\int_{-\infty}^{\infty} \delta(t - a)\,dt = 1$.

† λ_n are the single roots of the equation $B(s) = 0$.

As an illustration of the method, we solve the familiar equation of radioactive decay,

$$\frac{dN(t)}{dt} = -\lambda N(t)$$

with initial condition $N(0) = N_0$. Apply the Laplace transform to the equation, using the preceding table, to obtain

$$s\overline{N}(s) - \overline{N}(0) = -\lambda \overline{N}(s)$$

where $\overline{N}(s)$ is the transform of $N(t)$. Solving algebraically,

$$N(s) = \frac{\overline{N}(0)}{s + \lambda} = \frac{N_0}{s - (-\lambda)}$$

Now perform the inverse transform using $a = -\lambda$:

$$e^{at} \sim \frac{1}{(s - a)}$$

to obtain $N(t) = N_0 e^{-\lambda t}$, as expected.

INDEX

311